THEORIES AND EXPERIMENTS IN HIGH-ENERGY PHYSICS

Studies in the Natural Sciences

A Series from the Center for Theoretical Studies

University of Miami, Coral Gables, Florida

Volume 1 — IMPACT OF BASIC RESEARCH ON TECHNOLOGY
Edited by Behram Kursunoglu and Arnold Perlmutter • 1973

Volume 2 — FUNDAMENTAL INTERACTIONS IN PHYSICS
Edited by Behram Kursunoglu, Arnold Perlmutter, Steven M. Brown, Mou-Shan Chen, T. Patrick Coleman, Werner Eissner, Joseph Hubbard, Chun-Chian Lu, Stephan L. Mintz, and Mario Rasetti • 1973

Volume 3 — FUNDAMENTAL INTERACTIONS IN PHYSICS AND ASTROPHYSICS
Edited by Behram Kursunoglu, Steven Weinberg, Arthur S. Wightman, Geoffrey Iverson, Arnold Perlmutter, and Stephan L. Mintz • 1973

Volume 4 — QUANTUM STATISTICAL MECHANICS IN THE NATURAL SCIENCES
Edited by Behram Kursunoglu, Stephan L. Mintz, Susan M. Widmayer, Mou-Shan Chen, C. S. Hui, Joseph Hubbard, Joseph F. Malerba, Laurence Mittag, and George Soukup • 1974

Volume 5 — FUNDAMENTAL THEORIES IN PHYSICS
Edited by Stephan L. Mintz, Laurence Mittag, Susan M. Widmayer, Chui-Shuen Hui, and Joseph F. Malerba • 1974

Volume 6 — PROGRESS IN THE NEUROSCIENCES AND RELATED FIELDS
Edited by Behram Kursunoglu, Stephan L. Mintz, Susan M. Widmayer, Chui-Shuen Hui, Joseph Hubbard, and Joseph F. Malerba • 1974

Volume 7 — TOPICS IN ENERGY AND RESOURCES
Edited by Behram Kursunoglu, Stephan L. Mintz, Susan M. Widmayer, Chui-Shuen Hui, Joseph Hubbard, Joseph Malerba, and George Soukup • 1974

Volume 8 — PROGRESS IN LASERS AND LASER FUSION
Edited by Behram Kursunoglu, Arnold Perlmutter, Susan M. Widmayer, Uri Bernstein, Joseph Hubbard, Christian Le Monnier de Gouville, Laurence Mittag, Donald Pettengill, George Soukup, and M. Y. Wang • 1975

Volume 9 — THEORIES AND EXPERIMENTS IN HIGH-ENERGY PHYSICS
Edited by Behram Kursunoglu, Arnold Perlmutter, Susan M. Widmayer, Uri Bernstein, Joseph Hubbard, Christian Le Monnier de Gouville, Laurence Mittag, Donald Pettengill, George Soukup, and M. Y. Wang • 1975

A Continuation Order Plan is available for this series. A continuation order will bring delivery of each new volume immediately upon publication. Volumes are billed only upon actual shipment. For further information please contact the publisher.

ORBIS SCIENTIAE

THEORIES AND EXPERIMENTS IN HIGH-ENERGY PHYSICS

Chairman
Behram Kursunoglu

Editors
Arnold Perlmutter
Susan M. Widmayer

Scientific Secretaries
Uri Bernstein
Joseph Hubbard
Christian Le Monnier de Gouville
Laurence Mittag
Donald Pettengill
George Soukup
M. Y. Wang

Center for Theoretical Studies
University of Miami
Coral Gables, Florida

PLENUM PRESS • NEW YORK AND LONDON

1975

Library of Congress Cataloging in Publication Data

Orbis Scientiae, 2d, University of Miami, 1975.
Theories and experiments in high-energy physics.

(Studies in the natural sciences ; v. 9)
"Held by the Center for Theoretical Studies, University of Miami."
Includes bibliographical references and index.
1. Particles (Nuclear physics)—Congresses. I. Perlmutter, Arnold, 1928- II. Widmayer, Susan M. III. Miami, University of, Coral Gables, Fla. Center for Theoretical Studies. IV. Title. V. Series.
QC793.3.H507 1975 539.7'21 75-16281
ISBN 0-306-36909-5

Part of the Proceedings of Orbis Scientiae held by the Center for Theoretical Studies, University of Miami, January 20-24, 1975

A Division of Plenum Publishing Corporation
227 West 17th Street, New York, N.Y. 10011

United Kingdom edition published by Plenum Press, London
A Division of Plenum Publishing Company, Ltd.
Davis House (4th Floor), 8 Scrubs Lane, Harlesden, London, NW10 6SE, England

Printed in the United States of America

Preface

This volume contains a portion of the presentations given at the session on High Energy Physics and Astrophysics of Orbis Scientiae II, held at the Center for Theoretical Studies, University of Miami, from January 20 through January 24, 1975. This, second in the new series of meetings held at the CTS, strove to implement the goals professed in the organization of Orbis Scientiae in 1974, namely to encourage scientists in several disciplines to exchange views, not only with colleagues who share similar research interests, but also to acquaint scientists in other fields with the leading ideas and current results in each area represented. Thus, an effort has been made to include papers in each session that discuss fundamental issues in a way which is comprehensible to scientists who are specialists in other areas. Also in keeping with the philosophy of Orbis Scientiae, the major topics each year are to be varied, with the invariant being the inclusion of developments in fundamental physics.

The discussions of the current state of the art in high energy physics represented in this volume include new theories and experiments in the field.

Special gratitude is due to the following for their contributions as organizers and moderators of the sessions on high energy physics and astrophysics: Abdus Salam, Jogesh Pati, Karl Strauch, O. W. Greenberg, Sheldon Glashow, George Sudarshan and W. John Cocke. The editors wish to express their appreciation to Mrs. Helga Billings and Mrs. Jacquelyn Zagursky for their dedication in the preparation of the manuscripts for publication and for their capable assistance during the meetings.

A companion volume, entitled Progress in Laser Fusion and Lasers, incorporates the papers delivered at Orbis Scientiae II complementary to those included in the present one.

The Orbis Scientiae II was supported in part by the United States Energy Research and Development Administration, High Energy Physics Division.

The Editors

Contents

Some of the participants in attendance at the High Energy Physics Sessions of the Orbis Scientiae II

RECENT RESULTS FOR e^+e^- ANNIHILATION AT SPEAR*

Presented by H. L. Lynch

Stanford Linear Accelerator Center

Stanford University, Stanford, CA. 94305

J. E. Augustin, A. M. Boyarski, M. Breidenbach, F. Bulos, J. T. Dakin, G. J. Feldman, G. E. Fischer, D. Fryberger, G. Hanson, B. Jean-Marie, R. R. Larsen, V. Lüth, H. L. Lynch, D. Lyon, C. C. Morehouse, J. M. Paterson, M. L. Perl, B. Richter, P. Rapidis, R. F. Schwitters, W. Tanenbaum, F. Vannucci
Stanford Linear Accelerator Center
Stanford University, Stanford, CA. 94305

and

G. S. Abrams, D. Briggs, W. Chinowsky, C. E. Friedberg, G. Goldhaber, R. J. Hollebeek, J. A. Kadyk, A. Litke, B. Lulu, F. Pierre, B. Sadoulet, G. H. Trilling, J. S. Whitaker, J. Wiss, J. E. Zipse
Lawrence Berkeley Laboratory
University of California, Berkeley, CA. 94720

---

*Work supported by Energy Research and Development Administration

I. INTRODUCTION

In this presentation I shall assume that everyone is familiar with the existence of two narrow resonances coupling to electrons[1,2,3] at masses of 3.1 and 3.7 GeV. Properties of these resonances will be described at length. I shall also discuss upper limits which we can place for the production of other such resonances in the range 3.2 to 5.9 GeV.[4] Lastly, I shall discuss some tantalizing structure at 4.1 GeV.[5] This talk will concentrate upon the experimental facts; various speculations will be left for other speakers. It should be emphasized that most results described are preliminary and are subject to refinement.

II. APPARATUS

In order to save time I shall give only a very short description of the experimental apparatus[6]: The storage ring itself circulates one beam each of positrons and electrons which collide at 0°, and the energy resolution (standard deviation) of the order of 1 MeV for a center-of-mass energy of 3 GeV. This high resolution is dominated by quantum fluctuations in the synchrotron radiation. The absolute energy of the machine is known only to about 0.1%. The interaction region is of order of a millimeter transverse to the beam and a few centimeters along the beam.

The magnetic detector is schematized in Fig. 1, and consists of a counter around the interaction region, some spark chambers, some more counters for measuring time-of-flight, and some more for electron identification. The solenoidal magnet produces a nearly uniform field of about 4 kG along the beam. The time-of-flight system allows π/K separation up to about 600 MeV/c. The

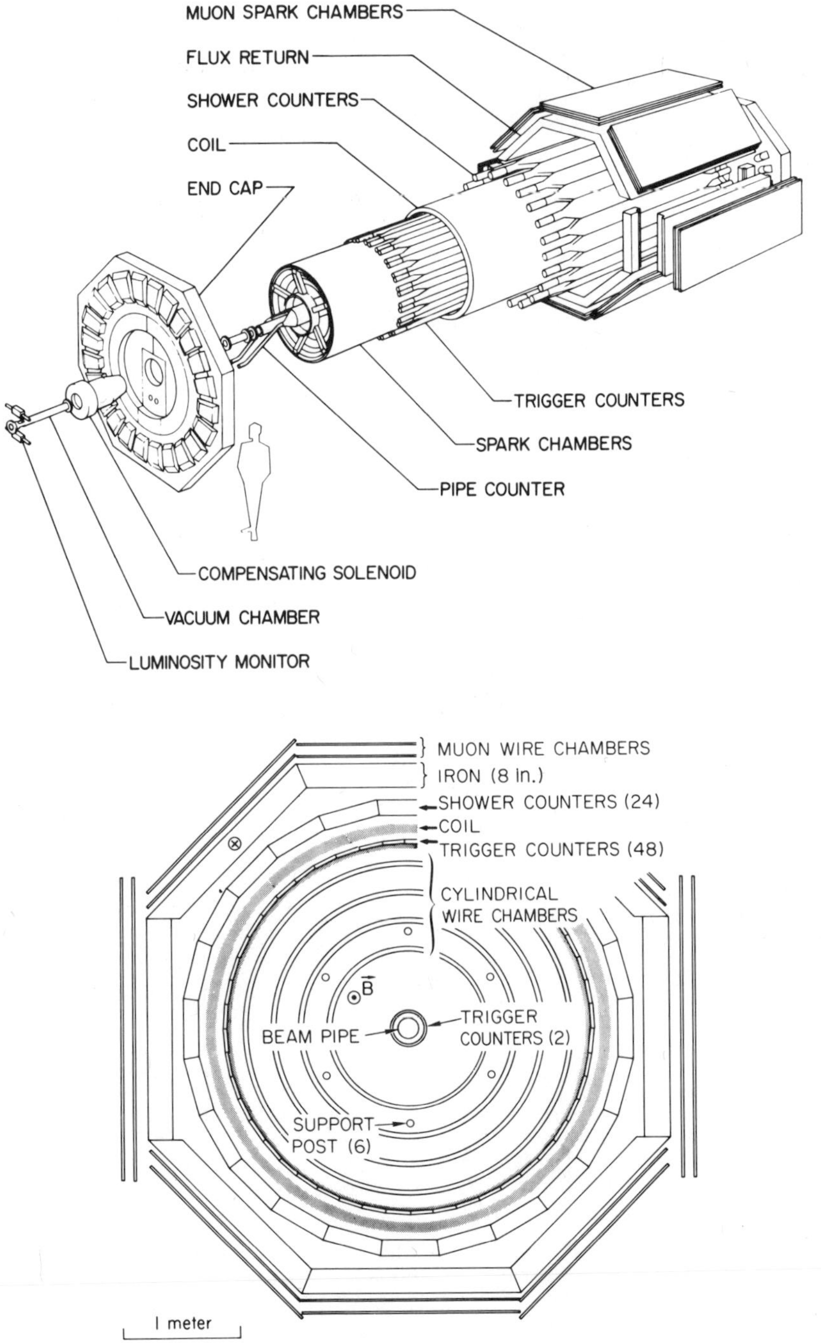

Fig. 1 (a) Telescoped view of detector; (b) end view of detector.

trigger requires two or more charged particles; this means, for example, that no totally neutral final states can be studied.

Backgrounds for the data on the resonances are extremely small and have no effect on results, being of the order of 0.01% to 0.1%.

III. PROPERTIES OF $\psi(3.1)$

There are several properties of the $\psi(3.1)$ which can be easily extracted from the data. Figure 2 shows

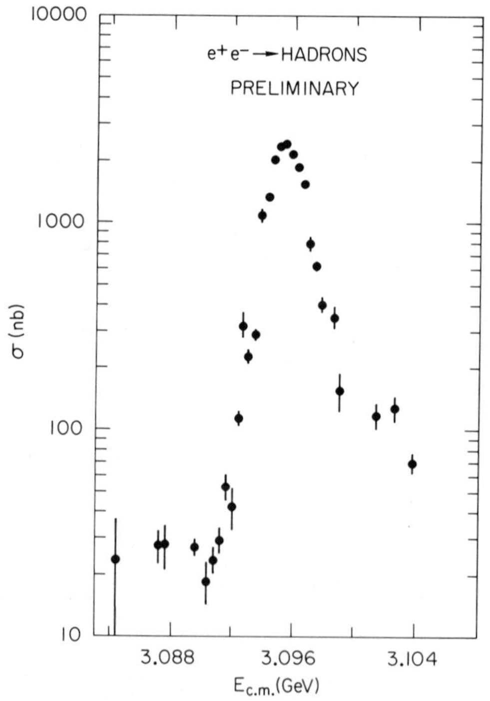

Fig. 2 Total cross section for hadron production *vs* center-of-mass energy for $\psi(3.1)$, corrected for detector acceptance.

the total hadron cross section as a function of the center-of-mass energy. The two most striking features of the figure are the magnitude of the peak cross section, ∿2500 nb, and the very narrow width, ∿2.5 MeV FWHM, a width which is fully compatible with the expected resolution of the storage ring. This means that what is plotted is not really the cross section but rather a convolution of the cross section with the machine resolution. To a very good approximation the shape of the curve depends only upon the area of the cross section vs. w. On very general grounds the cross section for resonance production can be related to partial widths

$$\sigma_c(w) = \frac{\pi(2J+1)}{w^2} \frac{\Gamma_e\Gamma_c}{(m-w)^2+\Gamma^2/4} \quad , \tag{1}$$

where J is the spin of the resonance, Γ_e is the partial width for decay into e^+e^-, Γ_c is the partial width to any channel c, w is the center-of-mass energy, m is the mass, and Γ is the total width of the resonance. Thus, the data for $e^+e^- \rightarrow \psi \rightarrow$hadrons are described by

$$\int \sigma_H dw = \frac{2\pi^2(2J+1)}{m^2} \Gamma_e B_H \quad , \tag{2}$$

where B_H is the branching fraction into hadrons. Using the data of Fig. 2 and making appropriate radiative corrections[7] the integral cross section may be obtained, $\int \sigma_H dw$ = 10.8±2.7 nb GeV. Assuming a spin J=1, on the prejudice that $\psi(3.1)$ is produced by single photon annihilation of the original e^+ and e^-, the product $\Gamma_e B_H$ can be determined. The branching fractions to leptons may be determined using the data of Fig. 3 (which, by the way, manifests gross violations of QED); assuming

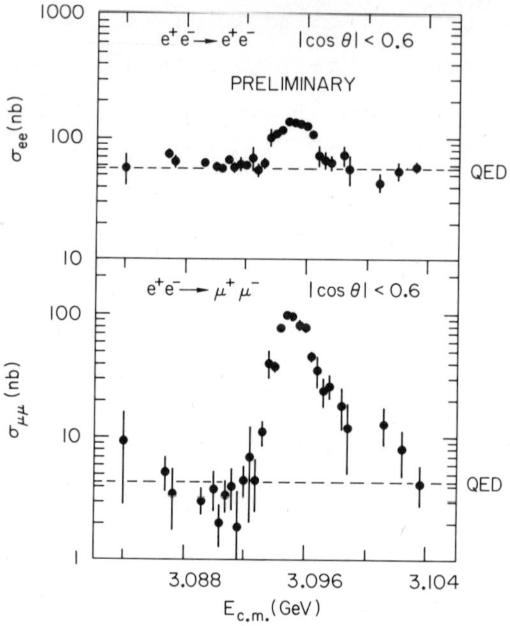

Fig. 3 Cross section for production of lepton pairs integrated over the range $|\cos\theta| < 0.6$ vs. center-of-mass energy; (a) electrons, (b) muons. No correction has been applied for the loss of events having $|\cos\theta| > 0.06$.

that there are no totally unobserved decay modes, Γ_e and Γ may be determined, $\Gamma_e = 5.2 \pm 1.3$ keV; $\Gamma = 77 \pm 19$ keV. The errors stated are strongly correlated and are entirely dominated by systematic errors, which are due, for example, to setting errors in energy and variations of machine resolution with experimental conditions. The demands made upon the machine for energy setting are extremely severe, and much effort was needed to maintain relative setting errors to less than 0.1 MeV center-of-mass energy.[8]

The assumption of J=1 can be tested experimentally by looking at the decay $\psi \to \mu^+\mu^-$. If the state $\psi(3.1)$ has the same quantum numbers as a photon, then, and only then, there can be interference of this channel

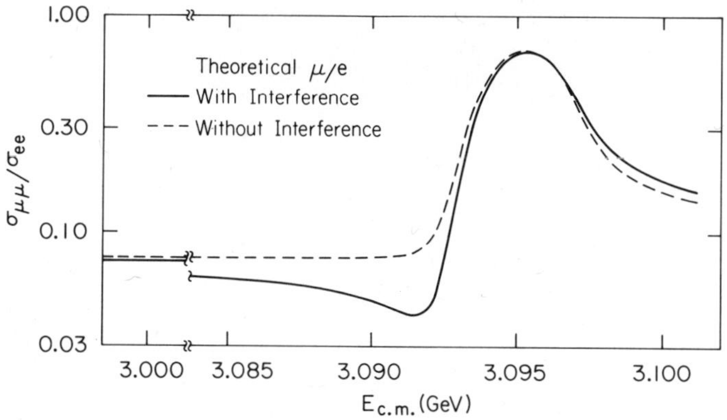

Fig. 4 Predictions for the ratio of μ-yield to e-yield for no interference and complete interference.

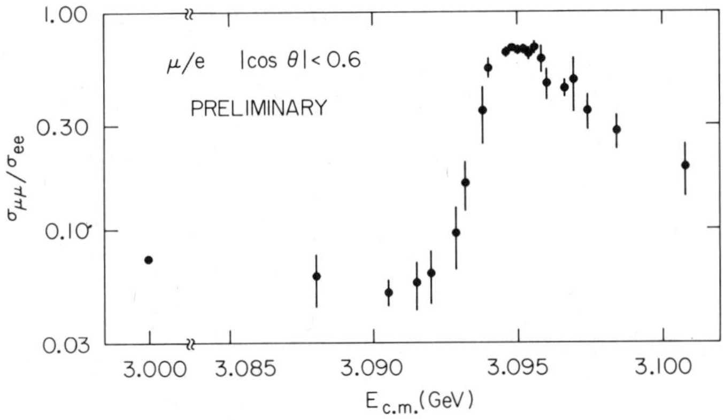

Fig. 5 Experimental data for the ratio of μ-yield to e-yield. The hypothesis of no interference can be excluded by having a confidence level of less than 0.15%.

with normal μ-pair production by QED. Figure 4 shows the prediction for the ratio of yields for $\psi \to \mu^+\mu^-$ to $\psi \to e^+e^-$ using the parameters already obtained. The choice of the ratio is convenient because systematic errors are minimized. Two cases are shown, with and without interference, corresponding respectively to pure axial vector and pure vector interaction. Figure 5 shows our data, which have been more coarsely binned to improve the statistical accuracy of each point. The amount of data in the interference region is limited so that a fit is not very fruitful; however, the hypothesis that there is no interference may be unambiguously tested: For this case the expected μ rate should rise rapidly for $w \geq 3.093$ GeV, but be quite flat below 3.093 GeV. There is a total of 89 μ-pair events and 1532 e-pair events below 3.093 GeV. Given those e-pair events, one expects 122 μ pairs; thus, the observed yield of μ pairs is ∿3 standard deviations below that expected for no interference. Furthermore, the above observed yield is compatible with the interference hypothesis. We conclude that ψ(3.1) must have the same quantum numbers as the photon, having rejected the hypothesis of no interference. The observation of this interference is the most convincing and direct evidence of the vector nature of the ψ(3.1).

The observation of interference does not rule out the possibility that ψ(3.1) is a mixture of vector and axial vector properties. The angular distribution of the μ pairs is sensitive to such a mixture. In particular, if ψ(3.1) has both vector and axial vector properties (i.e., a parity violation) there will be an asymmetry in the μ-pair angular distribution at the resonance energy. The observed asymmetry is less than

.04 in absolute value at the resonance energy, and is compatible with 0 in the region 5 MeV above and below the resonance. This implies a V-A mixing angle of less than 8°.

IV. PROPERTIES OF $\psi(3.7)$

We can carry through some of the same kinds of analysis on the $\psi(3.7)$ as on the $\psi(3.1)$. Figure 6 shows the hadronic cross section. The integrated cross section is $\int \sigma_H dw = 3.7 \pm 0.9$ nb GeV, and $\Gamma_e = 2.2 \pm 0.6$ keV. Again the errors are strongly correlated and dominated by systematics. In contrast to the $\psi(3.1)$, however, the

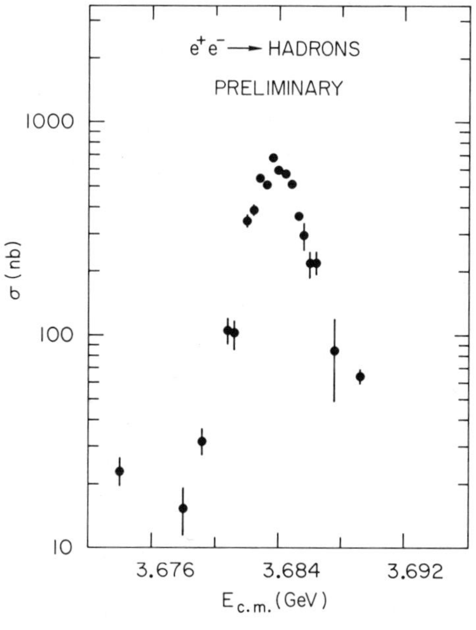

Fig. 6 Total cross section for hadron production *vs*. center-of-mass energy for $\psi(3.7)$, corrected for detector acceptance.

$\psi(3.7)$ has a very small branching ratio to leptons, so that the determination of Γ from Γ_e is difficult. An upper limit on Γ may be obtained from the width of the hadronic yield <u>vs</u>. w. A total width $\Gamma > 1$ MeV is incompatible with the expected resolution of the machine, while a lower limit of $\Gamma = 0.2$ MeV is obtained by attributing all μ-pair events reconstructed near 3.684 GeV to $\psi \to \mu^+\mu^-$ (i.e., including QED events). This number will eventually be determined when our constrained fitting programs have been thoroughly tested and loss or contamination mechanisms well studied. Because of the small branching fraction we cannot yet make the definitive test for interference, and we can only assume, not prove, that ψ(3.7) has spin 1. Much more data will be required to perform this test.

V. DECAY MODES OF ψ(3.1) AND ψ(3.7)

The leptonic decays of the ψ(3.1) have already been discussed. If this conference were a few weeks later it would be possible to be much more quantitative in the discussion of the hadronic decay modes which have been seen. At this time constrained event fitting programs are being developed, and the reported branching modes can only be discussed qualitatively. These results promise to be quite exciting, but for now I can only tease your appetite.

One clear result is that the cross section for 1C (one constraint) events involving an odd number of pions, e.g., $2\pi^+ 2\pi^- \pi^0$, is substantially greater than that for 4C (four constraint) events, e.g., $2\pi^+ 2\pi^-$. We have clean signals for the modes $\pi^+\pi^-\pi^0$, $2\pi^+ 2\pi^- \pi^0$, and $3\pi^+ 3\pi^- \pi^0$. The 5- and 7-pion modes have cross sections of the order of 50 nb (compared to the total hadronic cross section of 2500 nb), while the 3-pion mode is a little smaller. Clear ρ^0 and $\rho^\pm$ signals are seen in the 3-pion state; clear signals for $\rho^\pm$ and ω are seen in the 5-pion state.

The 4C events have a significantly smaller cross section than the 1C events. The decay $\psi(3.1)\to p\bar{p}$ has been seen with a cross section $\sim$2 nb (no correction for detection efficiency). The states $2\pi^+ 2\pi^-$, $\pi^+\pi^-K^+K^-$, and $3\pi^+ 3\pi^-$ are all clearly seen. These multipion cross sections are sufficiently small that the direct photon-hadron coupling with a vacuum polarization enhancement by the $\psi(3.1)$ form an important part of the observed yield. Figure 7a shows a normal e^+e^- annihilation to a single photon, which in turn couples to a final state f. If one writes a dispersion relation for the photon propagator (or alternatively for the vacuum polarization tensor) the effect shown in Fig. 7b results, where the reaction $e^+e^- \to\gamma\to\psi\to\gamma\to f$ takes place.

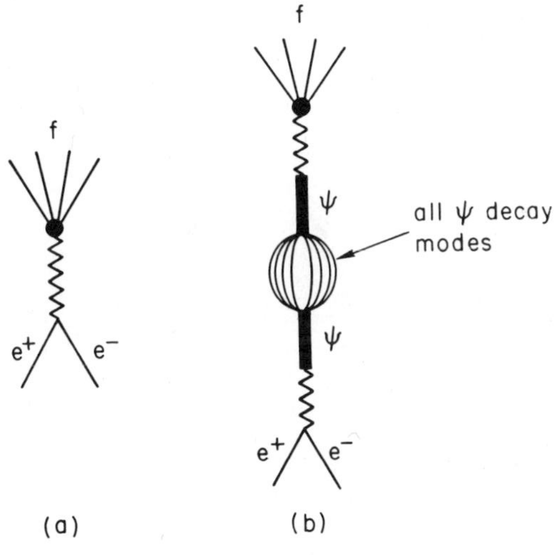

Fig. 7 Graphs of photon production of a final state f. (a) normal single photon, (b) single photon enhanced by ψ intermediate state.

A nice example of such a final state is that of μ pairs, which were seen to have a large enhancement near the $\psi(3.1)$. Thus, one expects any direct $\gamma\to f$ channel to be enhanced in the same way as the μ-pair channel. Since the μ-pair channel is enhanced by a factor of ∿20 one expects the nonresonant production of $2\pi^+ 2\pi^-$ or $3\pi^+ 3\pi^-$ to be enhanced by the same factor. Both these channels were measured to have cross sections ∿1 nb at w=3.0 GeV, meaning that one expects to see ∿20 nb on the resonance; this is in fact about what is seen. If one assumes isospin and G parity conservation in the decay, then the assignment of even isospin and negative G parity is favored for ψ(3.1).

Isolating exclusive channels in the decay of ψ(3.7) has proven to be much more elusive than for ψ(3.1). The only clearly established channel so far is a cascade from ψ(3.7)→ψ(3.1) + hadrons, and a 4C fit may clearly distinguish for ψ(3.7)→ψ(3.1) + $\pi^+\pi^-$ where the ψ(3.1)→ leptons. An example of such a decay is shown in Fig. 8. The branching fraction for ψ(3.7)→ψ(3.1) + anything is large, viz. ∿1/2.

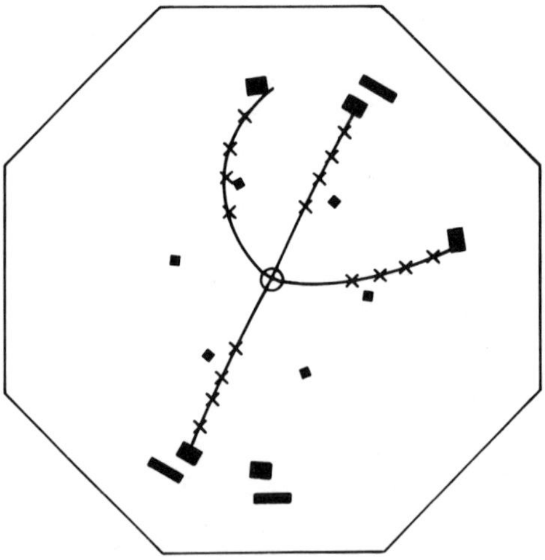

Fig. 8 Reconstructed end view of an event ψ(3.7)→ ψ(3.1) + $\pi^+\pi^-$, where the ψ(3.1) decays into a pair of electrons.

VI. ARE THERE OTHER RESONANCES?

A storage ring is both very good and very bad for finding narrow resonances. One of the ring's fundamental properties is its very high energy resolution, or stated alternatively its very narrow band-pass. Thus one must look very carefully in fine steps to find a narrow resonance lest it be missed entirely. On the other hand, when the resonance is found, the signal to noise ratio is immense; when the cross section rises by a factor of 100 over the normal rate (which was itself considered large a few years ago) there is no mistaking the existence of something so spectacular. Our discovery of $\psi(3.1)$ is a beautiful case of serendipity. Our original experiment[5] aimed at taking data in 200 MeV steps on σ_H over as large a range of center-of-mass energy as possible. The avowed purpose was to check scaling and look for structure in the s dependence of σ_H. The first phase of this data taking was completed by March, 1974. By then we noted an anomaly in σ_H at 3.2 GeV, and in May we acquired more data with finer steps. At first glance the new data showed no unusual behavior, but upon close examination, several runs taken at 3.1 GeV were internally inconsistent. Because of work being done on SPEAR, the next opportunity for data taking was in November. We then measured several points near 3.1 GeV and very soon found the $\psi(3.1)$. Thus, the original anomaly at w=3.2 GeV was just the radiative tail of the $\psi(3.1)$, and the data at w=3.10 were inconsistent because of small setting errors in the machine energy. Having found the $\psi(3.1)$ we immediately began a fine resolution scan and soon found the $\psi(3.7)$. The raw data of the scan are shown in Fig. 9,[4] where the $\Psi(3.7)$ is clearly visible but no other

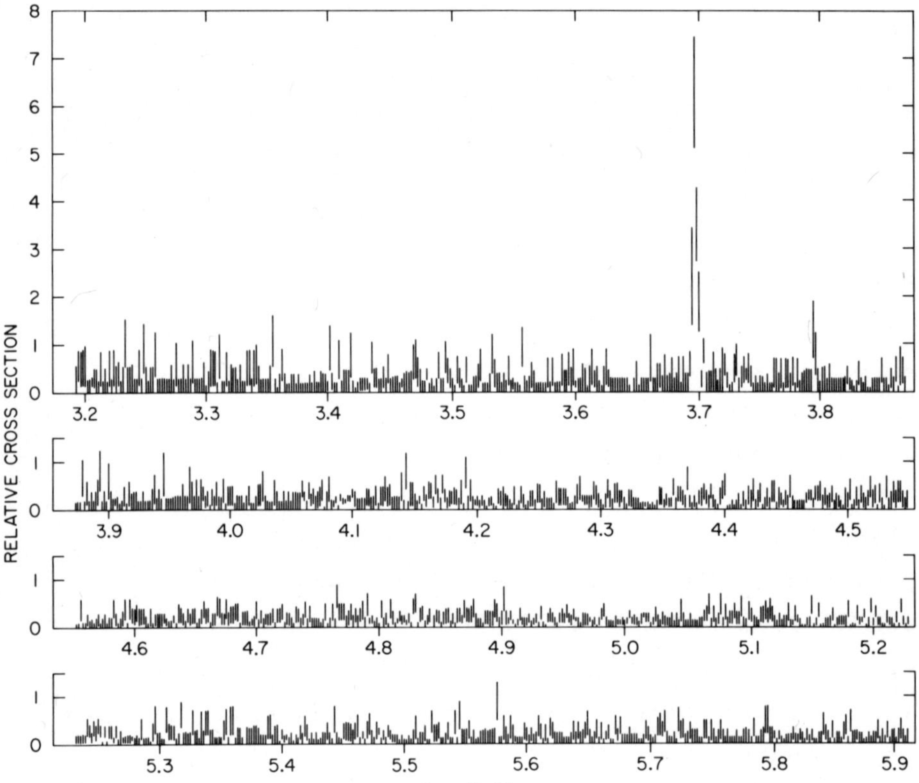

Fig. 9 Raw data for fine mesh energy scan. The ordinate is proportional to the total cross section for hadron production.

resonances appear from 3.2 to 5.9 GeV.[9] The region below 3.2 GeV has not been completed for technical reasons. Table I shows the upper limits we place on $\int \sigma_H dw$ for the production of more, narrow, resonances.

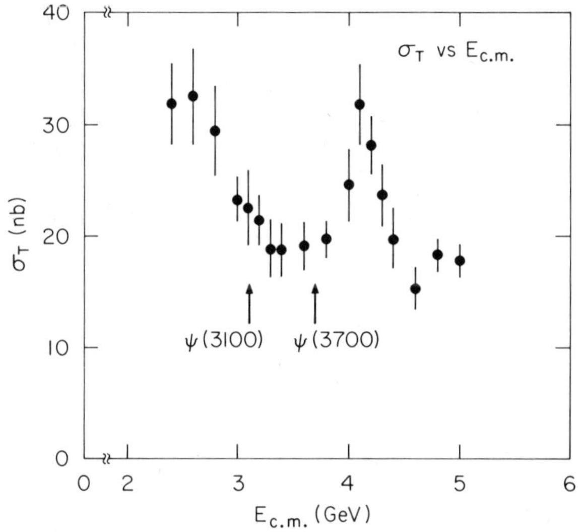

Fig. 10 Total cross section for hadron production vs. center-of-mass energy.

Returning now to the original experiment, the coarse energy scan, the results may be seen in Fig. 10.[5] The observed total cross section falls from 37 nb at w=2.6 GeV to a valley of ∿18 nb in the 3.0 to 3.6 GeV region and has a peak of ∿30 nb at w∿4.1 GeV. This peak is clearly quite different in character from the ψ(3.1) and ψ(3.7), since it is rather broad, 250 to 300 MeV. It is interesting to note, however, that the integrated "resonant" cross section is ∿5.5 nb GeV, of the same order of magnitude as that of the ψ(3.1) and ψ(3.7). At this time we have too few events on or near this peak to attempt a seriously studying exclusive channels. We plan to accumulate much more data in the near future for this purpose. In addition there are insufficient data to clearly distinguish whether the structure at 4.1 GeV is a resonance or just the opening of a new channel. Our data taking in the immediate future will concentrate on this region.

VII. EFFECTS OF $\psi(3.1)$ and $\psi(3.7)$ ON TESTS OF QED

We have recently submitted for publication tests of QED based upon studying e^+e^- and $\mu^+\mu^-$ final states at 3.0, 3.8, and 4.8 GeV.[6] One must ask what effects would one see in these tests due to the two resonances? Because the e^+e^- cross section into our detector is $\sim$13 times the $\mu^+\mu^-$ cross section, any lepton contamination is more serious in the $\mu^+\mu^-$ channel. For the test at w=3.0 GeV the most important effect is the interference of the $\psi(3.1)$ with QED; the μ production is depressed by about 2% and the e-pair yield is very slightly raised. We originally quoted a ratio of μ pairs/e pairs divided by the expected ratio for QED = 0.95±0.04. Using present information this becomes 0.97±0.04. For the test at w=3.8 GeV the most serious contamination is in the μ pairs due to the cascade $\psi(3.7)\rightarrow\psi(3.1)$ + (nothing seen) and subsequently $\psi(3.1)\rightarrow\mu^+\mu^-$. (Such events would have been accepted as valid QED events in the original analysis.) Such an effect yields an excess of $\sim$1.4% μ pairs and a very slight excess of e pairs. The radiation by the incident beams can produce some $\psi(3.7)$ which can again decay into μ pairs. This effect is expected to be of the order of 0.4% excess for μ pairs and much less for e pairs. There is also a 0.4% excess in μ pairs due to $\psi(3.1)$ interference effects. Lastly, if $\psi(3.7)$ has the same quantum numbers as the photon, then there can be an interference, which will produce an excess of

0.8% μ pairs. Taken together we expect an enhancement of 2.2 to 3.0% in the μ pairs and much less for the e pairs. Our quoted μ/e ratio compared to QED is 1.05±0.03 which becomes 1.02 or 1.03±0.03. An extremely high precision experiment on QED might have lead to discovery of the ψ's. Given a factor of 30 more data (assuming systematic errors could be appropriately reduced) one could, in principle discover that something was happening between 3.0 and 3.8 GeV because of the change of sign of the discrepancy in the μ/e ratio from QED. It is hardly likely, however, that this would happen in practice. The lesson is clear: tests of QED may not be as definitive as they appear at first sight.

VIII. CONCLUSION

We have to date 3 bona fide vector mesons, the ρ, ω, and φ, and we are offering a particle, the ψ(3.1) which also shares the quantum numbers of the photon. It is interesting to compare some of their properties shown in Table II. Also, included in the table are the ψ(3.7) and the 4.1 GeV enhancement, on the assumption that they are produced by single photon annihilation, and thus have spin 1; the case for this assumption is not proven. A striking feature of the table is that the partial widths to electrons of all these states are fairly similar, spanning a bit less than a factor of 10. At the same time the total widths differ enormously. Explaining these widths may reveal some exciting new ideas in physics. Finally, there is a glaring hole in the mass spectrum between the φ and ψ(e.1). Unfortunately, SPEAR cannot be operated in that region, so we eagerly await other laboratories to study that region.

TABLE I

Upper limits at the 90% confidence level for the radiatively corrected integrated cross section of a possible resonance. The units are nb MeV.

Mass Range (GeV)	Resonance width (FWHM in MeV) 0[a]	10	20
3.200 to 3.500	970	1750	2230
3.500 to 3.690	780	1090	1540
3.720 to 4.000	1470[b]	1530	1860
4.000 to 4.400	620	1260	1820
4.400 to 4.900	580	1080	1310
4.900 to 5.400	780	1100	1720
5.400 to 5.900	800	1120	1470

[a] Width less than the mass resolution

[b] See footnote 9

TABLE II

Particle	Mass GeV	Γ_{tot} MeV	Γ_e keV
ρ	0.770 ±0.010	150 ±0.010	6.5 ±0.5
ω	0.7828±0.0006	10 ±0.4	0.76±0.17
φ	1.0197±0.0003	4.2 ±0.2	1.34±0.084
ψ(3.1)	3.095 ±0.005	0.077±0.019	5.2 ±1.3
ψ(3.7)	3.684 ±0.005	0.2 - 1.0	2.2 ±0.6[a]
?(4.1)	4.15 ±0.1	250-300	4 ±1.2[a]

[a]Assuming J=1 and the branching fraction into hadrons $\simeq$1.

REFERENCES AND FOOTNOTES

1. J. J. Aubert *et al.*, Phys. Rev. Letters 33, 1404 (1974).

2. J. E. Augustin *et al.*, Phys. Rev. Letters 33, 1406 (1974).

3. G. S. Abrams *et al.*, Phys. Rev. Letters 33, 1453 (1974).

4. A. M. Boyarski *et al.*, "Search for Narrow Resonances in e^+e^- Annihilation", submitted to Phys. Rev. Letters.

5. J. E. Augustin *et al.*, "Total Cross Section for Hadron Production by e^+e^- Annihilation", submitted to Phys. Rev. Letters.

6. J. E. Augustin *et al.*, Phys. Rev. Letters 34, 233 (1975).

7. The radiative correction is large, ∿30%, but well understood, since we are concerned only with the soft photon region.

8. This tolerance is 30 times smaller than the original design specifications for stability of the ring, and that such precision was actually reached is a monument to superb work done by technical people involved in the design and maintenance of the ring. The reader will also note that the absolute energy scale differs from our previously published results due to a calibration error in the primary laboratory reference.

9. The largest fluctuation is centered at 3.795 GeV, where 8 events were detected for 2 expected. There is an independent reason for considering this a fluctuation rather than a signal. A narrow resonance with an integrated cross section of 1470 nb MeV located at 3.795 GeV would yield a radiative tail of about 13 nb at 3.800 GeV. We have previously taken extensive data at 3.800 GeV and these data cannot reasonably support the existence of a radiative tail of that size (see Ref. 5). If this fluctuation is excluded, then the limit on a narrow resonance in the region 3.720 to 4.000 GeV changes from 1470 to 850 nb MeV.

MEASUREMENTS OF $e^+e^- \rightarrow e^+e^-$, $e^+e^- \rightarrow \mu^+\mu^-$ AND $e^+e^- \rightarrow \gamma\gamma$ AT CENTER OF MASS ENERGIES CLOSE TO 3105 MeV*

Presented by R. Hofstadter

R.L. Ford, B.L. Beron, E. Hilger†, R. Hofstadter, R.L. Howell, E.B. Hughes, A.D. Liberman, T.W. Martin, L.H. O'Neill and J.W. Simpson

High Energy Physics Laboratory and Department of Physics, Stanford University, Stanford, California 94305

and

L.K. Resvanis

Department of Physics, University of Pennsylvania Philadelphia, Pennsylvania 19104

We report here independent evidence for the decay of the recently discovered $\psi(3105)$ particle[1-3] into

---

*Work supported by the National Science Foundation under Grant GP38611 and the National Aeronautics and Space Administration under Grant NGR452.

†Visitor from Physikalisches Institut, Universität Bonn, Bonn, Germany

electron-positron pairs and new evidence for the decay of this particle into muon pairs. We also report the results of a measurement of the reaction $e^+e^- \to \gamma\gamma$ at center of mass energies in the vicinity of 3105 MeV. These measurements were begun immediately following the discovery of the $\psi(3105)$ at SPEAR[1]. At that time an apparatus primarily designed for the study of quantum electrodynamics (QED) was operating in the second interaction region at SPEAR and was applied immediately thereafter to the study of the $\psi(3105)$. This apparatus is very similar to that described recently by Beron, et al.,[4] and is capable of identifying the reactions $e^+e^- \to e^+e^-$, $e^+e^- \to \mu^+\mu^-$ and $e^+e^- \to \gamma\gamma$. The detection apertures and procedures used to recognize each of these reactions are identical to those described by Beron et al.,[4] except that the detection aperture for the reaction $e^+e^- \to \mu^+\mu^-$ is larger by a factor of 2.6. All of the measurements reported in this letter were made with the detection apparatus set to accept particles produced at angles θ close to 90° with respect to the colliding beams.

Fig. 1 shows the observed event rate for the reaction $e^+e^- \to e^+e^-$ at center of mass energies in the vicinity of 3105 MeV[5]. A clear enhancement associated with the $\psi(3105)$ is observed with a width consistent with the upper limit of 1.9 MeV reported by Augustin, et al.[1] and Abrams, et al.[6]. The event rates shown in Fig. 1, and those in the subsequent figures of this letter, are normalized with respect to the observed rate of $e^+e^- \to e^+e^-$ events in an independent apparatus viewing the interaction region at angles close to 3.5^o. This latter apparatus, or luminosity monitor, is a substitute at the present time for a precision monitor

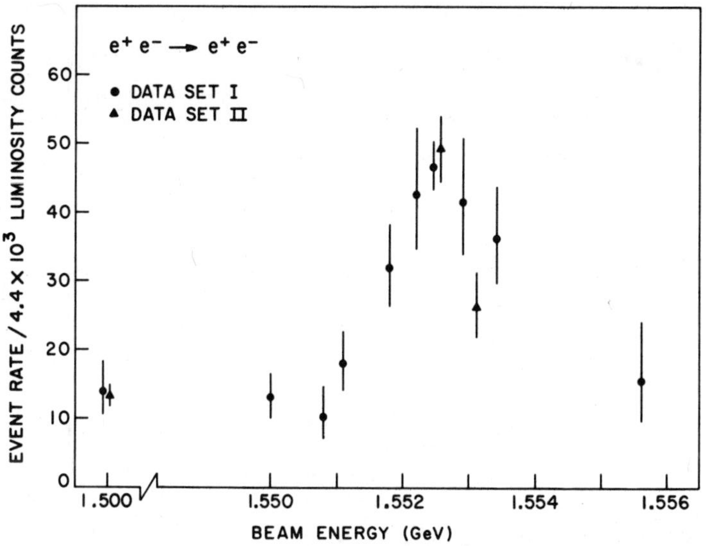

Fig. 1. The observed rate of $e^+e^- \rightarrow e^+e^-$ events for 4.4×10^3 luminosity counts as a function of beam energy. (4.4×10^3 luminosity counts are equivalent to an integrated luminosity of $2.6 \times 10^{33} cm^{-2}$ at 1.5525 GeV.) The two data sets distinguished in this figure correspond to those identified in Fig. 2. The total event yield in this figure is 587. The error bars are purely statistical, as are those in Figs. 2 and 3.

that is in preparation for later work. The statistical accuracy of the present monitor is adequate, but the absolute calibration is subject to a systematic uncertainty of ± 12% principally due to uncertainties in counter geometry. To within this level of accuracy the event rates shown in Fig. 1 outside the peak are consistent with the expected event rate of 18.6 ± 2.3 from QED.

Fig. 2 shows the observed event rate for the

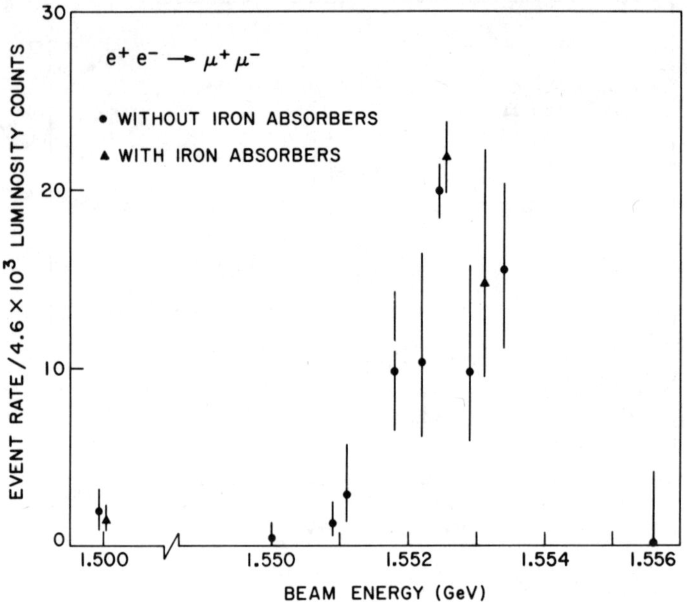

Fig. 2. The observed rate of $e^+e^- \rightarrow \mu^+\mu^-$ events for 4.6×10^3 luminosity counts as a function of beam energy. (4.6×10^3 luminosity counts are equivalent to an integrated luminosity of $2.7 \times 10^{33} cm^{-2}$ at 1.5525 GeV.) The total event yield in this figure is 393.

reaction $e^+e^- \rightarrow \mu^+\mu^-$, which also has a strong enhancement centered at 3105 MeV. Outside this peak the event rate is again consistent with the expected event rate of 0.9 ± 0.1 from QED. The detected particles in these events, in addition to geometrical and timing criteria, are required to penetrate a minimum of 20 in. of NaI(Tℓ) (1.4 pion absorption units) and to deposit energies in these crystals consistent with 1.5 GeV muons. For 42% of the data included in Fig. 2, the detected particles were also required to penetrate an additional 16 in. of steel (2.4 pion absorption lengths). The rate of events observed at 3105 MeV is not significantly changed by this additional range requirement, which confirms the identity of the detected particles as muons. Quantitatively, this result also implies that the admixture of collinear charged hadron pairs in the measured rate without the steel absorbers cannot exceed 11% of the rate of muon pairs (with 95% confidence).

Although the peak event rates shown in Figs. 1 and 2 are influenced both by radiative corrections and by the energy spread in the colliding beams[7], the ratio of these event rates, after subtraction of the measured QED background, can be used to estimate the ratio of the $\psi(3105)$ decay rates into electron-positron and muon pairs. If the $\psi(3105)$ is a resonance with unit spin and odd parity, the peak event rates, minus the QED background, are not affected by interference with the QED amplitudes and both decays are expected to occur with an angular dependence proportional to $(1 + \cos^2\theta)$. When this angular dependence is used to normalize the observed rates to the same detection aperture, which is approximately 2.0 times larger in the present apparatus for $e^+e^- \rightarrow e^+e^-$ than for $e^+e^- \rightarrow \mu^+\mu^-$, the ratio of the decay rates $\Gamma(e^+e^- \rightarrow e^+e^-)/\Gamma(e^+e^- \rightarrow \mu^+\mu^-)$ has the value of 0.93 ± 0.10. In addition, if the resonance profile for the reaction $e^+e^- \rightarrow e^+e^-$ is integrated over energy and also over the unobserved angular range, an estimate of the ratio Γ_{ee}^2/Γ can be obtained, where Γ_{ee} is the partial decay width of the $\psi(3105)$ into electron-positron pairs and Γ is the total decay width. Such an analysis, including a radiative correction, leads to the value of 0.36 ± 0.10 keV for this ratio.

Fig. 3 summarizes the observed event rates for the reaction $e^+e^- \rightarrow \gamma\gamma$ at center of mass energies close to

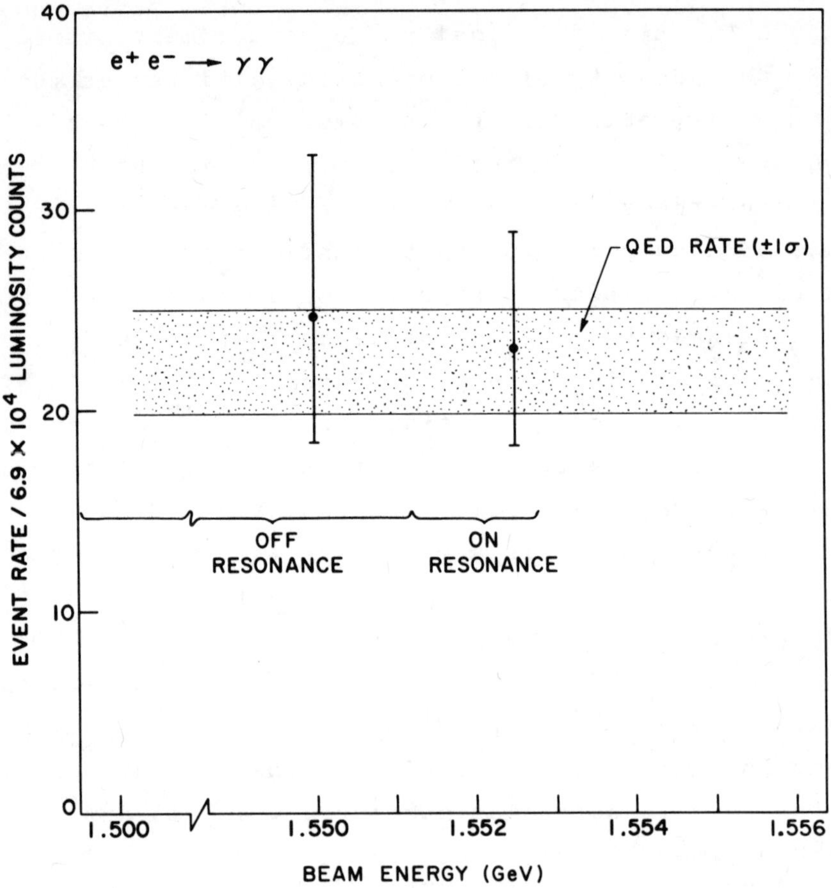

Fig. 3. The observed rate of $e^+e^- \to \gamma\gamma$ events for 6.9×10^4 luminosity counts as a function of beam energy. (6.9×10^4 luminosity counts are equivalent to an integrated luminosity of $4.1 \times 10^{34} cm^{-2}$ at 1.5525 GeV.)

3105 MeV. The available data are combined to show the average rates observed at center of mass energies in the ranges 3000 - 3102 MeV and 3102 - 3107 MeV. 15 events and 23 events are observed within these two ranges respectively. When these event numbers are normalized to the same luminosity, both are consistent with the number expected from QED, which is also indicated in Fig. 3.

We conclude from this initial study of the $\psi(3105)$ that this particle, if its spin-parity assignment is 1^-, decays with approximately equal probability into electron-positron and muon pairs and that to within the precision of the present data the rate of the reaction $e^+e^- \to \gamma\gamma$ at center of mass energies close to 3105 MeV is consistent with that expected from QED.

ACKNOWLEDGEMENTS

We gratefully acknowledge the support and cooperation of both the staffs of the Stanford Linear Accelerator Center, especially the SPEAR operations group, and of the High Energy Physics Laboratory at all stages of this experiment. We are also grateful to Professor M.R. Yearian, Director of the High Energy Physics Laboratory, for his continued support of this project.

REFERENCES

1. J.-E. Augustin et al., Phys. Rev. Lett. 33, 1406 (1974).
2. J.J. Aubert et al., Phys. Rev. Lett. 33, 1404 (1974).
3. C. Bacci et al., Phys. Rev. Lett. 33, 1408 (1974).
4. B.L. Beron et al., Phys. Rev. Lett. 33, 663 (1974).
5. The absolute beam energies used in this experiment were provided to us by the SPEAR operations group and are subject to correction should this group announce a recalibration of the energy scale.
6. G.S. Abrams et al., Phys. Rev. Lett. 33, 1453 (1974).
7. The energy spread in the colliding beams at SPEAR has also been found to depend upon the stored currents (B. Richter, private communication). In principle it is therefore necessary that comparisons of peak event rates, such as that of the muon-pair rate with and without the additional iron absorbers, be normalized with respect to simultaneous measurements of the rate of electron-positron pairs. This was done for only 38% of the muon-pair data reported here. However, no significant changes were observed in the peak event rates of either electron-positron pairs or muon pairs throughout this experiment. This is not unexpected because the average stored currents were essentially unchanged. We therefore assume that a continuous normalization with respect to electron-positron pairs is not necessary.

ELECTRON-POSITRON ANNIHILATION AND THE STRUCTURE OF HADRONS*

Frederick J. Gilman
Stanford Linear Accelerator Center
Stanford University, Stanford, California 94305

I. INTRODUCTION

The last two months have been very exciting ones in elementary particle physics. They have been filled with the most rapid and unexpected discoveries that I can recall. The highlight of this period is undoubtedly the finding of very narrow boson resonances,[1-4] the ψ's at 3.1 and 3.7 GeV.

Somewhat less noticed by many, but also of great importance, is the change that has taken place in our perception of the behavior of the fundamental quantity R, the ratio of $\sigma_T(e^+e^- \to \text{hadrons})$ to $\sigma(e^+e^- \to \mu^+\mu^-)$, the point cross section for muon pair production. For we have been confused and fooled for almost a year by partial and incomplete data - a year in which perhaps the most embarrassing questions one could ask many theorists were: "What's the origin of the behavior of $\sigma_T(e^+e^- \to \text{hadrons})$? Why doesn't it scale?" Now it

*Work supported by Energy Research and Development Administration.

appears the answer is "It does", or, a little more accurately, "It did", and that perhaps still higher energy data will show that "It will" scale again. Part of the reason for the earlier confusion is that there seems to be a step or threshold near 4 GeV and a new region above it, a transition whose physics is very likely connected to that of the narrow resonances just below.

In the following I will review what we know about $\sigma_T(e^+e^- \to \text{hadrons})$. Particular emphasis is put on scaling and the excitation of new hadronic degrees of freedom. Our present information on the ψ's is then reviewed in a phenomenological vein, from which we turn to a possible theoretical understanding of the new discoveries in terms of a new hadronic quantum number, a concrete example of which is charm.

II. THE BEHAVIOR OF R AND SCALING

Before looking at the latest data, let us recall what had been early theoretical expectations for the behavior of $R = \sigma_T(e^+e^- \to \text{hadrons})/\sigma(e^+e^- \to \mu^+\mu^-)$. On the basis of the parton model of point constituents, or of the more formal light cone algebra, one predicts that the cross section for e^+e^- annihilation into hadrons will scale, i.e., $\sigma_T(e^+e^- \to \text{hadrons}) \propto 1/Q^2$. Since the "point" cross section[5] for muon pairs,

$$\sigma(e^+e^- \to \mu^+\mu^-) = \frac{4\pi\alpha^2}{3Q^2} \qquad (1)$$

behaves as $1/Q^2$, theoretical expectation is that R will be constant and the constant may be interpreted as the sum of the squares of the charges (in units of e) of the fundamental fields making up the produced hadrons. In the case of three Gell-Mann - Zweig quarks[6,7] this gives

$$R = \sum_i Q_i^2 = \frac{4}{9}+\frac{1}{9}+\frac{1}{9} = \frac{2}{3} \quad , \tag{2a}$$

while if these quarks each come in three colors,

$$R = 3(2/3) = 2 \quad . \tag{2b}$$

Many other schemes may be invented either by adding more quarks and/or by allowing the photon (and consequently the charge) to be a nonsinglet with respect to color. A popular version of the latter possibility is the Han-Nambu scheme[8] with integrally charged quarks and R = 4.

A compilation of data on R from Orsay,[9] Frascati,[10] and SLAC[11] is found in Fig. 1. One clearly sees the $\rho(770)$, $\omega(783)$, and $\phi(1020)$ resonance peaks and then a value of R between 2 and 3 up to $\sqrt{Q^2} \simeq 3.6$ GeV. Within errors, these data are entirely consistent with <u>scaling</u>, i.e., R = constant, once Q^2 is above a few GeV^2 (and below $\approx$ 13 GeV^2). Furthermore, within the experimental errors[11] a value of $R = \sum_i Q_i^2 = 2$ is allowed, quite aside from any theoretical argument that R might well be somewhat larger than 2 in this region and approaching its asymptotic value from above. It therefore appears that the naive expectations might be right after all: scaling with R given by the sum of the squares of the charges of the operative quarks, i.e., the nine colored quarks composing the hadrons being produced, is completely consistent with the behavior of R until new physics asserts itself in the 3 to 4 GeV region.

At 3.1 GeV we get the first signal that something new is about to happen. At 3.7 GeV a second signal is

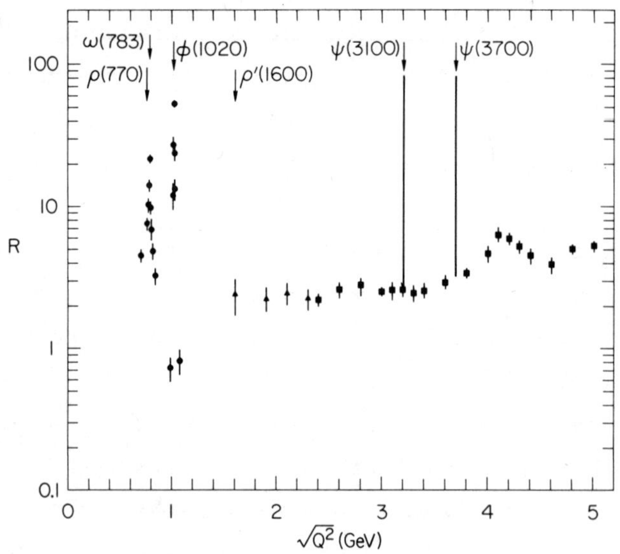

Fig. 1. $R = \sigma_T(e^+e^- \to \text{hadrons})/\sigma(e^+e^- \to \mu^+\mu^-)$ from measurements at Orsay,[9] Frascati,[10] and SLAC.[11]

immediately followed (or perhaps slightly preceded) by a rise in R. The general shape of R looks amazingly like sketches made years ago[12] to indicate what would happen due to the excitation of new hadronic degrees of freedom, whether color "thaw" or charm threshold.[13-16] The maximum in R at 4.1 GeV might be just a threshold effect or it could be a broad resonance sitting on top of a rising background, the latter being my personal feeling. In either case, a naive interpretation of the behavior of R leads to a threshold at or below 4 GeV: the broad width of the possible $\psi(4.1)$ compared to the very narrow $\psi(3.1)$ and $\psi(3.7)$ arises in the latter case precisely because one is presumably above threshold for actual decays of the resonance into new kinds of hadrons.

A look at specific channel cross sections from $\sqrt{Q^2} = 1.2$ to 1.8 GeV leads me to think that once accurate measurements are made of R in this threshold region for the "usual" quark degrees of freedom, it will appear qualitatively very much like the region from 3.8 to 4.4 GeV. The bump due to the $\rho'(1600)$, which will be less than one unit of R high, would then be the analogous structure to the larger bump in R at 4.1 GeV, even though its physics may be quite different in detail.

The presently available data[11] on R stops at $\sqrt{Q^2} = 5.0$ GeV, at which point $R \simeq 5$, i.e., double its value below the threshold. If scaling obtains and there are no further changes in R, then one has approximately doubled $\sum_i Q_i^2$ for the operative fundamental fermion fields above $\sqrt{Q^2}$ of ≈ 4 GeV.

Aside from measurements of R at higher Q^2, a better understanding of the physics above 4 GeV requires information on the final state particles. Such data would help first of all in establishing whether the structure at 4.1 GeV is a resonance - decay of such an object into a particular final state could be crucial in this regard. Present data are insufficient to draw any conclusions.

The inclusive single particle distributions are also of great interest. While not on the same level of rigor or as fundamental as the prediction of scaling of $\sigma_T(e^+e^- \to \text{hadrons})$, parton models and some extensions of light-cone ideas lead one to expect that $Q^2 d\sigma/dx$ should scale, where $x = 2P \cdot Q/Q^2$ and P_μ is the four-momentum of the observed hadron. Extensive data do exist at $\sqrt{Q^2} = 3.0$, 3.8, and 4.8 GeV on the inclusive charged particle distributions. Unfortunately, these energies are, respectively, below, in the middle of, and above the threshold or step in R. Consequently, one does not expect to see scaling of $Q^2 d\sigma/dx$ on comparing data at these particular three energies. Testing of scaling of $Q^2 d\sigma/dx$ awaits the accumulation of data at other energies below as well as above the threshold. Nevertheless, the data at $\sqrt{Q^2} = \sqrt{s} = 3.0$, 3.8, and 4.8 GeV shown[17] in Figure 2 are of some interest. For $x \gtrsim 0.5$, the distributions are the same! Is this an accident? If not, and the distribution at $\sqrt{Q^2} = 3.0$ GeV is already scaling and that characteristic of the component of R due to the nine colored Gell-Mann - Zweig quarks, then the new component of R is almost completely associated with particles at small x.

A look at the charged hadron multiplicity[11] in Figure 3 shows no obvious structure. Within errors it is consistent with a logarithmic rise with Q^2. Of course much is washed out in such a low moment of the data.

The proportion of π^-, K^-, and $\bar{p}$ shown[17] in Figure 4

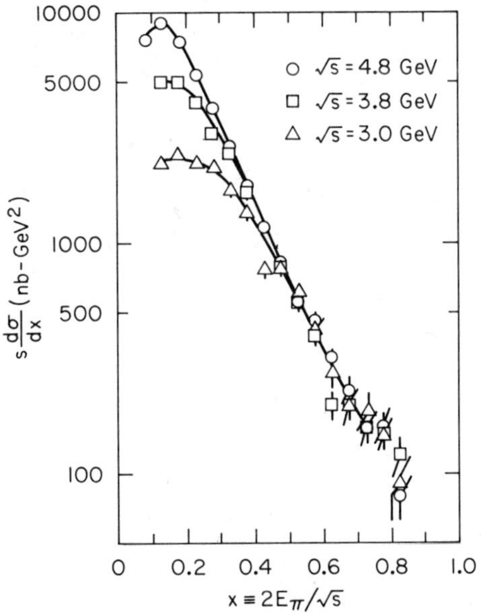

Fig. 2. The inclusive charged particle distribution[17] $s\ d\sigma/dx$ at $\sqrt{Q^2} = \sqrt{s} = 3.0$, 3.8, and 4.8 GeV.

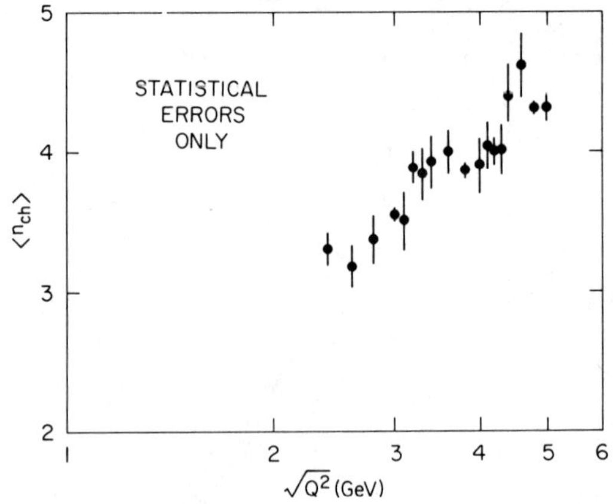

Fig. 3. The charged hadron multiplicity[11] versus $\sqrt{Q^2}$.

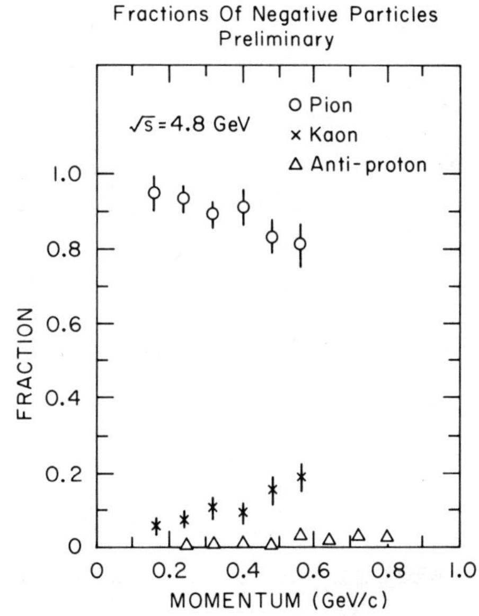

Fig. 4. Fractions[17] of π^-, K^-, and $\bar{p}$ at $\sqrt{Q^2}$ = 4.8 GeV.

shows that at $\sqrt{Q^2}$ = 4.8 GeV one has dominantly pions out to momenta of 600 MeV. As reported at this meeting[18,19] $K/\pi = 0.33 \pm 0.08$ or K/All = $0.25 \pm .05$ for momenta from 1.2 to 2.4 GeV at the same value of Q^2. Furthermore there is no dramatic difference in the SLAC-LBL results[17] at $\sqrt{Q^2}$ = 3.0 and 3.8 GeV from those at 4.8 GeV.

One quantity where there may be a change on crossing the threshold is in the proportion of the energy in charged hadrons in the final state. If all the final hadrons were pions, the simplest models[20] predict equal π^+, π^-, and π^o distributions, so that charged pions carry 2/3 of the energy. In practice, one expects a somewhat lower number because of η's, K's, etc. The experimental data[17] are shown in Figure 5. A biased eye sees a perfectly respectable value of ≈ 0.6 until about 4 GeV, with a decrease which makes the result look like an inverted version of R. But how is this increased proportion of energy carried by neutrals manifested? By photons? Or neutrinos? At present we do not know.

III. PHENOMENOLOGY OF THE ψ's

To establish some basis for the next section we enumerate here some of the basic facts now known about the ψ's and the consequent phenomenology. We start with the first to be discovered, which is now assigned a mass[21,22]

$$M = 3.095 \pm .005 \text{ GeV}$$

and J^{PC} is inferred to be 1^{--} from the three standard deviation interference[21,22] below the resonant energy in $e^+e^- \to \mu^+\mu^-$, the angular distribution of the muons,

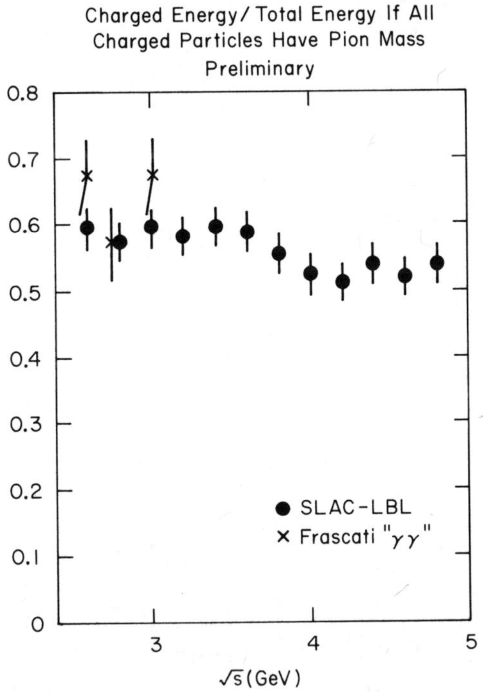

Fig. 5. Fraction of the total energy in charged hadrons.[17]

the lack of a $\gamma\gamma$ decay,[23,24] etc. The width into leptons is directly determined from the integrated cross section into hadrons:[25]

$$\int_{\text{Resonance}} \sigma_T(e^+e^- \to \text{hadrons})\, d\sqrt{Q^2} = \frac{6\pi^2}{M^2}\, \Gamma_{ee} \left(\frac{\Gamma_{\text{hadrons}}}{\Gamma_{\text{total}}}\right). \quad (3)$$

Using the preliminary values[21,22] for $\psi(3.1)$,

$$\int_{\text{Resonance}} \sigma_T(e^+e^- \to \text{hadrons})\, d\sqrt{Q^2} = 10{,}800 \text{ nb - MeV } (\pm 25\%)$$

and

$$\Gamma_{ee} = \Gamma_{\mu\mu} = .068\ \Gamma_{\text{total}} \quad ,$$

one finds

$$\Gamma_{ee} = \Gamma_{\mu\mu} = 5.2 \text{ keV}$$

$$\Gamma_{\text{total}} = 77 \text{ keV} .$$

These values agree within errors with the quantity $\Gamma^2_{ee}/\Gamma_{\text{total}}$ extracted from Frascati[3] and DESY data.[23,26] The leptonic width may be directly converted into a vector meson-photon coupling (see Fig. 6a). Writing eM^2/f at the ψ-photon vertex and using

$$\Gamma_{ee} = \left(\frac{4\pi\alpha^2}{3}\right) \frac{M}{f^2} \quad , \quad (4)$$

gives $f^2/4\pi = 10.6$. This is to be compared with $f^2_\rho/4\pi \simeq 2.5$, $f^2_\omega/4\pi \simeq 19$, and $f^2_\phi/4\pi \simeq 11$.

For the $\psi(3.7)$ we now have

$$M = 3.684 \pm .005 \text{ GeV}.$$

The value[21,22]

$$\int_{\text{Resonance}} \sigma_T(e^+e^- \to \text{hadrons})d\sqrt{Q^2} = 3700 \text{ nb - MeV } (\pm 25\%)$$

gives

$$\Gamma_{ee} = 2.2 \text{ keV}$$

and a corresponding coupling $f^2/4\pi = 29.8$. The branching ratio to leptons is still not completely settled and we have only the limits on the total width[21,22]

$$200 \text{ keV} < \Gamma_{total} < 800 \text{ keV} .$$

No other narrow states have been found in a scan[27] from 3.2 to 5.9 GeV. If one considers the structure at 4.1 GeV to be a single resonance, then[11]

$$\int_{\text{Resonance}} \sigma_T(e^+e^- \to \text{hadrons})d\sqrt{Q^2} \simeq 5500 \text{ nb - MeV}$$

leads to

$$\Gamma_{ee} = 4.0 \text{ keV}$$

and a corresponding $f^2/4\pi = 18.2$. The total width of the peak is in the 250 to 300 MeV range, making the branching ratio into a lepton pair $\approx 1.6 \times 10^{-5}$.

The data on decay modes are now beginning to pour forth from the 50,000 decays of the $\psi(3.1)$ observed by the SLAC-LBL magnetic detector. If the $\psi(3.1)$ couples to lepton pairs as in Figure 6a, it couples to hadrons as in Figure 6b with the exactly calculable rate,

$$\Gamma(\psi(3.1) \to \gamma \to \text{hadrons}) = R(\sqrt{Q^2} = 3.1\ \text{GeV}) \times \Gamma(\psi(3.1) \to \gamma \to e^+e^-)$$

$$\simeq 2.5\ (5.2\ \text{keV}) = 13\ \text{keV} = .17\Gamma_{\text{total}}. \qquad (5)$$

This leaves 77 - 13 - 2(5.2) ≃ 54 keV for "direct" decays of the $\psi(3.1)$ into hadrons. In particular, inasmuch as $2\pi^+ 2\pi^-$ is ≈ 1/20 of the cross section at 3.0 GeV (just off resonance), one calculates from Eq. (5) that

$$\Gamma(\psi(3.1) \to \gamma \to 2\pi^+2\pi^-) \simeq (\tfrac{1}{20})\Gamma(\psi(3.1) \to \gamma \to \text{hadrons}) \simeq .0085\ \Gamma_{\text{total}}. \qquad (6)$$

The $2\pi^+2\pi^-$ channel has recently been cleanly separated[21,22] from $\pi^+\pi^-K^+K^-$ and its partial width is consistent with Eq. (6), and hence with being entirely a second order electromagnetic, rather than "direct" decay mode.

A more important decay mode of $\psi(3.1)$ is five pions, including $\omega\pi\pi$ and $\rho\pi\pi\pi$. Three pion and seven pion modes are also seen.[21,22] Particularly the five pion mode occurs at a rate beyond that deduced from Eq. (5) and hence is "direct". If it occurs via strong interactions, then one concludes G=-1 and I = 0 or 2 for the $\psi(3.1)$, an assignment which is consistent with other observed modes[21,22] like $\pi^+\pi^-p\bar{p}$, $p\bar{p}$, $\pi^+\pi^-K^+K^-$, and $\Lambda\bar{\Lambda}$. It is also consistent with the lack of observation of $\pi\pi$ or $K\bar{K}$ modes at DESY:[26]

$$\Gamma(\psi(3.1) \to \pi\pi) < .025\ \Gamma_{ee} = .0017\ \Gamma_{\text{total}}$$

$$\Gamma(\psi(3.1) \to K\bar{K}) < .025\ \Gamma_{ee} = .0017\ \Gamma_{\text{total}}\ ,$$

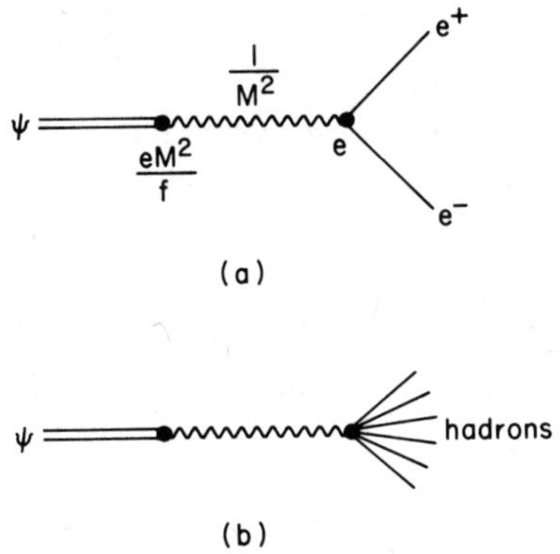

Fig. 6. Decay of a ψ through a single virtual photon into (a) e^+e^- and (b) hadrons.

since these decays are forbidden for strong interaction "direct" decays by G parity for the $\pi\pi$ mode and by SU(3) symmetry if the $\psi(3.1)$ is an SU(3) singlet for the $K\bar{K}$ mode.[28,29]

For the $\psi(3.7)$ less detailed information on decay modes is available from the 30,000 decays observed.[21,22] The branching ratio[21]

$$\frac{\Gamma(\psi(3.7\to\psi(3.1)+\text{ any})}{\Gamma(\psi(3.7)\to\text{ all})} = 0.5 \quad (\pm 25\%)$$

includes that for the observed decay $\psi(3.7)\to\pi^+\pi^-\psi(3.1)$ and the strongly suspected $\psi(3.7)\to\pi^0\pi^0\psi(3.1)$. Again, if this occurs due to strong interactions, then G=C=-, and I = 0 or 2 for the $\psi(3.7)$. In the next section we shall assume that both $\psi(3.1)$ and $\psi(3.7)$ have C=- I = 0, and G = -. Up to this point, no decay of the $\psi(3.7)$ to 4π, 5π, 6π, or 7π has been found which could not be a result of $\psi(3.7)\to\pi\pi\ \psi(3.1)$.

Since at least the first ψ has the quantum numbers of the photon it should be diffractively photoproduced at high energy with an amplitude as depicted in Fig. 7. At sufficiently high energy we assume the amplitude is pure imaginary with $d\sigma/dt \propto e^{bt}$. If we use the same ψ-photon coupling as determined at the ψ mass from Γ_{ee} = 5.2 keV, then, on integrating over t,

$$\sigma(\gamma N\to\psi N) = \frac{35\text{ nb}}{[\text{b GeV}^2]}\left[\frac{\sigma_T(\psi N)}{\text{mb}}\right]^2 . \qquad (7)$$

An upper limit for $\sigma(\gamma N\to\psi N)$ of $\approx$ 0.6 nb (after correction for the branching ratio to lepton pairs) has been established by a Rochester-Cornell[30] group at 11.1 GeV. At SLAC an upper limit[31] of 29 nb at 18.2 GeV has been superseded by measurement[32] of a cross

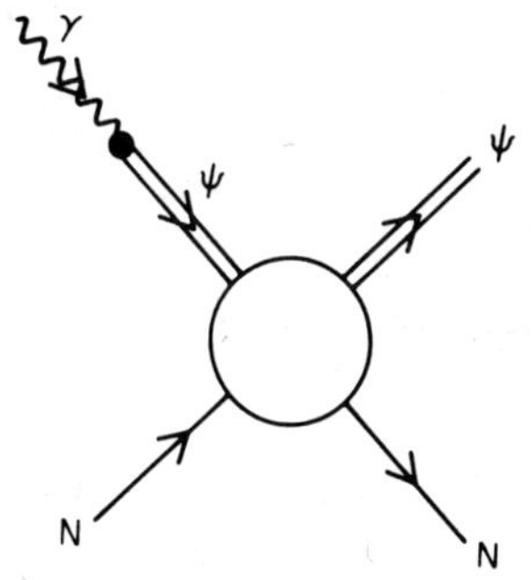

Fig. 7. A possible mechanism for ψ photoproduction.

section of 2 ± 1.2 nb at 18 GeV by one group and 1 to 5 nb at 19 GeV by another.[33] At FNAL, W.Y. Lee *et al*.[34] have observed a peak in the muon pair spectrum at 3.1 GeV resulting from photons striking a Beryllium target. A preliminary value[34] for the $\psi(3.1)$ photoproduction cross section per nucleus times the branching ratio into $\mu^+\mu^-$ lies in the 10 to 45 nb range. Assuming a differential cross section for Beryllium with both a coherent and an incoherent part,

$$\frac{d\sigma}{dt} \propto 81\ e^{40t} + 9\ e^{4t} \quad ,$$

leads on extraction of the $\gamma N \rightarrow \psi N$ cross section to values of $\sigma_T(\psi N)$ in the neighborhood of 1 mb through use of Eq. (7).

One must bear in mind that in this calculation we have assumed that the ψ-photon coupling is the same on the photon mass-shell as on the ψ mass-shell—something which could be wrong by a large factor.[35] Nevertheless, while the extracted values of $\sigma_T(\psi N)$ are considerably smaller than[36] $\sigma_T(\rho N) \simeq 28$ mb or $\sigma_T(\phi N) \simeq 13$ mb, such small cross sections are not unexpected to some,[37] and may still be taken to indicate that the $\psi(3.1)$ is a hadron with the J^{PC} quantum numbers of the photon.[38]

IV. CHARM

The existence of the narrow resonances and the rise in R have brought to the fore the question of excitation of new hadronic degrees of freedom. Such theories can be divided into those where the photon itself transforms as a nontrivial representation of a new multiplicative symmetry group of strong interactions and those where the photon is a singlet under such a group but there are additional additive strong interaction quantum numbers.[39] An example of the former is "color SU(3)", which will be discussed in detail by Professor Greenberg.[40] We concentrate on a popular example of the latter type: charm.[41,42]

At a fundamental level this involves adding a fourth quark with charge 2/3, isospin 0, and one unit of a new quantum number called charm,[43] which is conserved in strong and electromagnetic interactions. The four quarks (times three for color) are now called p,n,λ, and p' or u,d,s, and c, depending on one's geographical location, and the basic symmetry of strong interactions becomes SU(4) instead of SU(3) - the quarks falling in the fundamental four dimensional representation. An attractive aspect of this scheme is its origins in lepton-hadron symmetry and in providing an elegant way in the theory of weak interactions of keeping certain processes, which are observed or desired to be second order weak in magnitude, at that level.[43]

In such a theoretical framework, the ψ's are hadrons and interpreted as $c\bar{c}$ bound states. At least for the $\psi(3.1)$, one would like the quarks to lie in a relative s-wave ground state with net quark spin one. The resulting quantum numbers, $J^{PC} = 1^{--}$, I = 0 and therefore G = -1, are just those indicated by experiment as we have seen in the last section. The $\psi(3.1)$ would belong together with the other vector mesons, the ρ, ω, and ϕ, in the same SU(4) and quark model multiplets. In fact, the ratio of values of squared photon-vector meson couplings should then be 9:1:2:8 for $1/f_\rho^2 : 1/f_\omega^2 : 1/f_\phi^2 : 1/f_\psi^2$. Experimentally this is more like 9:1:2:2 (see the last section), but given SU(4) breaking, as evident in the large mass splittings, and the ambiguity in what quantity is to be compared with the SU(4) ratios, this is not any threat to the scheme.[44] The $\psi(3.7)$ is presumably the analogue of the $\rho'(1600)$ and its partners,[45] with J^{PC}, I, and G quantum numbers identical to the $\psi(3.1)$.

The critical tests of the charm scheme at the moment are <u>spectroscopic</u>. First, charmed particles with quark content $u\bar{c}$, $d\bar{c}$, $s\bar{c}$, (and $c\bar{u}$, $c\bar{d}$, $c\bar{s}$) should exist with J^P values 0^-, 1^-, etc. Most estimates[46] place the lowest mass charmed particles in the range 2.1 to 2.3 GeV, while identification of the step in R with the threshold for producing pairs of charmed particles would put the lowest such mass below 2 GeV. Second, additional $c\bar{c}$ states should exist with I = 0 and zero charm. The most obvious of these is the s-wave, quark spin zero, pseudoscalar state which is the quark model partner of the $\psi(3.1)$. Also present at somewhat higher masses if we take a clue from the observed meson states[47] composed of u, d, and s quarks are the L = 1 $c\bar{c}$ states with J^{PC} values 2^{++}, 1^{++}, 0^{++}, and 1^{+-}. Such states, as well as even more massive $c\bar{c}$ vector mesons, are also predicted by calculations using various potentials.[48]

An immediate question which arises as soon as one wants to make $\psi(3.1)$ and $\psi(3.7)$ hadrons is why are they so narrow? An answer is possibly provided by Zweig's rule,[7] which may be briefly stated for a meson decaying into two other mesons as in Figure 8: decay amplitudes corresponding to connected quark diagrams (Fig. 8a) are allowed, while those corresponding to disconnected diagrams (Fig. 8b) are forbidden. If one meson contains a quark which is not present in either of the other two, there is obviously no allowed diagram. For example, if

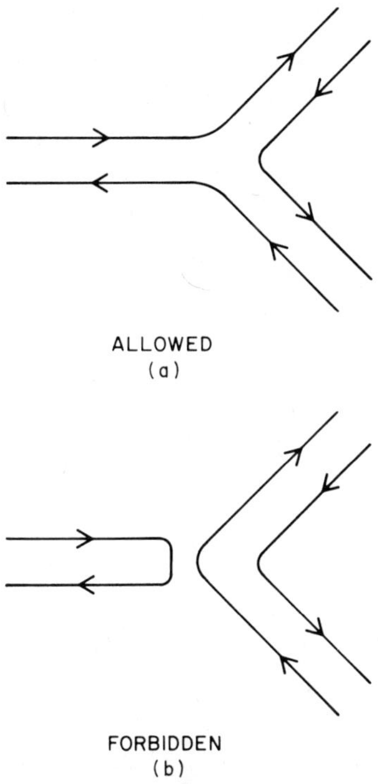

Fig. 8. The decay of a meson to two other mesons in a quark picture which is (a) allowed or (b) forbidden by Zweig's rule.

the ϕ meson had purely $s\bar{s}$ quark content, its decay to $\pi\rho$ would thus be forbidden.

How well does this "rule" work? One way of parametrizing its empirical accuracy is to compare the observed width for a forbidden process with what the width would be for a completely allowed process with the same kinematics. For example, the decay of an "ω" meson with high enough mass into $\pi\rho$ is perfectly allowed, where the "ω" is assumed to consist entirely of nonstrange u and d quarks. The coupling of ω to $\pi\rho$ can be obtained either from a vector dominance calculation[49] of $\omega \to 3\pi$, or from the current to constitutent quark transformation. The deduced couplings agree with one another,[50] and result in

$$\frac{\Gamma(\phi(1020)\to\pi\rho)}{\Gamma(\text{"}\omega\text{"}(1020)\to\pi\rho)} \simeq \frac{.0006\ \text{GeV}}{.19\ \text{GeV}} \simeq \frac{1}{300} \quad . \tag{8}$$

Similarly,

$$\frac{\Gamma(\phi(1020)\to\gamma\pi)}{\Gamma(\text{"}\omega\text{"}(1020)\to\gamma\pi)} \lesssim 1/100 \tag{9}$$

from the upper limit[51,52] on $\Gamma(\phi\to\gamma\pi)$.

For the f'(1516), decay into $\pi\pi$ is forbidden if its quark content is $s\bar{s}$. Taking the f(1260) to be composed only of nonstrange quarks, the present experimental limit on $f' \to \pi\pi$ and the known width for the allowed decay $f \to \pi\pi$ gives

$$\frac{\Gamma(f'(1516)\to\pi\pi)}{\Gamma(\text{"}f\text{"}(1516)\to\pi\pi)} \lesssim 1/50 \quad . \tag{10}$$

Note that the decay $f \to K\bar{K}$ is allowed and its observed rate[51] is consistent with that calculated from SU(3) and phase space.

Thus we see that empirically in the few cases where one can test it well, Zweig's rule is accurate to one part in a few hundred in decay rate. Moreover, it is not possible to tell if the observed decays like $\phi \to \pi\rho$ are due to breaking of the "rule" or due to a small nonstrange quark ("$u\bar{u} + d\bar{d}$") component of the $\phi(1020)$. In fact, the octet-singlet mixing angle for the vector mesons which follows from a quadratic mass formula gives a $u\bar{u} + d\bar{d}$ component to the ϕ which is completely consistent with its observed decay rate to $\pi\rho$ (or $\gamma\pi$). Thus, Zweig's rule is good <u>at least</u> to $\approx 1/200$ for ϕ decays. Of course, if the "rule" is broken, one automatically is forced into mixing[53] between the $s\bar{s}$ and $u\bar{u} + d\bar{d}$ states and it is less clear quantitatively where to assign the blame for the occurrence of forbidden decays.

If the $\psi(3.1)$ and $\psi(3.7)$ are $c\bar{c}$ states below the threshold for actual decay into pairs of charmed particles (which would be allowed by Zweig's rule), then their decays to ordinary hadrons are forbidden. The decays $\psi(3.7) \to \pi\pi\psi(3.1)$ and $\psi(3.7) \to \eta\psi(3.1)$ are also forbidden since they too correspond to disconnected diagrams. Experimentally there is a suppression, as[51] $\Gamma(\rho'(1600) \to \pi\pi\rho) \simeq 300$ MeV and $\Gamma(N^*(1470) \to (\pi\pi)_s N) \simeq 20$ MeV correspond to allowed quark diagrams and are 100 to 1000 times larger[54] than $\psi(3.7) \to \pi\pi\psi(3.1)$. From the observed width of $\psi(3.1) \to$ hadrons one needs Zweig's rule and/or the admixture of $u\bar{u}$, $d\bar{d}$, and $s\bar{s}$ quarks in $\psi(3.1)$ to be good to $\approx 1/5000$ in the decay rate, to be compared to the $\approx 1/200$ discussed above. Calculations using asymptotically free gauge theories for strong interactions, although model dependent, indicate at least that one expects a qualitative change toward increased accuracy of Zweig's rule as the mass of the decaying particle increases.[53] The pattern of the forbidden decays discussed above is shown in Figure 9.

With the exception of the $^1P_1$ state, all the other nearby $c\bar{c}$ states ($^1S_0$, $^3P_2$, $^3P_1$, $^3P_0$) are expected to have G = C = + and are therefore reachable from the ψ's by photon transitions.[55] In particular, the pseudoscalar state associated with the $\psi(3.1)$ is likely to lie below it, as the π or K are below the ρ and K* respectively, resulting in the picture shown in Figure 10. It can't lie very much below or else the allowed magnetic dipole transition[56] $\psi(3.1) \to \gamma\eta_c$ results in too large a total width for the $\psi(3.1)$. For example, in the SU(4) limit, the amplitude relation

$$A(\psi\to\gamma\eta_c) = \frac{4}{3}\,A(\omega\to\gamma\pi) \quad , \tag{11}$$

results in a 22 keV width for $\psi \to \gamma\eta_c$ if one uses simple p^3 phase space and a pseudoscalar mass of 3.0 GeV. While it is easy to obtain a smaller width by introducing mass factors in the amplitudes and/or phase space, or by making $M_\psi - M_{\eta_c}$ smaller (or negative!), this serves well to illustrate how small the $c\bar{c}$ quark content of any pseudoscalar state (including the η and η') more than a few hundred MeV below the $\psi(3.1)$ must be in order to avoid a large width for the $\psi(3.1)$. One also has the upper limit from DESY[23] for the $\psi(3.1)$:

$$\left[\frac{\Gamma(\psi\to\gamma\eta_c)}{\Gamma(\psi\to\text{all})}\right]\cdot\left[\frac{\Gamma(\eta_c\to\gamma\gamma)}{\Gamma(\eta_c\to\text{all})}\right] < .014 \quad ,$$

but this is probably not a stringent bound since most theories would have either bracketed quantity of order a few percent or less. Much more striking is the

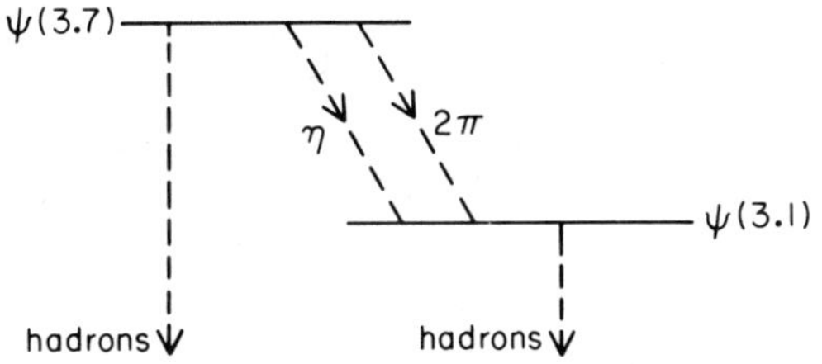

Fig. 9. The possible strong interaction transitions of the ψ(3.1) and ψ(3.7). Dashed lines indicate decays forbidden by Zweig's rule.

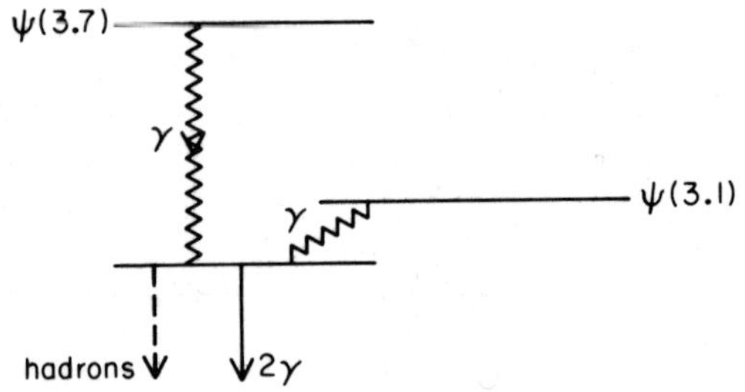

Fig. 10. The possible electromagnetic and strong decays involving a C = + state with $c\bar{c}$ quark content and a mass lower than 3.1 GeV. Dashed lines indicate decays forbidden by Zweig's rule.

≈ 600 MeV gamma ray from the transition $\psi(3.7)\to\gamma\eta_c$. If this is even a few percent decay mode of the $\psi(3.7)$ it should be readily detectable by Professor Hofstadter's group at SPEAR in the near future.

The other even charge conjugation states, the $^3P_2$, $^3P_1$, $^3P_0$, and the $^1S_0$ state associated with the $\psi(3.7)$, would lie between 3.1 and 3.7 GeV if even a rough analogy with the ordinary L = 1 meson states is relevant. The possible transitions involving one such state between 3.1 and 3.7 GeV are given in Fig. 11. The allowed electric dipole transitions from $\psi(3.7)$ to the ^3P states are estimated[55] to collectively contribute several hundred keV to $\psi(3.7)\to$ all. Furthermore, in addition to being forbidden by Zweig's rule, the decay of the ^3P states into hadrons is further suppressed in a potential picture[55] by the vanishing of the p-wave wave function at the origin. This makes the decays of the ^3P states proceed dominantly by electric dipole radiation into $\psi(3.1)$. The main decay chain is then

$$\psi(3.7)\to\gamma\,^3P\to\gamma\gamma\psi(3.1)\quad .$$

But we have heard earlier[21] that the branching ratio

$$\psi(3.7)\to\psi(3.1)+\text{ anything}$$

is of order $\frac{1}{2}$. Given the bound on the total width of the $\psi(3.7)$ as well as the importance of $\psi(3.7)\to\pi^+\pi^-\psi(3.1)$ and probable existence of $\psi(3.7)\to\pi^0\pi^0\psi(3.1)$, there do not appear to be many hundreds of keV for $\psi(3.7)\to\gamma\gamma\psi(3.1)$. As better numbers come out on the $\psi(3.7)$ branching ratios and total width, this situation should be of great interest.

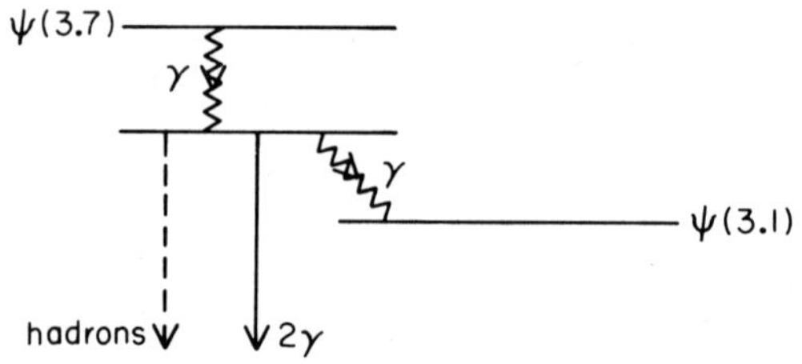

Fig. 11. The possible electromagnetic and strong decays involving a C = + state with $c\bar{c}$ quark content and a mass between 3.1 and 3.7 GeV. Dashed lines indicate decays forbidden by Zweig's rule.

Another situation of interest is the question of what are the other decays of the $\psi(3.7)$ besides $\psi(3.1)$ + anything. For up to now, specific channels like $4\pi^{\pm}$ + one neutral or $6\pi^{\pm}$ + one neutral which are not due to $\pi\pi\psi(3.1)$ decays have not been identified. Furthermore, if one uses the direct decays of $\psi(3.1) \to$ hadrons to estimate those for $\psi(3.7)$ in a potential picture,[55] the combination of phase space and the wave function at the origin gives values of order 50 keV for this quantity. But about half the total width is not $\psi(3.1)$ + anything. Where are the other decays? One possibility, $\psi(3.7) \to \gamma\eta_c$, we have already discussed. Another is $\psi(3.7) \to \gamma\,{}^3P$, but that for some reason the ${}^3P$ states decay into hadrons rather than $\gamma\psi(3.1)$. But if either the η_c or the ${}^3P$ states go into hadrons, they should decay at least a few percent of the time into $4\pi^{\pm}$, $6\pi^{\pm}$, etc. In that case, if a particular transition like $\psi(3.7)\to\gamma\eta_c$ was <u>the</u> principal other decay mode of $\psi(3.7)$, one should have $4\pi^{\pm}\gamma$, $6\pi^{\pm}\gamma$, etc. at a detectable level in $\psi(3.7)$ decay.[57] A much more exciting possibility is that the $\psi(3.7)$ lies just above threshold for decay into charmed particles. Whatever is the case, it should be very enlightening when we know which if any of these alternatives is chosen by Nature.

The most straightforward interpretation within a charm scheme for the rise in R near 4 GeV is that this is the threshold for producing pairs of charmed particles. Meson states (like the $\psi(4.1)$?) composed of $c\bar{c}$ above such a mass find it kinematically possible to decay into pairs of charmed particles via amplitudes allowed by Zweig's rule. Hence, such meson states are no longer narrow and have more typical hadronic widths. Asymptotically one expects R to approach $3(\frac{4}{9} + \frac{1}{9} + \frac{1}{9} + \frac{4}{9}) = 10/3$

if one has four quarks, u, d, s, and c, each coming in three colors. In asymptotically free gauge theories R approaches its asymptotic value from above. The value of R ($\sqrt{Q^2}$ =5.0) ≃ 5 is thus presently regarded by charm enthusiasts[41] as compatible with their expectations.

However, in such a picture a substantial part (≈ 1/2) of the cross section for $e^+e^- \to$ hadrons should involve production of charmed particles in the final state once one is above the threshold. Higher mass charmed particles will decay by strong or electromagnetic interactions, both of which conserve charm, cascading eventually into the lowest mass states carrying a unit of charm. These lowest mass states decay only weakly, and hence are very narrow. Furthermore, the most straightforward estimates[58] (as well as our experience with hyperons) indicate that nonleptonic decays dominate over semileptonic.[59] But in both cases, assuming a current-current form of the basic interaction, the origins of charm in weak interactions dictate that the charmed quark (c) is changed into a strange quark (s) by the large (cos θ) part of the Cabibbo current. As a result, states containing a charmed quark and $\bar{u}$ or $\bar{d}$ quark decay weakly dominantly into states with hadronic quantum numbers which include a unit of strangeness.[60] For meson decays, this unit of strangeness of the hadrons will manifest itself as a K meson among the decay products. Thus, following this naive argument, one expects first of all an increase in the number of K's per e^+e^- induced event once one crosses charmed particle production threshold. Secondly, from the nonleptonic decays one expects to find narrow peaks in the 2 GeV region in plots of the number of Kπ, Kππ, etc., events versus invariant mass. As discussed earlier, there is no dramatic increase of kaon production between 3.0 GeV (below the threshold) and 4.8 GeV (above the threshold). Striking peaks in $K\pi$, $K\pi\pi$, etc., mass plots have not been announced - and by now everyone is aware of the importance of looking for them. One way to avoid this last difficulty would be to demand decay into K+n π's where n is large ($\approx$ 4 or 5). Then most decays involve neutral pions, which remain undetected with the present magnetic detector, and this prevents reconstruction of the invariant mass of the entire K+nπ system resulting from charmed particle decay. However, then the value of $<n_{ch}>$ should rise once one is above threshold for charmed particle production and their subsequent decay to high multiplicity states. This doesn't seem to happen either (see Fig. 3). Another way out is to make semileptonic decays dominant, so one has an undetected neutrino in the decay products of charmed particles. Here the data[18,19] presented at this meeting on the inclusive muon spectrum ($1.0 < p_{\mu} < 2.4$ GeV) are an important restriction. For not only is the observed muon distribution in momentum and angle (collinearity and coplanarity) consistent with QED (including radiative corrections), but out of roughly 150 events all but a few have a total charged multiplicity of two, strongly indicating they mostly do not originate in multihadron events. It must be stressed that all these searches for various aspects of the charm picture are not yet conclusive, from the attempts to find evidence for the radiative transitions between $c\bar{c}$ states at the naively expected rates to the search for narrow peaks in $K\pi$ spectra and a change in the number of K's per event. Each is theoretically not crucial enough to kill the scheme, and in every case a change in the naive theoretical prediction by a factor of 2 to 5 will avoid any difficulty with present experimental results. Collectively, however, they make me, at least, somewhat uneasy.

V. CONCLUSION

In the last year many of our views on e^+e^- annihilation into hadrons have come almost full circle, except for one - its importance in understanding hadrons. As we have seen, the present data available on R are consistent with scaling, even precocious scaling, before new physics begins in the 3 to 4 GeV region. Below $\sqrt{Q^2} \simeq 3.6$ GeV, R is between 2 and 3 and consistent with, or consistent with approaching, the colored u, d, and s quark value of 2.

The new narrow resonances and the apparent threshold near $\sqrt{Q^2} = 4$ GeV are presumably related to the same physics and represent the excitation of new hadronic degrees of freedom. A possible explanation lies in the existence of a new hadronic quantum number, charm, and an associated fourth quark carrying a unit of this quantum number. The most crucial tests of this theory lie at the moment in spectroscopy - finding charmed particles and the other $c\bar{c}$ states expected to accompany the ψ's. We have examined these in some detail. Following the most naive theoretical estimates we have seen that presently there is not yet evidence for the expected spectroscopy, but that no really decisive test has been made. A scheme involving charm still seems to me the most attractive extant explanation for the totality of what has been observed.

Moreover, what has come out of all this is that the importance of quarks as the fundamental objects of hadron physics is clearer than ever. For hadron spectroscopy, current induced transitions between hadrons, deep inelastic scattering, and for e^+e^- annihilation, a theory based on abstraction from a field theory with fundamental fermion fields carrying quark quantum numbers again and again provides a basic understanding. When one finally writes down the complete story of strong interactions, and particularly that of hadron structure, near the beginning one will need to present the most basic hadronic measurement, that made by leptons shown in Figure 1.

ACKNOWLEDGEMENTS

I thank Professor Carl Kaysen for the hospitality of the Institute for Advanced Study, where part of this talk was conceived. Conversations with many colleagues at the Institute and at SLAC, and in particular with J.D. Bjorken and H. Harari, are greatly appreciated.

REFERENCES

1. J.-E. Augustin et al., Phys. Rev. Letters 33, 1406 (1974).
2. J.J. Aubert et al., Phys. Rev. Letters 33, 1404 (1974).
3. C. Bacci et al., Phys. Rev. Letters 33, 1408 (1974); Erratum, Phys. Rev. Letters 33, 1649 (1974).
4. G.S. Abrams et al., Phys. Rev. Letters 33, 1453 (1974).
5. $Q^2 = -q_\mu q_\mu$ is positive in the time-like region. $\alpha=e^2/4\pi \simeq 1/137$.
6. M. Gell-Mann, Phys. Letters 8, 214 (1964).
7. G. Zweig, CERN preprints TH.401 and TH.412, unpublished (1964).
8. M.Y. Han and Y. Nambu, Phys. Rev. 139, B1006 (1965).
9. D. Benaksas et al., Phys. Letters 39B, 289 (1972); ibid., 42B, 507 (1972); ibid., 48B, 155 (1974); ibid., 48B, 159 (1974); ibid., 40B, 685 (1972). G. Cosme et al., paper submitted to the Bonn Conference, August 1973 (unpublished).
10. G. Salvini, talk presented at the Italian Society of Physics, October 28 - November 2, 1974 (unpublished). The total cross sections used are "grand average" values from Frascati experiments.
11. J.-E. Augustin et al., SLAC-PUB-1520, 1975 (unpublished). A 10% uncertainty in overall normalization is not included in Fig. 1.
12. See, for example, J.D. Bjorken in Proceedings of the 6th International Symposium on Electron and Photon Interactions at High Energies, H. Rollnik and W. Pfeil, eds. (North-Holland, Amsterdam, 1974), p. 25.
13. The possibility of a step and/or bump in R at charm threshold and asymptotic approach to 10/3 was stressed before the recent experimental data by

K. Wilson, ref. 14, J. Kogut, ref. 15, and T. Appelquist and H.D. Politzer, ref. 16.

14. K. Wilson, remarks at the London Conference, July 1974 (unpublished).
15. J. Kogut, invited talk at the American Physical Society meeting, William and Mary College, September 5-7, 1974, and Cornell preprint CLNS-285, 1974 (unpublished).
16. T. Appelquist and H.D. Politzer, Phys. Rev. Letters 34, 43 (1975).
17. B. Richter, in Proceedings of the XVII International Conference on High Energy Physics, J.R. Smith, ed. (Science Research Council, Chilton, Didcot, 1974), p. IV-37.
18. B.A. Barnett, invited talk at this conference.
19. G.K. O'Neill, Bull. Am. Phys. Soc., Series II, 20, 95 (1975).
20. See, for example, F.J. Gilman, invited talk at the Irvine Conference, December 1973, and SLAC-PUB-1396, 1974 (unpublished).
21. H. Lynch, invited talk at this conference.
22. R.F. Schwitters, Bull. Am. Phys. Soc., Series II, 20, 95 (1975).
23. W. Braunschweig *et al.*, DESY preprints DESY 74/59, 1974 (unpublished) and DESY 74/62, 1974 (unpublished) and DESY 74/62, 1974 (unpublished).
24. R. Hofstadter, invited talk at this conference, and R.L. Ford *et al.*, Stanford University preprint HEPL 748, 1975 (unpublished).
25. We are assuming that J = 1 and all decay modes are detected in evaluating widths. See the discussion of widths and radiative corrections in J. Bjorken *et al.*, SLAC-PUB-1515, 1974 (unpublished), and

also K. Geer *et al.*, Ohio State preprint, COO-1545-147, 1974 (unpublished), and D.R. Yennie, Phys. Rev. Letters 34, 239 (1975).

26. G. Wolf, Bull. Am. Phys. Soc., Series II, 20, 95 (1975).

27. A.M. Boyarski *et al.*, SLAC-PUB-1523, 1975 (unpublished).

28. This has been particularly pointed out by H. Harari, SLAC-PUB-1514, 1974 (unpublished).

29. If one assumes that the $\pi\pi$ and $K\bar{K}$ decays are second order electromagnetic, i.e., $\psi(3.1)\to\gamma\to\pi\pi$ and $\psi(3.1)\to\gamma\to K\bar{K}$, then the DESY upper bounds translate to $|F_\pi(Q^2=(3.1)^2)|^2 < 0.1$ and $|F_K(Q^2=(3.1)^2)|^2 < 0.1$. The bound on $|F_\pi|^2$ is roughly a factor of four larger than an extrapolation based on $F_\pi(Q^2) \propto 1/Q^2$ and data at lower Q^2 values.

30. D.E. Andrews *et al.*, Phys. Rev. Letters 34, 233 (1975), and E.H. Thorndike, Bull. Am. Phys. Soc., Series II, 20, 95 (1975).

31. J.F. Martin *et al.*, Phys. Rev. Letters 34, 288 (1975).

32. University of Massachusetts - SLAC experiment as quoted at the Anaheim meeting, Bull. Am. Phys. Soc., Series II, 20, 95 (1975).

33. SLAC - University of Wisconsin experiment as quoted at the Anaheim meeting, Bull. Am. Phys. Soc., Series II, 20, 95 (1975).

34. Columbia University, University of Hawaii, Cornell University, University of Illinois, FNAL experiment as quoted at the Anaheim meeting, Bull. Am. Phys. Soc., Series II, 20, 95 (1975).

35. See, for example, the arguments of I. Bars and R. D. Peccei, Stanford University preprint ITP-480,

1974 (unpublished).

36. See, for example, the review of K. Gottfried, Proc. of the 1971 Int. Symposium on Electron and Photon Interactions at High Energies, N.B. Mistry, ed. (Cornell University, Ithaca, 1972), p. 221.

37. C.E. Carlson and P.G.O. Freund, University of Chicago preprint EFI 74-60, 1974 (unpublished).

38. Also relevant to the nature of the ψ's is their production in nucleon-nucleon collisions and other purely hadronic reactions. This has been treated by J.F. Gunion, University of Pittsburgh preprint, 1974 (unpublished); R. Blankenbecler *et al.*, SLAC-PUB-1531, 1975 (unpublished); R.M. Barnett and D. Silverman, Harvard University preprint, 1975 (unpublished); J. Kripfganz and J. Ranft, Leipzig preprint, 1975 (unpublished).

39. General reviews of the theoretical possibilities have been given in print by H. Harari, ref. 28; I. Bars *et al.*, SLAC-PUB-1522, 1974 (unpublished); and by the CERN Boson Theory Workshop, CERN preprint TH. 1964, 1974 (unpublished). See also ref. 41. Much of the material in this section covers the same ground as the above and other quoted references. My apologies are offered to the many people who have made the same analysis and arguments, whether in or out of print, who are not referenced here.

40. O.W. Greenberg, invited talk at this conference.

41. The case for charm has been particularly argued for by T. Appelquist and H.D. Politzer, ref. 16; A. De Rujula and S.L. Glashow, Phys. Rev. Letters **34**, 46 (1975); T. Appelquist *et al.*, Harvard preprint, 1974 (unpublished); and by M.K. Gaillard, B.W. Lee, and J.L. Rosner, FNAL preprint Pub-74/86-THY, 1974

(unpublished) and S. Borchardt *et al.*, Phys. Rev. Letters 34, 38 (1975) and Rochester preprint UR-505, 1974 (unpublished). Reviews of aspects of the charm option can be found in ref. 39 and in C. G. Callan *et al.*, Phys. Rev. Letters 34, 52 (1975); S. Kitakado *et al.*, DESY preprint, 1974 (unpublished); L. Clavelli and T.C. Yang, Maryland preprint, 1974 (unpublished); E. Takasugi and S. Oneda, Maryland preprints, 1974 (unpublished); P. Marcolungo, Padova preprint, 1974 (unpublished); Y. Hara, Tokyo preprint, 1975 (unpublished); K. Kajantie *et al.*, Helsinki preprint, 1975 (unpublished); J. Pasupathy, Tata Institute preprint, 1974 (unpublished). See also refs. 43 and 48.

42. Nothing prevents one from adding more than one new quark: see R.M. Barnett, Harvard preprint, 1974 (unpublished); M. Suzuki, Berkeley preprint, 1974 (unpublished); and many unpublished schemes.

43. J.D. Bjorken and S.L. Glashow, Phys. Letters 11, 255 (1964); S.L. Glashow, J. Illiopoulos, and L. Maiani, Phys. Rev. D 2, 1285 (1970). See also S. L. Glashow in *Experimental Meson Spectroscopy - 1974*, D. Garelick, ed., AIP Conference Proceedings No. 21, Subseries on Particles and Fields No. 8 (American Institute of Physics, New York, 1974), p. 387.

44. See in particular the asymptotically free gauge theory calculations of T. Appelquist and H.D. Politzer, ref. 16, and of A. De Rujula and S.L. Glashow, ref. 41.

45. Inasmuch as the recent partial wave analysis of the $\pi\rho$ system by F. Wagner, M. Tabak, and D.M. Chew, Berkeley preprint LBL-3395, 1974 (unpublished)

shows that the ω(1675) definitely has $J^P = 3^-$ and is therefore the partner of the g(1680), none of the partners of the ρ'(1600) can be claimed to have been seen. Establishment of the ω' and ϕ' is obviously of some interest.

46. Estimates of charmed particle masses are to be found in refs. 39 and 41. A lower bound of ≈ 1.84 GeV is provided by the narrow ψ(3.7) width.

47. See, for example, the review of the quark model states in F.J. Gilman, Proceedings of the Summer Institute on Particle Physics, M. Zipf, ed., SLAC Report No. SLAC-179, Vol. I, 307 (1974).

48. Such calculations are reported in the first three papers of ref. 41 and by E. Eichten et al., Cornell preprint, 1974 (unpublished); B.J. Harrington et al., Phys. Rev. Letters 34, 168 (1975); H.J. Schnitzer, Harvard preprint, 1974 (unpublished); T.P. Cheng and P.B. James, Missouri preprint, 1975 (unpublished); and J. Kogut and L. Susskind, Cornell preprint, 1975 (unpublished).

49. M. Gell-Mann, D. Sharp, and W. Wagner, Phys. Rev. Letters 8, 261 (1962).

50. See, for example, F.J. Gilman and M. Kugler, Phys. Rev. Letters 30, 518 (1973).

51. N. Barash-Schmidt et al., "Review of Particle Properties," Phys. Letters 50B, No. 1 (1974).

52. Using the observed rate for $\phi \to \gamma\pi$ of the Orsay experiments, ref. 9, one deduces ≈ 1/200 for the right-hand side of Eq. (9).

53. Such mixing and a model for the violations of Zweig's rule through the three-gluon channel in asymptotically free gauge theories have been discussed in detail by A. De Rujula and S.L. Glashow,

ref. 41. See also T. Appelquist and H.D. Politzer, ref. 16; and T. Appelquist et al., ref. 41.

54. The phase space for $N^*(1470)\to(\pi\pi)_s N(\rho'(1600)\to\pi\pi\rho)$ is less (greater) than that for $\psi(3.7)\to\pi\pi\psi(3.1)$.

55. These transitions are discussed in detail by T. Appelquist et al., ref. 41; E. Eichten et al., ref. 48; J. Borenstein and R. Shankar, Harvard preprint, 1974 (unpublished); and S. Rudaz, Cornell preprint, 1974 (unpublished). They have also been treated with varying thoroughness in many of the papers in refs. 39 and 41.

56. We use the notation η_c for the pseudoscalar state (associated with the $\psi(3.1)$) following M.K. Gaillard, B.W. Lee, and J.L. Rosner, ref. 41.

57. Another way out of this "difficulty" is for $\eta_c\to\gamma\gamma$ to be an important decay mode. One calculates $\Gamma(\eta_c\to\gamma\gamma) \simeq 300$ keV from p^3 phase space plus SU(4) symmetry ($A(\eta_c\to\gamma\gamma) = (\frac{4\sqrt{2}}{3})A(\pi^0\to\gamma\gamma)$) and $\Gamma(\pi^0\to\gamma\gamma)$ (or $\Gamma(\eta\to\gamma\gamma)$ with account of singlet-octet mixing.) However, aside from questions of whether this overestimates the true width, even with this large a $\gamma\gamma$ width the decay of η_c into hadrons is expected to be over an order of magnitude larger according to the papers in ref. 53.

58. See for example M.K. Gaillard, B.W. Lee, and J.L. Rosner, ref. 41.

59. G. Altarelli, N. Cabibbo, and L. Maiani, Ecole Normale Superieure preprint, 1974 (unpublished). See also R.L. Kingsley et al., Princeton preprint, 1975 (unpublished).

60. If one assumes that the piece of the weak nonleptonic Hamiltonian transforming like the regular, 15-dimensional representation of SU(4) dominates,

this is no longer true, as noted by J.D. Bjorken and H. Harari (private communication), and by A. Pais and V. Rittenberg, Rockefeller preprint, COO-2232B-69, 1975 (unpublished). Also H. Fritzsch (private communication).

ELECTRON-POSITRON ANNIHILATION TO HADRONS AND COLOR SYMMETRIES OF ELEMENTARY PARTICLES

OR

THE OUTLOOK FOR COLOR: GRAY OR ROSY?

O. W. Greenberg*

Center for Theoretical Physics

Department of Physics and Astronomy

University of Maryland

College Park, Maryland 20742

1. INTRODUCTION

In this talk I survey several versions of the color model, and discuss the use of this model to account for the recently discovered ψ (or J) resonances.[1] First, I discuss where color comes from, and in doing so I remind you of the successes of the quark model,[2,3] and, in particular, the symmetric quark model,[4,5] in accounting for the properties of baryons. Then I describe the variety of possible color models. Unlike the case of charm,[6] where there is a unique way of describing the ψ mesons as 1^- charmed quark-charmed anti-quark states, with color there are several possibilities,

*Supported in part by the National Science Foundation under Grant No. GP-43662X.

which, a priori, can have an equal chance to account for the ψ's. Next I discuss qualitative features which most of the color models have in common, and the problems they encounter, in particular, the problem of radiative decays. Finally I describe some specific color models which have been proposed to account for the present data on the ψ's, and I give experimental predictions which characterize the different models.

2. WHERE DOES COLOR COME FROM?

We are all familiar with the quark model,[2,3] in which the quantum numbers of hadrons are accounted for in terms of the quantum numbers of quarks, with mesons represented by $(q\bar{q})$ and baryons by (qqq). Table I lists the familiar quantum numbers of the quarks. Taking

TABLE I: Quantum Numbers of Quarks

	J^P	B	Y	I	I_z	Q	U	U_z
p	$\frac{1}{2}^+$	$\frac{1}{3}$	$\frac{1}{3}$	$\frac{1}{2}$	$\frac{1}{2}$	$\frac{2}{3}$	0	0
n	$\frac{1}{2}^+$	$\frac{1}{3}$	$\frac{1}{3}$	$\frac{1}{2}$	$-\frac{1}{2}$	$-\frac{1}{3}$	$\frac{1}{2}$	$\frac{1}{2}$
λ	$\frac{1}{2}^+$	$\frac{1}{3}$	$-\frac{2}{3}$	0	0	$-\frac{1}{3}$	$\frac{1}{2}$	$-\frac{1}{2}$

the quark as a 3, and the antiquark as a 3* under SU(3), we find the familiar reductions

$$B \sim (qqq) \sim 3\text{x}3\text{x}3 = 1+8+8+10$$

for baryons, and

$$M \sim (q\bar{q}) \sim 3 \text{ x } 3^* = 1 + 8$$

for mesons.

To classify hadrons, it is convenient to take account of the spin of the quark in addition to the degree of freedom associated with SU(3) symmetry. The quark is a 3 in SU(3) and a 2 in $SU(3)_S$, the spin SU(2), and following Gürsey and Radicati[7] and Sakita[8] we can consider the quark as a 6 in SU(6). Then $q = (p^{\uparrow}, p^{\downarrow}, n^{\uparrow}, n^{\downarrow}, \lambda^{\uparrow}, \lambda^{\downarrow}) \rightarrow (3,2)$ under $SU(6) \rightarrow SU(3) \times SU(2)_S$. Just as the reduction of $3 \times 3^*$ gives the SU(3) content of mesons, and the reduction of $3 \times 3 \times 3$ gives the SU(3) content of baryons, the analogous reductions in SU(6) give the classification of baryons and mesons under this larger group. For baryons, we have

$$B \sim (qqq) \sim 6 \times 6 \times 6 = 56 + 70 + 70 + 20,$$

where the Young diagrams are shown under the representations. As indicated, the 20 is antisymmetric under permutations of the SU(6) degrees of freedom, and would be expected to contain the S-wave three quark bound states corresponding to the lowest baryons. This possibility was considered by Sakita,[8] who gave the reduction

$$20 \rightarrow (8,2) + (1,4), \text{ under } SU(6) \rightarrow SU(3) \times SU(2)_S.$$

There is a spin-$\frac{1}{2}$ octet of baryons, but there is no even-parity spin-$\frac{3}{2}$ resonance at low mass. In addition, the magnetic moments for the (8,2) are completely wrong, not only in magnitude but in sign: they point the wrong way. The 56 is totally symmetric in the SU(6) degree of freedom, and would seem to be composed of bose quarks. Nonetheless, the reduction

$$56 \rightarrow (8,2) + (10,4) \text{ under } SU(6) \rightarrow SU(3) \times SU(2)_S,$$

given by Gürsey and Radicati, just includes the spin-1/2 nucleon octet containing N,Λ,Σ and Ξ, and the decuplet of spin-3/2 containing Δ, Σ*, Ξ* and Ω. The magnetic moments of these particles calculated by Bég, Lee, and Pais[9] and by Sakita[10] agree well with the nucleon octet magnetic moments provided the effective magnetic moments of the quarks are taken to be

$$\mu_i = 2.79\, q_i \frac{e\hbar}{2M_p c}$$

where $q_i e$ $(e > o)$ is the charge of the ith quark and M_p is the proton mass. This effective quark magnetic moment would occur if the quark were a Dirac particle with an effective mass

$$M^{eff}_{quark} = \frac{M_P}{2.79}$$

Heuristically, the three quarks in a proton behave, as far as their magnetic moments are concerned, as though each quark has about a third of the proton mass. This model correlates the radiative decays of ω and Δ with the magnetic moment of the proton, using the quark model, and taking all inner products between quark model space wave functions in the same SU(6) supermultiplet to be one. The results agree with experiment to within 20%. The predicted G_A/G_V ratio is too large, but of the correct order of magnitude. An SU(6) point of view leads to the Gürsey-Radicati mass formula.

$$M = M_o + M_1 Y + M_2 I\,(I+1) + M_3 J(J+1)$$

which relates the SU(3) mass splittings in the octet and decuplet, and accounts well for the masses of the 8 isospin multiplets in this 56 supermultiplet. The symmetric quark model rule[4,5] for the higher baryon supermultiplets is that the state must be totally symmetric in the SU(6) and orbital degrees of freedom of 3 quarks, without excitation of center of mass motion. Thus, including the total orbital angular momentum and parity, L^P, the supermultiplets $(56,0^+)$, $(70,1^-)$, $(56,2^+)$, $(56,0^+)$, etc., occur. These have been analyzed most recently by Jones, Laskinski, and Levi Setti[11] and by Dalitz and Horgan,[12] who showed that the quark model accommodates the known resonances and gives a good account of their masses and decays.

Mesons in the SU(6) model are $(q\bar{q})$ composites and have the SU(6) content

$$6 \times 6^* = 1 + 35,$$

$$1 \rightarrow (1,1),\ (\eta'),\ \text{under } SU(6) \rightarrow SU(3) \times SU(2)_S,$$

$35 \rightarrow (8,1)+(1+8,3),(\pi,K,\bar{K},\eta)+(\rho,\omega,K^*,\bar{K}^*,\phi)$, under $SU(6) \rightarrow SU(3) \times SU(2)_S$. Here again the SU(6) classification scheme is successful in correlating multiplets of the same parity and different spins in a single SU(6) supermultiplet. Here, because of the quarks and antiquarks are not identical, the meson classification does not depend on quark statistics.

Why are the three quarks in a baryon symmetric under permutations, rather than antisymmetric? The simplest answer is that some hidden three-valued degree of freedom is present. The most economical scheme to accomplish this is to assume parafermi quark statistics[4] of order three, in which up to three quarks are allowed to occupy the same quantum state. In this scheme states totally symmetric in the SU(6) degrees of freedom are allowed. These states are the only three-quark composite states which behave as fermions. The parastatistics has solved the problem of permutation symmetry. By Green's ansatz[13] and the Klein transformation[14] this model is in most ways equivalent to a model with three identical fractionally charged quark triplets.[15] This model was renamed the color model by Gell-Mann, et al.,[16] and, in the patriotic version, the extra three-valued degree of freedom was called red, white and blue.

The next model of this kind was suggested by Han and Nambu.[17] They considered three distinguishable triplets with quantum numbers chosen in such a way that these quarks have integral charge. Other color models are described below.

Han and Nambu called the SU(3) acting within a triplet SU(3)', and the SU(3) which mixes corresponding members of different triplets SU(3)". The Han-Nambu quark nonet transforms as (3,3*) under SU(3)' x SU(3)". I follow this notation and call the diagonal SU(3) group SU(3). (The reader should note that SU(3)' is often called SU(3), and SU(3)" is often called $SU(3)_{color}$ or SU(3)' in the literature). The identification of the terminology SU(3)" and $SU(3)_{color}$ is convenient and I use it. I make the identification of SU(3)' and SU(3) only for models in which the observed SU(3) is identified with SU(3)'.

To classify states in color models, the chain $SU(18) \rightarrow SU(6)' \times SU(3)'' \rightarrow SU(3)' \times SU(3)'' \times SU(2)_S$ can be used. In this classification, the S-wave baryons are in a totally antisymmetric 816 three-quark representation,[18] and the S-wave mesons are in

$$18 \times 18^* = 1 + 323, \text{ in } SU(18).$$

$1 \rightarrow (1,1,1)$; $323 \rightarrow (8,1,1) + (8+1, 1,3) + (8+1, 8, 1+3)$ under $SU(18) \rightarrow SU(3)' \times SU(3)'' \times SU(2)_S$.

3. STRUCTURE OF COLOR MODELS

The parastatistics or identical triplet color model has three identical quark triplets whose charges are given in the following natrix.

$$Q = \begin{array}{c} p \\ n \\ \lambda \end{array} \begin{pmatrix} \text{Red} & \text{White} & \text{Blue} \\ \frac{2}{3} & \frac{2}{3} & \frac{2}{3} \\ -\frac{1}{3} & -\frac{1}{3} & -\frac{1}{3} \\ -\frac{1}{3} & -\frac{1}{3} & -\frac{1}{3} \end{pmatrix}$$

The rows are labeled by the quark names p, n, and λ, and the columns are labeled by the colors red, white and blue. Here, the color degree of freedom does not contribute to the charge, which is given by the Gell-Mann-Nishijima formula

$$Q = I_3 + \frac{1}{2} Y,$$

where I_3 and Y are the third component of isospin and the hypercharge, respectively, of the observed SU(3) which is identified with the SU(3)' above. Let

$$\mathcal{Q} = \begin{pmatrix} 2/3 & & \\ & -1/3 & \\ & & -1/3 \end{pmatrix}$$

Then

$$\gamma \sim (8,1) \sim \mathcal{Q} \times 1 \text{ in } SU(3) \times SU(3)_{color},$$

and the photon does not excite the $SU(3)_{color}$ degrees of freedom. Thus, in this model, the ψ (or J) resonances can not be interpreted as color excitations. It has been speculated that this model provides a permanent quark binding mechanism in schemes in which the

$SU(3)_{color}$ degree of freedom is never excited and the ψ resonances are charmed quark-charmed antiquark composites.[19]

In the naive quark-parton model,

$$R \equiv \frac{\sigma(e^+e^- \to \text{hadrons})}{\sigma(e^+e^- \to \mu^+ \mu^-)} \to \sum_i Q_i^2, \quad s \to \infty \quad .$$

For this version of the color model, R = 2. The ranges of baryon and meson charges are 2, 1, ...-1 and 1, 0, -1, respectively, as in the Gell-Mann-Zweig quark model.

In the Han-Nambu model, as mentioned above, the quark nonet is taken as a (3,3*) under SU(3)' x SU(3)". This nonet reduces to

$$q \sim (3,3^*) \to 1 + 8$$

under the diagonal SU(3). The generators of diagonal SU(3) in the quark model nonet can be taken to be the matrices

$$\frac{1}{2}[\lambda_\alpha \times 1 - 1 \times \lambda_\alpha^T]$$

Here the charges are integral

$$Q = \begin{matrix} \\ p' \\ n' \\ \lambda' \end{matrix} \begin{matrix} \bar{p}'' & \bar{n}'' & \bar{\lambda}'' \\ \left(\begin{matrix} 0 \\ -1 \\ -1 \end{matrix} \right. & \begin{matrix} 1 \\ 0 \\ 0 \end{matrix} & \left. \begin{matrix} 1 \\ 0 \\ 0 \end{matrix} \right) \end{matrix}$$

The photon is

$$\gamma \sim (8,1) + (1,8) \to 8_{diagonal}$$
$$\sim \mathcal{Q} \times 1 - 1 \times \mathcal{Q} \ .$$

The R parameter is 4; the range of baryon and meson charges are both symmetric around zero: 3, 2, ..., -3 and 2, 1, ..., -2, respectively.

There are a number of variations of this model: (i) the observed SU(3) can be taken to be either the diagonal SU(3) or the SU(3)', (ii) the particle eigenstates in SU(3)" can be labeled either by the quantum numbers I, I_z, and Y, or by U, U_z, and Q. This latter choice depends on the assumed color-breaking interactions: if the main color-breaking interactions are due to electromagnetism, or to other U-spin scalar interactions, then the U, U_z, Q scheme is relevant; if medium-strong color-breaking interactions are dominant, then the I, I_z, Y scheme occurs.

Another variation of the model is one in which the quark nonet is taken as

$$q \sim (3,3) \rightarrow 6 + 3^*.$$

The SU(3)" 3 can be antisymmetrized just as well as the 3*, and although this model has not received as much consideration as the Han-Nambu model, it should be taken as a serious possibility. Note that the 3* states of this model have the same quantum numbers as a usual antiquark triplet. The charge matrix now contains fractional charges

$$Q = \begin{array}{c} \\ p' \\ n' \\ \lambda' \end{array} \begin{array}{c} \begin{array}{ccc} p'' & n'' & \lambda'' \end{array} \\ \begin{pmatrix} \frac{4}{3} & \frac{1}{3} & \frac{1}{3} \\ \frac{1}{3} & -\frac{2}{3} & -\frac{2}{3} \\ \frac{1}{3} & -\frac{2}{3} & -\frac{2}{3} \end{pmatrix} \end{array}$$

The photon has the form

$$\gamma \sim (8,1) + (1,8) \rightarrow 8 \sim \mathcal{Q} \times 1 + 1 \times \mathcal{Q}.$$

In this model the range of baryon charges is asymmetric as in the quark model, but the range is larger:

4,3,..., -2. The range of meson charges is the same in the Han-Nambu model, as is the R parameter.

The Tati model[20] differs from the models considered above in taking an SU(2) or SO(3) triplet for the second type of degree of freedom:

$$q \sim (3,\ SU(2)\ \text{or}\ SO(3)\ 3)$$
$$\sim (2+1,3) \to 2+4+3\ \text{under}$$
$$SU(2)_{I'} \times U(1)_{Y'} \times SU(2)_{I''} \to SU(2)_I\ .$$

Here the quark charges are fractional:

$$Q = \begin{array}{c} \\ p' \\ n' \\ \lambda' \end{array} \begin{array}{c} \begin{array}{ccc} \text{"}\pi^+\text{"} & \text{"}\pi^0\text{"} & \text{"}\pi^-\text{"} \end{array} \\ \begin{pmatrix} \frac{5}{3} & \frac{2}{3} & -\frac{1}{3} \\ \frac{2}{3} & -\frac{1}{3} & -\frac{4}{3} \\ \frac{2}{3} & -\frac{1}{3} & -\frac{4}{3} \end{pmatrix} \end{array}$$

The photon has the form

$$\gamma \sim (8,1) + (1,3) \sim Q \times 1 + 1 \times \begin{pmatrix} 1 & & \\ & 0 & \\ & & -1 \end{pmatrix}.$$

The range of baryon and meson charges are larger than before: 5, 4,...,-4 and 3, 2,...,-3. The R parameter is 8.

Models which have both charm and a color degree of freedom which can be excited clearly allow more possibilities than a model in which only charm or color can be excited. I will describe some such models in detail in Sec. 9, but mention here only the Pati-Salam gauge model[21] in which colored vector gluons which can manifest themselves as resonances appear in addition to the $(q\bar{q})$ composites, where $q \sim (4,3^*)$ under $SU(4)' \times SU(3)''$. The quarks are in the same fundamental 16 as the leptons. The charge matrix of the 16 is

$$Q = \begin{array}{c} p \\ n \\ \lambda \\ c \end{array} \begin{array}{c} \\ \left(\begin{array}{cccc} a & b & c & \text{leptons} \\ 0 & 1 & 1 & \nu_e \\ -1 & 0 & 0 & e^- \\ -1 & 0 & 0 & \mu^- \\ 0 & 1 & 1 & \nu_\mu \end{array} \right) \end{array}$$

Here $R_{\text{color}} = 4$, and $R_{\text{color + charm}} = 6$.

All the models in which color is excited predict a wider range of charges than the quark model. In particular, all of these models differ from the charm model in predicting multiply-charged meson states.

4. NUMEROLOGICAL INTERLUDE

Before discussing the ways in which color models can account for the ψ's, I include a numerological interlude in Table II, which is constructed using equal intervals in $(\text{mass})^2$. Note that (i) the ρ and ω, the ρ' and f, and other mesons fall in the same series as the ψ and ψ' as though the ψ's were low daughters of the ρ-f trajectory, (ii) the ψ,ψ' and ψ" are equally spaced in $(\text{mass})^2$.

5. WHAT IS THERE TO EXPLAIN ABOUT THE ψ RESONANCES?

The data concerning the ψ's has just been reviewed by Dr. Lynch, and further comments were made by Dr. Gilman. Here I collect some preliminary useful information about the ψ's. Table III gives the masses, and total and leptonic widths of the three ψ's.

Table II: Numerological Interlude[22]

No.	Mass (GeV)	Resonances	J^P	I^G	Observed Mass (GeV)
18	4.191	ψ''	1^-?	?	4.150
14	3.684	ψ'	1^-?	0^-	3.684
10	3.095	ψ	1^-	0^-	3.095
6	2.364	U, $(N\bar{N})$	?,?	1?,0?	2.360, 2.375
5	2.142	ρ''', T	?,?	1^+,?	2.100, 2.200
4	1.895	S	?	?	1.930
3	1.610	ρ'', A_3	$1^-,2^-$	$1^+,1^-$	1.600, 1.640
2	1.262	ρ', f	$1^-,2^+$	$1^+,0^+$	1.250, 1.270
1	0.771	ρ,ω	$1^-,1^-$	$1^+,0^-$	0.770, 0.783

TABLE III: Properties of the ψ's[1]

	J^P	Mass (MeV)	Total Width (MeV)	Leptonic Width (keV)
ψ	1^-	3095 ± 3	0.077 ± 0.019	5.2 ± 1.3
ψ'	1^-?	3684 ± 4	0.2 to 1.0	2.2 ± 0.6
ψ"	1^-?	4150 ± 100	250 to 300	4.0 ± 1.2

I will use ψ for ψ(3095), ψ' for ψ'(3684) and ψ" for ψ" (4150) throughout. The status of ψ" as a resonance is not as clearly established as that of ψ and ψ'. In addition, "hadron" will mean the uncharmed non-colored particles known before the discovery of the ψ's; sometimes I will emphasize this by a phrase like "ordinary hadrons." I will use H to denote a generic hadronic state. Table IV lists decay modes of ψ and ψ' for which preliminary rough branching ratios are available.

Table IV: Preliminary Rough Branching Ratios for ψ and ψ'.

Decay modes of ψ	Rough Branching ratio (%)
e^+e^-	6.8
$\mu^+\mu^-$	6.8
5π	3 to 4
ωπ	0.6 to 0.8
4π	0.6 to 0.8
$p\bar{p}$	0.08
$\Lambda\bar{\Lambda}$	<0.08

Other modes seen: 3π, ρπ, ρ3π, $\pi^+\pi^-$ K^+K^-

Decay modes of ψ'	Rough Branching ratio (%)
ψππ	50
H (hadrons)	20
e^+e^-	0.22 to 1.1
$\mu^+\mu^-$	0.22 to 1.1

The present data for production of ψ's in hadronic collisions and in photoproduction is: $\sigma(pBe \rightarrow \psi X)B \sim 0.1$ nb/nucleon, with 28.5 GeV protons,[23] or $\sigma(pN \rightarrow \psi X) \sim 1.5$ nb/nucleon; $\sigma(nBe \rightarrow \psi X)B \sim 3$nb/nucleon with neutrons peaked at 250 GeV,[24] or $\sigma(nBe \rightarrow \psi X) \sim 45$ nb/nucleon; $\sigma(\gamma Be \rightarrow \psi X)B = (1.8 \pm 0.5)$nb/nucleon from photons with a cut-off energy of 250 GeV,[24] or $\sigma(\gamma\ Be \rightarrow \psi X) \sim 26$ nb/nucleon. Use of vector dominance, assuming the $\psi\gamma$ coupling $f_{\psi\gamma}$ is the same for on-shell photons as for photons of mass M_ψ, leads to $\sigma_{tot}(\psi N) \sim 1$ mb. Comparison of photoproduction of ψ from Be and Pb leads to $\sigma_{tot}(\psi N) < 20$ mb, and consistent with 1 mb. This implies the bound

$$\frac{f_{\psi\gamma}(o)}{f_{\psi\gamma}(M_\psi{}^2)} > \frac{1}{20} \quad .$$

6. HOW CAN COLOR MODELS EXPLAIN THE ψ RESONANCES?[25]

Here, we consider the color models for the ψ's in a general way, leaving more detailed discussion to Sec. 9. The first question to be asked is: What new states can be excited in the reaction $e^+e^- \rightarrow \gamma \rightarrow$ meson? If we assume that the $Y = 0$ neutral vector meson states in $(1 + 8, 1)$ are used up by the ρ^o, ω and ϕ, then the photon can only excite new states which contain $(1,\gamma)$.[26] To discuss these possibilities, we must decide the orientation of the particle eigenstates in SU(3)". Figure 1 illustrates possible orientations. For the U-spin orientation, the relevant states are $(1,\gamma) + (8,\gamma)$.

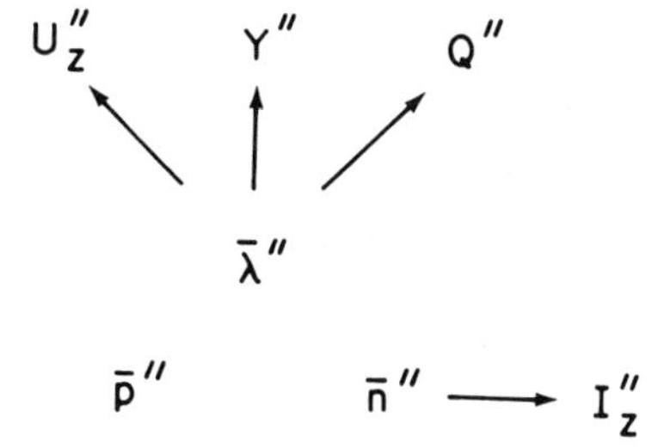

Figure 1: Orientation of Particle Eigenstates in SU(3)

which are excited via the $(1,\gamma)$ part of the state. For the I-spin orientation, the possible states are in $(1,\rho^\circ) + (8,\rho^\circ)$ and $(1,\omega_8) + (8,\omega_8)$.[27] The simplest possibility with U-spin orientation is I: to have the $\psi \sim (1,\gamma)$. In this case the other ψ's would be in different radial or orbital states than the lowest one. This situation would resemble that of the charm model for the ψ's. The simplest model with I-spin orientation is II: to have two narrow ψ's $\sim (1,\rho^\circ)$ and $(1,\omega_8)$.[28] There are two possibilities analogous to these two, in which the singlet under SU(3)' is replaced by ω-like and ϕ-like mixtures of singlet and octet, like the usual ω and ϕ. For the U-spin orientation, III: the states are (ω,γ) and (ϕ,γ).[29-32] For the I-spin orientation, IV: the states are (ω,ρ°), (ϕ,ρ°), (ω,ω_8) and (ϕ,ω_8).[33,34] These four possibilities are collected in Table V.

Table V: Colored Vector Mesons Excited by the Photon

Diagonal States Under SU(3)' \ Orientation in SU(3)"	U"-spin	I"-spin
1'	I $(1,\gamma)$	II $(1,\rho^\circ),(1,\omega_8)$
ω',ϕ'	III (ω,γ), (ϕ,γ)	IV $(\omega,\omega^\circ),(\phi,\rho^\circ)$ $(\omega,\omega_8),(\phi,\omega_8)$

Now we discuss these four cases in turn.

I. There is only one 1^3S_1 colored state which is excited by the photon; presumably $\psi(3095)$ is this state. The remaining (1,8) vector states, none of which are multiply charged, have masses close to 3095 MeV. The higher ψ's are in different radial or orbital states, such as 2^3S_1 or 2^3D_1; such assignments are similar to those made in the charm model. The (8,8) states, which include multiply-charged mesons, could lie at higher masses. This version fails to use the group-theory possibilities of the three-triplet model, which allow more than one ψ among the 1^3S_1 states. As in the four versions of the color model discussed here, the narrow width for decay to the usual hadrons is due to conservation of color: terms in the symmetry-breaking Hamiltonian H_{SB} which transform as 8" are small, and thus

$$\Gamma(8'' \rightarrow 1'') \propto |\langle 1'' \, | H_{SB} | 8'' \rangle|^2$$

is small, i.e.

$$\psi \not\rightarrow \text{usual hadrons},$$
$$(\cdot,8) \not\rightarrow (\cdot,1).$$

II.[28] Two 1^3S_1 colored states are excited by the photon: $(1,\rho^\circ)$ and $(1,\omega_8)$; presumably $\psi(3095)$ and ψ' (3684) are the states. The narrow width for these states to decay to hadrons is due to the smallness of $\langle 1''|H_{SB}|8''\rangle$ just discussed; however if the 8" part of H_{SB} is small enough to make these ψ's narrow, then the partial width for $\psi'(3684) \rightarrow \psi(3095)\pi\pi$ would be much smaller than observed. Therefore this $\psi' \rightarrow \psi\pi\pi$ mode must be due to a rather large 27" part of H_{SB}. Furthermore, this decay violates I" conservation as well as SU(3)" symmetry. In ordinary SU(3), isospin symmetry is less broken than SU(3) symmetry, and contributions to H_{SB} transforming as a 27 are small. The necessity for H_{SB} to break I" strongly and to have a large term transforming as a 27" is discouraging for this version of the model.

III.[29-32] Two 1^3S_1 colored states, (ω,γ) and (ϕ,γ) are excited by the photon. These states have narrow widths for decays to the usual hadrons because $\langle 1''|H_{SB}|8''\rangle$ is small, but they can decay to each other because of terms in H_{SB} which transform as 8'. Several authors[29,31,32] assign the $\psi(3095)$ and $\psi'(3684)$ to these states, and use the ratio of the leptonic widths,[35]

$$\frac{\Gamma_{e^+e^-}((\omega,\gamma))}{\Gamma_{e^+e^-}((\phi,\gamma))} = \frac{2}{1}$$

to assign $\psi(3095)$ to (ω,γ) and $\psi'(3684)$ to (ϕ,γ). Then $\psi'(3684) \to \psi(3095)\pi\pi$ is allowed by conservation of color, and suppressed, to some degree, by the Zweig rule, because ψ and ψ' are composed of disjoint sets of quarks, in analogy with the usual argument which prohibits $\phi \to \rho\pi$. T. C. Yang[30] uses the mass formula

$$\frac{M^2(a,\gamma)}{M^2(a,1)} = \text{const., independent of } a$$

to assign $\psi(3095)$ to (ω,γ) and $\psi''(4150)$ to (ϕ,γ). Note that (ρ^o,γ) is pure (8,8) and is not excited by the photon.

IV.[33,34] The photon excites four 1^3S_1 colored states, two of which have narrow widths for decays to the usual hadrons for the same reason as before. The argument given under II applies against transitions between (ω or ϕ,ρ^o) and (ω or ϕ,ω_8) without emission of colored particles. This argument poses a serious problem for the model of Sanda and Terazawa. Their model, however, can accommodate all three known ψ's in 1^3S_1 states together with a predicted fourth ψ at 4.9 GeV. (See Table VI). Ignoring Zweig's rule, the decays $\psi'' \rightarrow \psi H$ and $\psi''' \rightarrow \psi' H$ are allowed transitions between octet color states,

Table VI: Photon-excited resonances in the Sanda-Terazawa Model

Resonance	Assignment	Ratio of leptonic widths[35]	Hadronic width
$\psi'''(4900)$ (predicted)	(ϕ,ω_8)	1	large
$\psi''(4150)$	(ϕ,ρ°)	3	large
$\psi'(3684)$	(ω,ω_8)	2	small
$\psi(3095)$	(ω,ρ°)	6	small

which agrees with the large width of ψ'' and predicts a large width for ψ'''.

These four models all use SU(3)' x SU(3)" to classify states, rather than the diagonal SU(3) subgroup. I discuss further properties of these models in Sec. 9.

Pati and Salam have considered models in which the $(q\bar{q})$ states are supplemented by the colored vector gluons which bind the quarks in hadrons. I describe the Pati-Salam models in Sec. 9.

Models of the ψ's in which their narrow hadronic widths are due to conservation of color can be constructed using the other versions of the color model such as the (3,3) model and Tati's model, mentioned in Sec. 3. These models are qualitatively similar to the ones I have just described; I will not consider them in detail here.

The variant of the Han-Nambu model in which the quark nonet transforms as (3,3) under SU(3)' x SU(3)", rather than as (3,3*) allows construction of a model of ψ's in which their narrow hadronic widths are due to the Zweig rule, as in the charm model, rather than to color symmetry. Consider a different use of the (3,3) nonet, in which the reduction

$$(3,3) \rightarrow 6 + 3^*$$

under the diagonal subgroup allows the usual mesons to be formed out of this 3* and its anti-triplet 3** = 3, since 3* x 3 = 1 + 8. The new resonances will be built[36] from 6 x 6* = 1 + 8 + 27, and Zweig's rule makes some of them narrow. Mesons in 6 x 3 = 8 + 10 and 6* x 3*= 8 + 10* will also occur.

For further discussion of this model, it is convenient to introduce the following notation for the quark nonet: the 6 and 3* will be labeled as in Table VII.

Table VII: The 6 and 3* reduction of the (3,3) nonet.

		A_{-2}			$\bar{p}^{-2/3}$	$\bar{n}^{1/3}$
	B_{-2}		B_1			
C_{-2}		C_1		C_4	$\lambda^{-1/3}$	

In Table VII, the superscripts on the 3* states are the electric charge in units of |e|, and the subscripts on the 6 states are three times the electric charge, the rows in the 6 and, separately, in the 3* have the same values of I; in addition, Y increases down, and I_z increases to the right. I will use the symbols B and C to denote the corresponding isospin multiplet, where convenient. The nonet matrix is

$$\begin{array}{cccc} & p'' & n'' & \lambda'' \\ p' & C_4 & 2^{-\frac{1}{2}}(C_1 + \bar{\lambda}) & 2^{-\frac{1}{2}}(B_1 - \bar{n}) \\ n' & 2^{-\frac{1}{2}}(C_1 - \bar{\lambda}) & C_{-2} & 2^{-\frac{1}{2}}(B_{-2} + \bar{p}) \\ \lambda' & 2^{-\frac{1}{2}}(B_1 + \bar{n}) & 2^{-\frac{1}{2}}(B_{-2} - \bar{p}) & A_{-2} \end{array}$$

Since among $\bar{p}$, $\bar{n}$, and $\bar{\lambda}$, we expect $M(\bar{p}, \bar{n}) < M(\bar{\lambda})$ in the 3*, we expect $M(A) < M(B) < M(C)$ in the 6. Further, since 6 is triangular, we expect equal spacing:

$$M^2(C) - M^2(B) = M^2(B) - M^2(A).$$

In analogy with ideal nonet mixing for the usual ω and ϕ, assume that there are three I=0 vector mesons constructed of 6 and 6* which are each composed of quarks in a different isospin multiplet of the 6:

$$\psi = A\bar{A}$$

$$\psi' = \frac{1}{\sqrt{2}}\,(B_1\bar{B}_1 + B_{-2}\bar{B}_{-2})$$

$$\psi'' = \frac{1}{\sqrt{3}}\,(C_4\bar{C}_4 + C_1\bar{C}_1 + C_{-2}\bar{C}_{-2}).$$

The ψ state will be the unique lowest-mass vector meson in 6 x 6*. The equal spacing between the quark isospin multiplets in the 6 leads to equal spacing between these three mesons:

$$M^2(\psi'') - M^2(\psi') = M^2(\psi') - M^2(\psi).$$

Assign these states as in Table VIII, which also contains their predicted leptonic widths.

Table VII: Assignments, masses and leptonic width ratios[35] in the 6*-3 model

	Assignment	Mass	Leptonic width ratio
ψ''	$3^{-\frac{1}{2}}C.\overline{C}$	4191	8
ψ'	$2^{-\frac{1}{2}}B.\overline{B}$	3684 input	9
ψ	$A\overline{A}$	3095 input	6

Note that these states are mixtures of SU(3) 1, 8, and 27 states.

7. THE PROBLEM OF RADIATIVE DECAYS OR WHAT THE PHOTON BRINGETH THE PHOTON TAKETH AWAY

The problem of radiative decays is the most serious difficulty for most color models. From the standpoint of group theory

$$\psi \rightarrow \text{usual hadrons in an SU(3)' singlet} + \gamma$$
$$(1,8) \rightarrow (1,1) \times (1,8)$$

is allowed. I will use the quark model in the most naive way to see how big this problem of radiative decays might be. First, recall the quark model[37] calculation for M1 radiative decays of vector mesons V, to pseudoscalar mesons, P, in the same SU(6) supermultiplet:

$$\Gamma(V \rightarrow P\gamma) = \frac{1}{3\pi}\,\mu_{VP}^2 \left(\frac{M_V^2 - M_P^2}{2M_V}\right)^3 ,$$

where

$$\mu_{VP} = \langle P|\mu_q \;\Sigma_i\; q_i \sigma_{zi}|V(S_z=0)\rangle \quad ,$$

μ_q is the quark magneton, and q_i is the charge of the ith quark in units of $|e|$. The proton magnetic moment,

$$\mu_p = \langle p\uparrow | \mu_q \Sigma_i q_i \sigma_{zi} | p\uparrow \rangle$$

fixes

$$\mu_q = \mu_p = \frac{2.79\ e\hbar}{2M_p c} .$$

The prediction for $\omega \to \pi^o\gamma$ is then

$\Gamma(\omega \to \pi^o\gamma) = 1.18$ MeV, vs. 0.87 MeV experimentally.[22] The corresponding calculation for $\psi \to \eta'\gamma$, assuming ψ and η' are in the same SU(18) supermultiplet, taking η' to be pure SU(3) singlet, and assigning ψ to (ω,γ) as in the models of Ref. 29-32 gives

$$\Gamma(\psi \to \eta'\gamma) = 35 \text{ MeV}.$$

This assignment gives a larger width than any other (ω, 8) assignment, because (ω,γ) is oriented in the photon direction in SU(3)"; however, the k_γ^3 kinematic factor alone increases $\Gamma(\psi \to \eta'\gamma)$ by a factor of 50 compared to $\Gamma(\omega \to \pi^o\gamma)$, so other assignments give widths in the MeV range. (Note that $\psi \not\to \pi^o\gamma$, because of the conservation of I'.) Although the data on radiative decays is in a preliminary state, it seems safe to assume that experimentally $\Gamma(\psi \to \eta'\gamma) < 50$ KeV. The, replacing μ_p by μ_{color} for M1 colored photon emission

$$\left(\frac{\mu_{color}}{\mu_p}\right)^2 \lesssim 1.4 \times 10^{-3}, \text{ or } \frac{\mu_{color}}{\mu_p} \lesssim \frac{1}{26} .$$

An even larger suppression factor for colored photon emission would be necessary if we consider that the large mass of ψ allows many different channels for radiative decay, such as $\psi \to \pi\pi\gamma$, $\psi \to K\bar{K}\gamma$, $\psi \to E\gamma$, $\psi \to 4\pi\gamma$ etc. One can connect the possible smallness of μ_{color} and the possible suppression of M1 transitions with high masses for colored baryons via the magnetic moment formula; this would lead to colored baryon masses $\gtrsim$ 26 GeV. Such a suppression would not operate for E1 transitions.

Pati and Salam[21], Bars and Peccei,[28] and Krammer, et al.[32] have proposed that dynamical effects suppress real colored photon emission, but that couplings of high mass (time-like) virtual colored photons to high-mass colored states (such as the ψ's) are not suppressed. According to this proposal, the following processes, among others, would be suppressed:

$$\psi \to \text{usual hadrons} + \gamma$$
$$eN \to \text{colored hadrons},$$
$$pp \to \psi\gamma \quad + \text{usual hadrons},$$

and the usual estimate to extract $\sigma_{tot}(\psi N)$ from $\sigma(\gamma N \to \psi N)$ would have to be revised (see Fig. 2), since

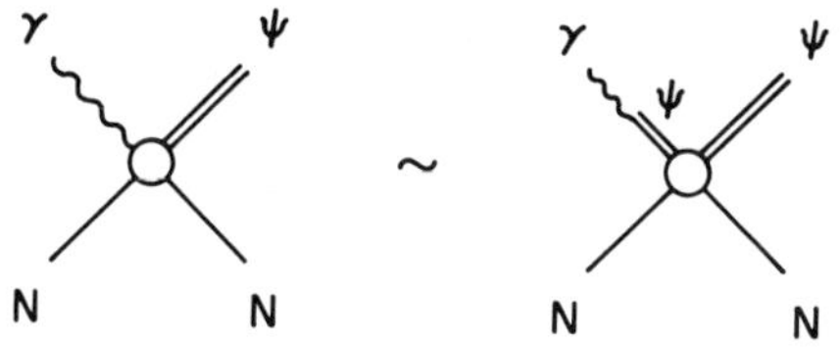

Fig. 2 Relation between $\gamma N \to \psi N$ and $\psi N \to \psi N$ from vector dominance.

the $\psi\gamma$ coupling involves a real photon. This revision would lead to an estimate for $\sigma_{tot}(\psi N)$ increased by ~ $[f_{\gamma\psi}(o)]^{-1}$ from the estimate made without taking this suppression into account. Typical processes for which no damping would occur are:

$$e^+e^- \to \gamma \to \psi \ ,$$

$$e^+e^- \to \gamma \to \psi\pi^+\pi^- \ .$$

Kramer, et al.,[32] suggest that the partial width[38] for $\eta \to 2\gamma$ supports the hypothesis that effective coupling constants for colored photon emission are suppressed compared to those for ordinary photon emission. I don't find their arguments compelling, because (i) $\Gamma(\eta\to 2\gamma)$ is very sensitive to changes in the singlet-octet mixing angle and could be used to determine this angle, and (ii) their estimate of the coupling constant does not take account of the expected suppression of contributions to $\eta \to 2\gamma$ from ψ and ψ' due to the large ψ and ψ' masses, using

$$\Gamma(P \to 2\gamma) \propto \left| \sum_V \frac{\langle o|j|V\rangle\langle V|\Sigma(q_i\sigma_{zi})|P\rangle}{M_V} \right|^2$$

where the matrix elements represent dimensionless Clebsch-Gordan coefficients, and P and V stand for pseudoscalar and vector mesons.

These dynamical suppression effects can be expressed in terms of a photon-ψ form factor $f_{\gamma\psi}(q^2)$ which, on the ψ mass shell, enters the leptonic width, $\Gamma(\psi \to e^+e^-) \propto [f_{\gamma\psi}(M_\psi^2)]^2$, and decreases as q^2 decreases.

The q^2-dependence of $f_{\gamma\psi}$ can be determined from the A-dependence of ψ photoproduction from different elements. As mentioned in Sect. 5, present data[24] is consistent with no change in $f_{\gamma\psi}$ between $q^2 = M_\psi^2$ and $q^2 = 0$, and places the limit

$$\frac{f_{\gamma\psi}(o)}{f_{\gamma\psi}(M_\psi^2)} > \frac{1}{20}$$

on the q^2-dependence of f. This result already casts serious doubt that the q^2-dependence of f can give the suppression of radiative decays needed to avoid radiative decays needed to avoid radiative widths which conflict with experiment. Further increase of this lower bound is higher statistics are collected may rule out this mechanism.

Another argument for suppression of radiative decays involving colored photon emission can be made in the framework of the quark model.[29] Matrix elements, such as

$$\langle \eta' | \mu | \psi \rangle \text{ and } \langle \pi^o | \mu | \omega \rangle$$

which we calculated group-theoretically above, contain an inner product between the space wave functions of the initial and final mesons:

$$M_{fi}(|\vec{k}|) = \int f_f^* (\vec{r}) \, e^{i\vec{k}.\vec{r}} \, f_i(\vec{r}) d^3r \ .$$

A purely group-theoretical calculation of M_{fi} for the states i and f in the same supermultiplet requires the assumptions: (a), that the space wave functions are the same for all states in the same supermultiplet, and (b), that M_{fi} is dependent of $|\vec{k}|$. It is plausible that these assumptions could be approximately valid for decays like $\omega \to \pi^o\gamma$, in which both mesons are in the same SU(6) multiplet and the meson mass differences and thus also $|\vec{k}|$ are not too large, but that these assumptions could be violated strongly for decays such as $\psi \to \eta'\gamma$, for which the mesons are in the same SU(18) multiplet, but not in the same SU(6)' multiplet nor in the same SU(3)" multiplet, and for which the meson mass differences and $|\vec{k}|$ are large.

Calculations, analogous to those above, of radiative widths of ψ and ψ' with ordinary photon emission in transitions to color pseudoscalar mesons, P, place lower limits on the mass of these colored pseudoscalars, if we assume an upper limit for the width. For example, if

$$\Gamma(\psi'(\phi,\gamma) \to P(\eta,\gamma)\gamma) < 50 \text{ keV},$$

then

$$M(P(\eta,\gamma)) > 3.5 \text{ GeV}.$$

Here, since the transition is within an SU(6) multiplet, the photon is uncolored, and the vector-pseudoscalar mass difference is not too large, the radiative widths will not be suppressed by the mechanisms discussed above.

T. C. Yang[30] suggests a different mechanism than that of other authors to suppress radiative decays. He assumes that all transitions between colored and non-colored states occur via an SU(3)-singlet semi-strong interaction which has a coupling constant $g_{ss}^2/4\pi$, suppressed by 1/10 to 1/100 relative to the strong coupling constant, $g^2/4\pi$, which gives the strength of transitions among colored or among non-colored states. Then colored photon emission in radiative ψ decay involves the semi-strong interaction and is suppressed. The same assumption also suppresses ordinary photon emission in the radiative ψ decay to a colored pseudoscalar just discussed.

If the naive estimates made above are correct, and if strong dynamical suppression of colored photon emission does not intervene, then the ψ's are not color excitations. In that case, either color is never excited, or when color is excited the signature for vector meson states will be very large radiative widths which will show up as a decrease at the mass of the resonance in the fraction of the total center of mass energy detected in charged particles.

8. MASS FORMULAS IN COLOR MODELS

The successful mass formulas for bayrons and mesons in SU(3) and SU(6) can usually be derived by finding the most general tensor operator which can be constructed in terms of one- or two-body operators, and which transforms as a singlet or the hypercharge member of an octet under SU(3), and is invariant under rotations. Examples of such formulas are the Gürsey-Radicati mass formula for the baryons in the $(56,0^+)$ and the mass formulas for the higher baryons in the $(70,1^-)$,[5] and still higher representations.[12] The extension of this point of view to the color models would lead to the consideration of one- or two-body operators in SU(18) or one of its subgroups such as SU(6)' x SU(3)" or SU(3)' x SU(3)" which transform, for example, as 1' or Y' under SU(3)' and 1" under SU(3)". I conjecture that if the states are unmixed in the SU(6)' x SU(3)" chain, these assumptions imply that SU(3)' splittings among states in (1+8,8) will be the same as the corresponding splittings in (1+8,1); in particular that

$$M^2(\phi,\gamma) - M^2(\omega,\gamma) = M^2(\phi) - M^2(\omega) = 0.427 \text{ GeV}^2.$$

and

$$M^2(\omega,\gamma) - M^2(\rho,\gamma) = M^2(\omega) - M^2(\rho) = 0.020 \text{ GeV}^2.$$

These relations seem to be violated badly with the assignments given in Ref. 29, 31, 32.

Relaxation of the condition that the mass operator be constructed from one- or two-body operators leads to very unconstrained mass formulas, in which the masses of the color octet states are independent of the masses of the color singlet states, since the mass operator can then be taken to have the form

$$M = M(1'')\,[C_2^{(3)''}-6] + M(8'')C_2^{(3)''} ,$$

where

$$C_2^{(3)}(1) = 0, \quad C_2^{(3)}(8) = 6$$

To give an overall picture of possible patterns of masses for the S-wave colored mesons in models in which states are mixed in the SU(6)' x SU(3)" chain, the SU(3)"-splittings are small, I give masses of colored vector states in Table IX using the assumption that SU(6) $(\text{mass})^2$ splittings in the color octet are (a) the same as in the color singlet, i.e.

$$M^2(X,8) - M^2(X,1) = M^2(\psi(3105)) - M^2(\omega), \qquad \text{(a)}$$

and (b) the color octet masses have a constant ratio[30] to their singlet analogs, i.e.

$$\frac{M^2(X,8)}{M^2(X,1)} = \frac{M^2(\psi(3105))}{M^2(\omega)} \qquad \text{(b)}$$

Table IX: Predicted masses of colored vector mesons

States	Mass (MeV) (additive formula(a))	Mass (MeV) (multiplicative formula(b))
$(\rho,8)$	3092	3045
$(\omega,8)$	3095 (input)	3095 (input)
$(K^*,8),(\bar{K}^*,8)$	3124	3528
$(\phi,8)$	3163	4032

Neither of these mass patterns agrees well with present data. With either spectrum, the (ω,γ) - (ρ,γ) splitting is small. In that case, several authors[29,39] have pointed out that assuming $\psi'(3684)$ is (ϕ,γ) the decay

$$\psi'(\phi,\gamma) \to V(\rho,\gamma)^{\pm}\pi^{\mp},$$

which is allowed by color conservation, but suppressed somewhat by the Zweig rule, would have a significant width and a clear monoenergetic pion signal. The Zweig suppression can't be too strong, because $\psi'(3684) \to \psi(3095)\pi\pi$, which has less phase space, is seen. Thus $V(\rho,\gamma)$ must be assumed to have a mass not much below $M(\psi'(3684))-m_\pi = 3546$ MeV. Then this $V(\rho,\gamma)$ state will have a very large width since

$$V(\rho,\gamma) \to \psi(\omega,\gamma)\pi$$

is allowed by both color symmetry and the Zweig rule.

An outstanding signature of models with 1'+8' mixing and small SU(3)" breaking is the presence of doubly charged mesons in the mass range of the ψ's. Such mesons should be produced in pairs in electron-positron colliding beams above the production threshold $\sqrt{s} \sim 6.2$ GeV.

In Sec. 9, I list mass thresholds for fully allowed strong decays of $\psi(3095)$ as (ω,γ) and (3684) as (ϕ,γ) to various colored pseudoscalar states.

9. DETAILED PROPERTIES OF VARIOUS MODELS

a. Colored ω and ϕ model[29,31,32]

The leading idea of this model as mentioned in III. of Sec. 6 above, is to construct the colored vector mesons in as close analogy to the usual ρ,ω and ϕ as possible; in particular, to use the same ideal nonet SU(3)' mixing for the new mesons as for ω and ϕ. Thus

ψ is assigned to (ω,γ) and ψ' to (ϕ,γ), while ψ'' is either an (ω,γ) recurrence, or is associated with a threshold for production of $(8,\gamma)$ + mesons. In this model, if only electromagnetism breaks color symmetry, there are two octets, $(\omega,8)$ and $(\phi,8)$, near 3.1 GeV and 3.7 GeV, respectively, all of whose members are narrow and whose masses are split only by electromagnetism. Aside from $(\omega,\gamma) = \psi$ itself, all the members of the $(\omega,8)$ octet decay only via weak interactions with lifetimes estimated roughly (since the weak interaction theory has not been developed in detail for this model) to be $\tau_{\text{lept.}} \sim 10^{-12}$ sec and $\tau_{\text{non-lept.}} \sim 10^{-14}$ sec.[29] This octet includes doubly-charged particles. The prediction of doubly-charged particles with the lifetimes just given and masses near 3.1 GeV is the most striking feature of this model. These particles and their singly-charged partners should be produced in e^+e^- collisions above about 6.2 GeV, as well as in hadronic collisions above the relevant threshold.

As mentioned in Sec. 8, the color models have mass constraints in the form of lower limits on various colored states which are necessary to prevent the two narrow ψ's from decaying via an allowed transition. Such decays would also give mono-energetic mesons or unique missing masses. In Table X, I list some mass thresholds for colored resonances which make the listed decays energetically forbidden. (The required lower limits on the masses of the colored states should be somewhat lower to take advantage of phase space suppression when the decay is close to its energy threshold.)

Table X: Lower limits on masses to avoid allowed decays of ψ and ψ'

Lower Limit (GeV)	Decay which is energetically forbidden
$M(\rho,\gamma) > 3.55$	$\psi' \to (\rho,\pi)^{\pm}\pi^{\mp}$
$M(\pi,\gamma) > 2.82$	$\psi \to (\pi,\gamma)^{o}\pi^{+}\pi^{-}$
$M(\pi,\gamma) > 3.41$	$\psi' \to (\pi,\gamma)^{o}\pi^{+}\pi^{-}$
$M(K^{*},\gamma) > 3.19$	$\psi' \to (K^{*},\gamma)^{\pm}\bar{K}^{\mp}$
$M(K,\gamma) > 3.19$	$\psi' \to (K,\gamma)^{\pm}K^{\mp}$
$M(\eta,\gamma) > 2.90$	$\psi' \to (\eta,\gamma)\omega$

The upshot of these lower bounds is that ψ must be the lowest mass colored meson. Analogous arguments can be made for other color models.

Assuming the 4.1 GeV structure to be a third ψ, classified as an (ω,γ) recurrence, Bars and Peccei[29] attribute its large width to the following final states: (a), $(\rho,\gamma)\pi$, $(K^{*},\gamma)\bar{K}$, $\psi\eta$, $\psi'\eta$, and (b), $\psi\pi\pi$, $(\pi,\gamma)\pi\pi$, where the decays in (a), have mono-energetic π's, K's or η's and those in (b), have unique missing masses as signatures. The decays $\psi' \to \psi\pi\pi$ and $\psi' \to \psi\eta$ are allowed by color symmetry, but suppressed by the Zweig rule.

Note that the 4.1 GeV structure cannot have energetically allowed decays to color-anti-color states, because this would require color states at 2.05 GeV, which would violate the bounds given in Table X above.

Bars and Peccei[29] suggest second order electromagnetic effects as the main source of violation of color symmetry. Since the electromagnetic current transforms as (1,8)+(9,1) under SU(3)' x SU(3)", the color breaking second order contributions transform as (1,8) x (1,8) and (1,8) x (8, 1), where the first term preserves SU(3)' isospin and G parity while the second term violates both. The presently known decay modes of ψ and ψ' seem to conserve both isospin and G parity, which seems to be evidence against purely electromagnetic color breaking. If non-electromagnetic color breaking is added, it must be done in such a way as to preserve the U-spin orientation of the color eigenstates.

The assignment of ψ' to (ϕ,γ) leads to the prediction that the production of ψ' in hadronic collisions and electron-nucleon collisions will be suppressed relative to production of ψ, since the hadronic targets in these collisions do not contain λ quarks. This assignment of ψ' also leads to a larger partial width by a factor of two to four for $\psi' \to K\bar{K}n\pi$.[29]

b. T. C. Yang model[30]

This model is similar to the Bars-Peccei model in using the Han-Nambu model with U-spin orientation in SU(3)", and in assigning ψ to (ω,γ). Yang notes that

$$M_\psi/M_\omega = 3.995 \approx M_{\psi''}/M_\phi = 4.07,$$

and gives arguments[40] for the multiplicative mass formula (b) of Sec. 8 for vector mesons. On this basis, he assigns ψ'' to (ϕ,γ), and predicts $M(K^*,\gamma) \approx 3.56$ GeV. Yang's assigns ψ' to a recurrence of (ω,γ). He finds

$$\frac{\Gamma(\psi \to e^+e^-)}{\Gamma(\psi'' \to e^+e^-)} = 2, \text{ vs. 1.3 experimentally.}$$

The decay $\psi'(3684) \to \psi(3095)\pi\pi$ is suppressed by the same assumption (Section 7) that Yang makes to suppress radiative decays.

Yang's assignment of ψ'' to (ϕ,γ) and his dynamical assumption lead to srong consequences for the decay of the broad ψ''. The modes

$$\psi'' \rightarrow \begin{cases} (\eta,\gamma)\omega & (\eta',\gamma)\omega \\ (\eta,\gamma)\phi & (\eta',\gamma)\phi \end{cases}$$

dominate the 250 to 300 MeV ψ'' width. Then the ψ'' decays should have strong ω and ϕ signals, and the missing spectrum, when the ω and ϕ have been identified, should correspond to two resonances (η,γ) and (η',γ). These resonances have allowed decays to $(\pi,\gamma)\pi\pi$, 2γ, and $(\rho,\gamma)\gamma$, and should be broad, i.e. Γ's > 50 MeV. The assumption of SU(3)' - singlet dominance of semi-strong transitions between colored and non-colored states leads to a Zweig-like rule which prohibits $\psi''\rightarrow\psi\pi\pi$ and $\psi''\rightarrow\psi\eta$, and leads to $\Gamma(\psi''(4150) \rightarrow \psi(3095)\pi\pi \sim$ 1-10 KeV, in contrast to a much larger width in other models.

c. Four resonance model[33,34]

This model uses the Han-Nambu model with 1 + 8 mixing in SU(3)' as in the models just discussed, but with I-spin orientation in SU(3)". Sanda and Terazawa[34] note that

$$\frac{M_{\psi''}}{M_{\psi}} = 1.34 \approx \frac{M_{\phi}}{M_{\omega}} = 1.30,$$

and also suggest a multiplicative mass formula. Using the leptonic widths and the mass formula, they assign the known ψ's and the fourth ψ needed in this scheme as shown in Table IV in Sec. 6. Their hypothesis that the SU(3)" state cannot change in strong interactions implies suppression of the following decays:

$$\psi \rightarrow H,\ \psi' \rightarrow H,\ \psi' \rightarrow \psi H,\ \psi''' \rightarrow \psi'' H,\ \psi''' \rightarrow \psi H$$

but allows

$$\psi'' \rightarrow \psi H \text{ and } \psi''' \rightarrow \psi' H$$

so that ψ'' and ψ''' are broad in this scheme. Note that the Zweig rule has been ignored in considering these last two decays to be allowed. Their assumption also implies that isospin and hypercharge are conserved in transitions among colored states just as among non-colored states, so that the observed G-parity conservation for $\psi \rightarrow (2n + 1)\pi$ and $\psi' \rightarrow \psi\pi\pi$ is expected.

This model predicts at least 14 more colored vector mesons between 3.1 GeV and 4.2 GeV, none of which are doubly charged, as well as additional colored mesons, some of which are doubly charged, with comparable masses.

The narrow widths of $\psi(3095)$ and $\psi'(3684)$ in this model are due to color conservation, but the decay $\psi'(3684) \rightarrow \psi(3095)\pi\pi$, which has very little phase space, and requires a rather large $\psi'\psi\pi\pi$ coupling constant, is also prohibited by color conservation. Further, the ψ and ψ' have a large mass splitting. These facts seem to me to pose a serious, perhaps fatal, difficulty for this model, since good SU(3)" symmetry is required to produce narrow widths for the two lower ψ's.

d. Pati-Salam models[21]

Unlike the case for all the other color models, Pati and Salam start from a unified gauge theory which provides important motivation for their point of view, but still allows flexibility in accommodating the demands of experiment. The most important consequence of their underlying gauge theory is the expectation that their colored octet gauge fields will appear as (1,8) colored resonances, in addition to the colored states corresponding to $(q\bar{q})$ composites which appear in other models. This extra (1,8) colored gauge octet allows the two narrow ψ's to be assigned to states with the same color quantum numbers, but in two different (1,8) octets, a situation which would require a recurrence of the (1,8) octet in other models. From the phenomenological point of view I am taking this survey, there is no clear distinction between gauge and composite vector mesons. Pati and Salam expect the gauge mesons to be pure (1,8), but allow either pure (1,8) or (1 + 8, 8) mixed states for the composites.

In their original model,[41] Pati and Salam assigned one of ψ and ψ' to a linear combination of the $U'' = 0$ (γ) and $U'' = 1$, $U_z'' = 0$ states of a (1,8) gauge octet and the other to the corresponding states of a (1,8) ($q\bar{q}$) composite octet, and considered two possibilities: (i) that resonances corresponding to orthogonal linear combinations of $U'' = 0$ and $U'' = 1$, $U_z'' = 0$ are excited in electron-positron annihilation, so that two more particles with the same spin and parity exist close to ψ and ψ', or (ii) that the particle eigenstates are pure U''- spin singlet, so that only the ψ and ψ' exist. More recently, Pati and Salam have proposed three variations[42] of their model: I. that ψ and ψ' are the ($1,\gamma$) gauge and the ($q\bar{q}$) states, respectively and ψ'' is the $\phi_c \sim (c\bar{c})$ orthocharmonium state, II. that ψ is the ($1,\gamma$) gauge meson, while ψ' and ψ'' are the (ω,γ) and (ϕ,γ) ($q\bar{q}$) states, respectively, and III. that ψ and ψ' are ϕ_c and its recurrence, while ψ'' is the ($1,\gamma$) gauge state.

Model I, which is closest to their original model, allows $\psi' \rightarrow \psi\pi\pi$ to be a strong decay with a width reduced by phase space, but inhibited by the Zweig rule, and does not require extreme ($c\bar{c}$) purity of $\phi_c \sim \psi''$, since ψ'' has higher mass than the other ψ's and a hadronic width. Important signatures for model I are mono-energetic photons from $\psi \to \eta'\gamma$ and $\psi' \to \eta'\gamma$, and the presence of neutral or singly charged partners of the gauge octet near 3.1 GeV and the $(q\bar{q})$ octet near 3.7 GeV. The charged members of these octets should be pair-produced by strong interactions in-say-pp collisions, and by electromagnetic interactions in-say-e^+e^- collisions above their respective thresholds, 6.2 GeV and 7.4 GeV, and the $(1,\rho)^{\pm}$ and $(1,K^*)^{\pm}$ members should decay weakly with lifetimes $\lesssim 10^{-14}$ sec either leptonically or non-leptonically, but not semi-leptonically (ignoring order-α corrections). The absence of semi-leptonic decay modes is due to the fact that in the basic Pati-Salam model the gauge bosons which mediate (weak) interactions between leptons and hadrons at energies accessible to present accelerators are SU(3)"-singlets, while the gauge bosons which carry color do not interact with leptons, except via the electromagnetic field. By contrast, the new resonances in the charm scheme can have significant semi-leptonic decay modes. Thus the absence or presence of semi-leptonic decay modes should separate the color and charm models.

Model II assigns all three ψ's to colored states: ψ to $(1,\gamma)$ in the gauge octet, and ψ' and ψ'' to (ω,γ) and (ϕ,γ) in $(q\bar{q})$ colored states. The decay $\psi'' \to \psi\eta$ accounts for the large width of ψ'' and the decay $\psi' \to \psi\eta$ accounts for a large part (100 to 300 keV) of the width of ψ'; thus mono-energetic η's in these two decays are important signatures for this model. The decay $\psi'' \to \psi'\pi\pi$ is suppressed by the Zweig rule. The spectrum of this model is similar to model I, except that doubly charged partners of (ω,γ) and (ϕ,γ) are expected near 3.7 GeV and 4.1 GeV, respectively.

Model III is very similar to the charm model: ψ and ψ' are assigned to charm-anti-charm composite states, and only ψ'' is a color excitation, in this case a $(1,\gamma)$ gauge meson. Here, $(1,8)$ colored pseudoscalars are assumed to lie lower, and the large width of ψ'' is due to $\psi'' \to (1,8) + n\pi$.

e. $6-3^*$ model

As mentioned in Sec. 5, the annihilation Zweig rule suppresses transitions between states in $6 \times 6^*$ and states in $3^* \times 3$. We assume that this suppression is much stronger than the suppression that acts within each of these sets of states. Then the lowest-mass states in $6 \times 6^*$ have narrow widths for decays to ordinary mesons.[43]

In contrast to other color models, large radiative widths to the usual mesons are not expected here, since the electromagnetic current does not produce transitions between quarks in the 6 and 3^* representations. Further properties of this type of model depend on the specific assignments.

With the assignments discussed in Sec. 6, $\psi' \to \psi\pi\pi$ suppressed by the weaker Zweig rule acting within the $6 \times 6^*$ states. If the breaking of the Zweig rule occurs in such a way that states in a 1" state are mixed, then the decays of the ψ's conserve isospin and G parity, and

$$\psi' \to \text{hadrons in } I^G = 0$$
$$\psi' \to \psi + \text{nonstrange hadrons in } I^G = 0^-$$
$$\to \text{nonstrange hadrons in } I^G = 0^-$$
$$\psi' \to \psi' + \text{nonstrange hadrons in } I^G = 0^-$$
$$\to \text{nonstrange hadrons in } I^G = 0^-$$

but

$$\psi'' \not\to \psi + \text{hadrons.}$$

This assignment gives leptonic widths which disagree

with experiment.

Possible decays of the ψ's to pseudoscalar states in $6 \times 6^*$ and to vector or pseudoscalar states in 6×3 and $6^* \times 3^*$ have not yet been analyzed.

This model has a very serious, perhaps fatal, problem with decays to baryon-antibaryon states: such decays are allowed both group-theoretically and by the Zweig rule, since the baryons must use all nine quarks to satisfy the requirement of the symmetric quark model.
However,

$$\psi \not\rightarrow N\bar{N},\ N^*\bar{N}^*,\ \Delta\bar{\Delta},\ \text{and}\ \Delta^*\bar{\Delta}^*,\ \text{etc.},$$

by the Zweig rule, since the Ω quark is not present in N and Δ states.

One could consider the 6 of this model to be a new set of quarks, unrelated to the usual ones.[45] This is uneconomical, but has the advantage that the Zweig rule then also suppresses decays to baryon-anti-baryon states.

10. CONCLUDING REMARKS

As far as color models of the ψ's are concerned, we do not seem to be in the position of the man in Wigner's anecdote[46] "who, having to open several doors in succession, always hit on the right key on the first or second trial." The color models provide us with a variety of keys, but none of them is obviously the right key to expose the mysteries of the ψ's. Whether, with some jiggling, one of the keys will turn out to be the right one is still unclear. A three-valued color degree of freedom must exist in hadron physics; however it is possible that color is exactly conserved and permanently bound along with quarks, in which case color is irrelevant for the ψ's.

In most color models, radiative decays should be major decay modes of the ψ's, and present data already requires suppression of the rates for colored photon emission by a factor of about 700 relative to ordinary photon emission. Detection of mono-energetic photons from two-body radiative decays, and measurement of the partial widths of such modes, is very important. Study of the A dependence of photo-production of ψ's allows the separation of the γψ coupling for on-shell photons from the ψ-nucleon cross section, and allows calculation of the suppression factor $f_{\psi\gamma}(o)/f_{\psi\gamma}(M_\psi^2)$, which, as just mentioned, must be ~ 1/25 for most color models. If present indications (discussed in Sec. 7) that this suppression does not exist are strengthened, serious doubt would be case on most color models. In that case, I would speculate that the true photon-excited color mesons, if such exist, have not yet been found, and that their signature would be a dip in the fraction of the center-of-mass energy seen in charged particles. This dip would occur at the mass of the colored meson and its width would be $\gtrsim$ 50 MeV.

Another qualitative property of most color models is the existence of doubly-charged mesons which are stable under the strong and electromagnetic interactions, and decay weakly with lifetimes ~ 10^{-14} sec. These particles, which can be produced in hadronic collisions as well as in e^+e^- collisions, will not leave tracks, but will appear as sharp peaks in missing mass distributions.

ACKNOWLEDGEMENTS

I thank my Maryland colleagues, L. Clavelli, J. C. Pati, C. H. Woo and T. C. Yang for many helpful discussions and for comments on this manuscript, and B. Barnett and G. T. Zorn for discussions of the experimental data. I thank I. Bars, M. A. B. Bég, F. Gilman, R. Larsen, H. Lynch, H. Pagels and R. D. Peccei for comments about the models and for information about the data.

FOOTNOTES AND REFERENCES

1. H. Lynch, these Proceedings, reviews of the present data on these resonances.

2. M. Gell-Mann, Phys. Lett. 8. 214 (1964).

3. G. Zweig, CERN Preprints 8182/TH.401 and 8419/TH. 412 (1964).

4. O. W. Greenberg, Phys. Rev. Lett. 13, 598 (1964).

5. O. W. Greenberg, University of Maryland Technical Report No. 680, 1967 (unpublished); O. W. Greenberg and M. Resnikoff, Phys. Rev. 163, 1844 (1967).

6. S. L. Glashow, J. Iliopoulos, and L. Maiani, Phys. Rev. D 2, 1285 (1970). F. Gilman discusses the charm model of the ψ's in SLAC-PUB-1537, to appear in these Proceedings.

7. F. Gürsey and L. A. Radicati, Phys. Rev. Lett. 13, 173 (1964).

8. B. Sakita, Phys. Rev. 136, B1756 (1964).

9. M. A. B. Bég, B. W. Lee, and A. Pais, Phys. Rev. Lett. 13, 514 (1964).

10. B. Sakita, ibid, 13, 643 (1964).

11. M. Jones, R. Levi Setti and T. Lasinski, Nuovo Cimento 19A, 365 (1974).

12. R. Horgan and R. H. Dalitz, Nucl. Phys. B66, 135 (1973); R. Horgan, ibid, B71, 514 (1974).

13. H. S. Green, Phys. Rev. 90, 270 (1953).

14. O. Klein, J. Phys. Radium 9, 1 (1938).

15. This evident fact seems first to have been stated in the literature in O. W. Greenberg and D. Zwanziger, Phys. Rev. 150, 1177 (1966).

16. M. Gell-Mann, Acta Phys. Austriaca Supp. 9, 733 (1972); W. A. Bardeen, H. Fritzsch, and M. Gell-Mann, in Scale and Conformal Symmetry in Hadron Physics, ed. R. Gatto (Wiley, New York, 1973), p. 139; M. Gell-Mann, in Proc. XVI International

Conference on High Energy Physics, ed. J. D. Jackson and A. Roberts (NAL, Batavia, 1973), Vol. 4, p. 333.

17. M. Y. Han and Y. Nambu, Phys. Rev. 139, B1006 (1965); Y. Nambu, in Preludes in Theoretical Physics, ed. A. de Shalit, H. Feshbach, and L. Van Hove (North-Holland, Amsterdam, 1966), p. 133.

18. O. W. Greenberg and C. A. Nelson, Phys. Rev. Lett. 20, 604 (1968), and Phys. Rev. 179, 1354 (1969).

19. Such models have been studied by many authors, including S. Borchardt, V. S. Mathur, and S. Okubo, Phys. Rev. Lett. 34, 38 (1975); T. Appelquist and H. D. Politzer, op. cit., p. 43; A. De Rújula and S. L. Glashow, op. cit., p. 46; and C. G. Callan, R. L. Kingsley, S. B. Treiman, et al., op. cit., p. 52. F. Gilman, SLAC-PUB-1537, to appear in these Proceedings, analyzes the present status of this model.

20. T. Tati, Prog. Theor. Phys. 35, 126 (1966).

21. J. C. Pati, these Proceedings, and references cited there.

22. Data taken from Ref. 1 and Particle Data Group, Phys. Lett. 50B, No. 1 (1974).

23. J. J. Aubert, U. J. Becker, P. J. Biggs, et al., Phys. Rev. Lett. 33, 1404 (1974).

24. W. Lee, private communication.

25. H. Harari SLAC-PUB-1514, 1974 (unpublished); CERN Boson Theory Workshop, CERN preprint TH.1964, 1974 (unpublished); and I. Bars, M. Chanowitz, S. D. Drell, et al., SLAC-PUB-1522, 1975 (unpublished) give general discussions of the ψ's from many points of view, including that of color.

26. Radial and orbital excitations of states discussed in the text can also be excited, provided they have $J^{PC} = 1^{--}$.

27. I use 8 to refer to an octet, and a symbol to refer to a given member of the octet. I use 1 to refer either to a singlet or to its only member.

For example, $(8,\rho^o)$ means a state in the (8,8) of $SU(3)' \times SU(3)''$ with $I'' = 1$, $I_Z'' = 0$.

28. W. Alles, Bologna preprint, 1974 (unpublished).

29. I. Bars and R. D. Peccei, Stanford University preprints ITP-480, 1974 and ITP-484, 1975 (unpublished).

30. T. C. Yang, University of Maryland Technical Report No. 75-052, 1975 (unpublished).

31. W. Alles, Bologna preprint, 1975 (unpublished).

32. M. Krammer, D. Schildknecht and F. Steiner, DESY 74/64 (1974).

33. B. G. Kenny, D. C. Peaslee and L. J. Tassie, Phys. Rev. Lett. 34, 429 (1975).

34. A. I. Sanda and H. Terazawa, Rockefeller University Report No. COO-2232B-70, 1975 (unpublished).

35. I ignore factors due to mass ratios here.

36. O. W. Greenberg, in preparation. I thank C. H. Woo for many helpful discussions about this model.

37. R. Van Royen and V. F. Weisskopf, Nuovo Cimento 50A, 617 (1967); erratum, ibid, 51A, 583 (1967).

38. A. Browman, J. DeWire, B. Gittelman, et al., Phys. Rev. Lett. 32, 1067 (1974). Note that their result, $\Gamma(\eta \to 2\gamma) = (324 \pm 46)$ eV is a factor of 3 less than the previously accepted value.

39. L. Clavelli, and M. A. B. Bég and H. Pagels, private communications.

40. M. A. B. Bég has pointed out that Yang's arguments for the multiplicative mass formula seem to require a Wigner symmetry, rather than the Goldstone symmetry present in a chiral theory (private communication).

41. J. C. Pati and A. Salam, Phys. Rev. Lett. 34, 613 (1975).

42. J. C. Pati and A. Salam, University of Maryland Technical Report No. 75-056, 1975 (unpublished).

43. The Zweig rule asserts that transitions whose duality diagrams are disconnected have smaller amplitudes than those whose duality diagrams are connected. Amplitudes whose duality diagrams contain a single meson whose quark-anti-quark lines are disconnected from the rest of the duality diagram ("hairpin" or "annihilation diagrams" are suppressed by a larger factor than those corresponding to other disconnected duality diagrams. Unitarity implies that Zweig rule suppressions cannot be absolute, since, for example $\phi \rightarrow K\bar{K}$ and $K\bar{K} \rightarrow 3\pi$ each have connected duality diagrams, so $\phi \rightarrow 3\pi$, which has a disconnected hairpin diagram, can go via unitarity.[44] It is difficult to distinguish corrections to the Zweig rule from mixings of the quark content of the mesons; for example, $\phi \rightarrow 3\pi$ could go via unitarity corrections as just illustrated, or because $\phi \sim \lambda\bar{\lambda} + \varepsilon(p\bar{p} + n\bar{n})$, etc. For the discussion of the 6-3* model, I use the mixing point of view, but still call it the "Zweig rule", and assume that quark mixings between 6 x 6* states and 3* x 3 states are extremely small, leading to narrow widths of ψ and ψ', and that there is some, but less, suppression of quark mixings inside 6 x 6* or inside 3* x 3 states.

44. H. Pagels has emphasized the necessity of unitarity corrections to the Zweig rule (private communication).

45. L. Clavelli (private communication).

46. E. P. Wigner, Symmetries and Reflections (Indiana University Press, Bloomington, 1967) p. 222.

ELECTRON-POSITRON INCLUSIVE HADRON REACTIONS*

(Presented by Bruce A. Barnett)

Department of Physics and Astronomy

University of Maryland, College Park, MD.

and

MP^2 Experimenters:

T. Atwood, B. Barnett, G. Zorn, L. Trasatti

Department of Physics and Astronomy

University of Maryland, College Park, MD.

M. Cavalli-Sforza, G. Goggi, G. Montovani,

A. Piazzoli, B. Rossini, N. Scannicchio

Universita Degli Studia Di Pavia

Pavia, Italy

D. Coyne, G. O'Neill, H. Sadronzinski

Department of Physics

Princeton University, Princeton, New Jersey

*Supported in part by the Atomic Energy Commission and the National Science Foundation.

I would like to present some of the preliminary results of an experiment studying e^+-e^- interactions at the SPEAR colliding beam facility at SLAC. This experiment was predominately a single arm magnetic spectrometer for measuring e^+-e^- inclusive cross sections.

The main characteristics of the experiment are as follows:

1) The event trigger required only a single charged particle passing through the magnetic spectrometer.
2) The spectrometer was at 90° to the e^+-e^- beams and covered only about 1% of the total 4π steradians solid angle.
3) The experiment had $e/\mu/\pi/K/p$ identification for particles passing through the spectrometer by means of a Cerenkov counter, shower counters, range-hadron filter, and time of flights.
4) Particles travelling at $\approx$ 90° to the e^+-e^- beams opposite to the spectrometer were partially identified by a shower counter and range-hadron filter.
5) A central detector, called the "polymeter," covered 99% of the 4π steradian solid angle and measured the charge multiplicity of events which triggered our system. It consisted of four units, each containing three porportional wire chambers having wires parallel to the e^+-e^- beams.
6) Four systems existed for detecting the electron or positron from a "2γ" process, one system being above and below the vacuum pipe at each end of the interaction region. Each

system consisted of two proportional wire planes and a lead-scintillation counter sandwich shower counter.

7) The experiment contained no "triggered" detectors; that is to say that all particle location was achieved by using proportional wire chambers or scintillation counters.

8) The experiment was set up and debugged during the autumn of 1973, and the data was taken during the first half of 1974, prior to the discovery of the ψ particles.

The accompanying Figures 1 and 2 show diagrams of the apparatus from above and from the side. The positions of all of the proportional wire chambers are shown, where the label of "X" means the wires run vertically and the label of "Y" means the wires run horizontally. The time of flight measurement was made using a scintillation counter, not shown in the diagrams, positioned between the proportional wire chamber CIX and the polymeter, and the first two scintillation counter planes of the shower counter. The Cerenkov counter was filled with 90 P.S.I.G. of propane, giving a pion threshold of 1.05 GeV/c. The shower counters were made of a five layer sandwich of 1/4 inch lead and 3/4 inch scintillation counters. The hadron filters each consisted of three iron-scintillation counter sandwiches. The total thickness of the iron was 26 inches.

A summary of the particle identification is as follows:

1) Electrons should produce large pulses in the Cerenkov counter and the shower counters, and should not penetrate the hadron filter.

2) Muons should produce a pulse in the Cerenkov

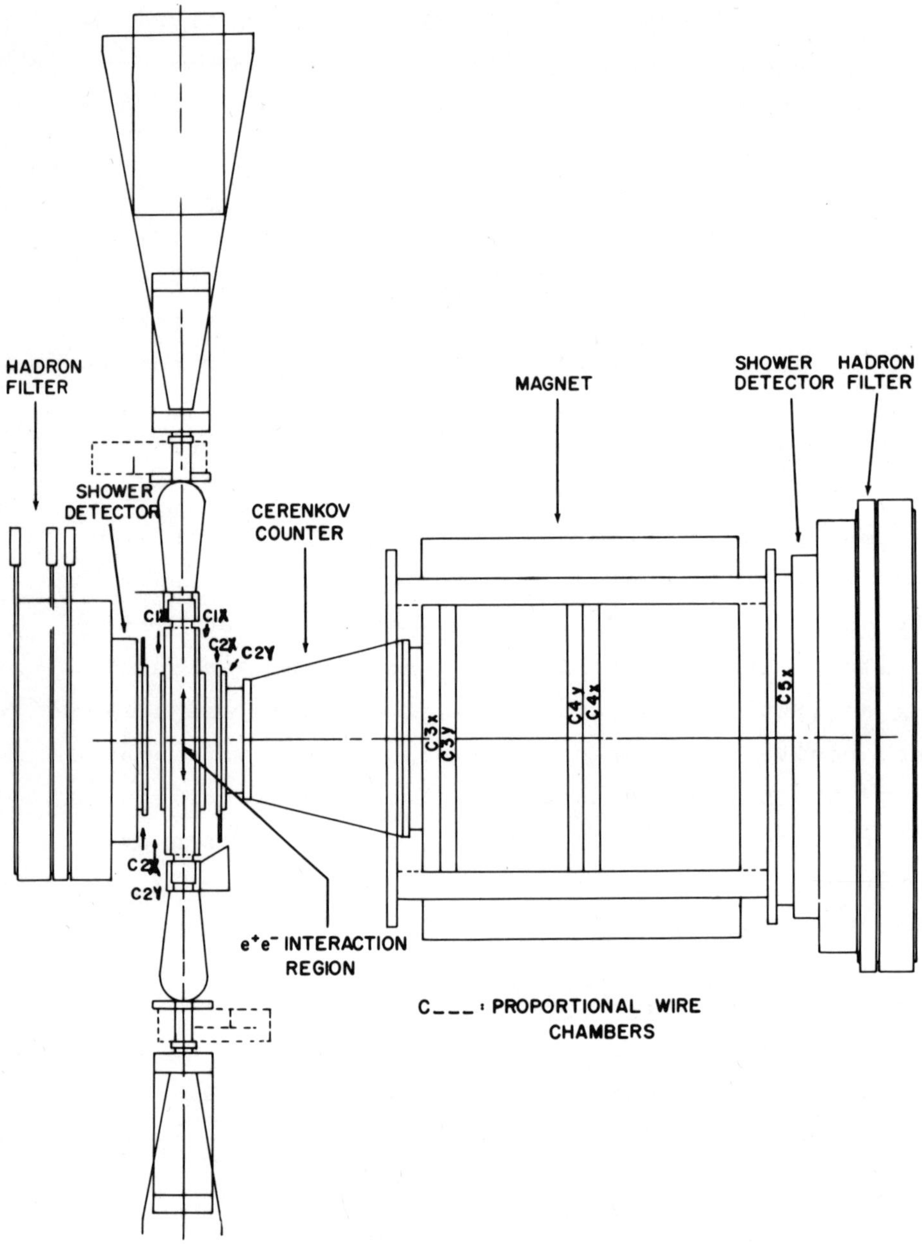
HADRON
FILTER
SHOWER
DETECTOR
CERENKOV
COUNTER
MAGNET
SHOWER
DETECTOR
HADRON
FILTER
C1X
C1X
C2X
C2Y
C3x
C3y
C4y
C4x
C5x
C2X
C2Y
e+e- INTERACTION
REGION
C___: PROPORTIONAL WIRE
CHAMBERS

Figure 1

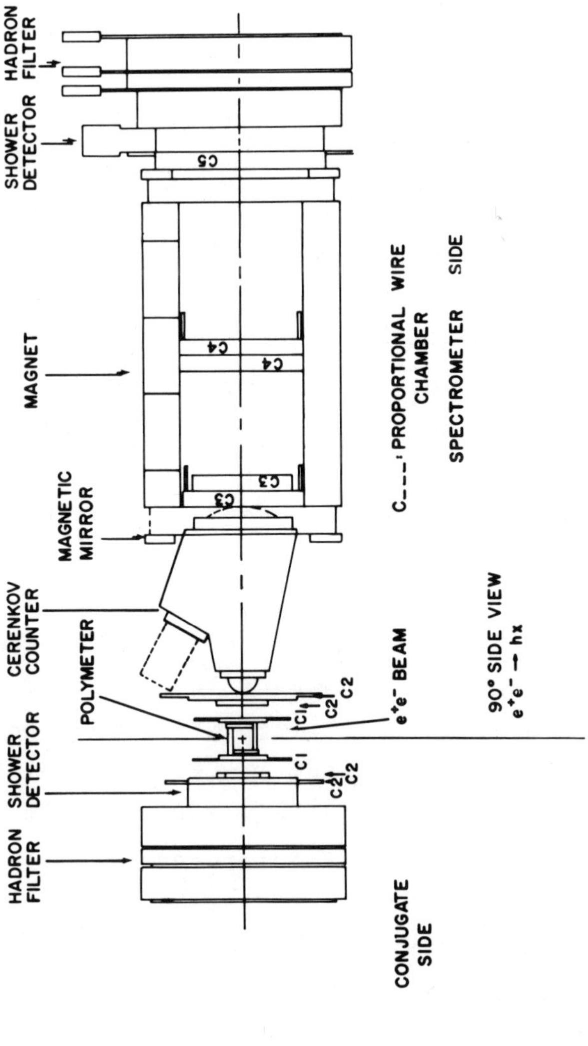
HADRON FILTER
SHOWER DETECTOR
C5
MAGNET
C4
C4
C3
C3
MAGNETIC MIRROR
CERENKOV COUNTER
POLYMETER
C1
C2
C2
e+e- BEAM
C1
C2
C2
SHOWER DETECTOR
HADRON FILTER
CONJUGATE SIDE
C___: PROPORTIONAL WIRE CHAMBER
SPECTROMETER SIDE
90° SIDE VIEW
e+e- → hx

Figure 2

counter above 800 MeV/c, should not shower, and should penetrate the hadron filter.

3) Pions should produce a pulse in the Cerenkov counter above 1.05 GeV/c, should not shower, and should not penetrate the hadron filter.

4) Kaons should produce no pulse in the Cerenkov counter, should not shower, and should not penetrate the hadron filter.

5) Protons would look like kaons, but are distinguishable by time of flight.

Figure 3 shows the behavior of the Cerenkov counter for the events identified as being hadrons above 1.0 GeV/c. The rising line represents the average pulse height expected for pions with a threshold at 1.05 GeV/c so that there is a clear separation of the band of pions from the band of kaons and protons above 1.2 GeV/c. There are a total of 13 events identified as either kaons or protons in our present sample at $\sqrt{S}$ = 4.8 GeV/c.

The time of flight measurement on these 13 events was examined to separate the protons from the kaons. No valid measurement could be made for three of these events because an extra counter in the shower counter system fired. Of the remaining ten events, all had times of flight corresponding to kaons rather than protons. These numbers can be interpreted as giving a proton to kaon ratio of $P/K < .33$ with a 95% confidence level for momenta greater than 1.2 GeV/c. Calling all 13 events kaons, since no evidence of protons was found, allowed us to find the K/π ratio after appropriate decay corrections. The result, $K/\pi = .33 \pm .10$, is shown in Figure 4, where our data point is for all hadrons above 1.2 GeV/c.

Also shown on this graph are the SLAC-LBL[1] e^+-e^-

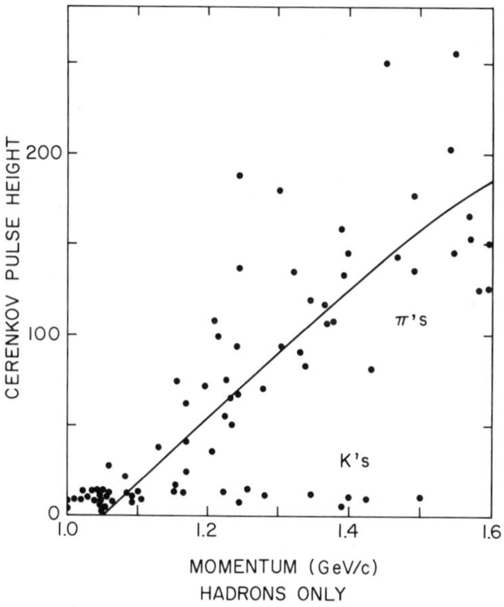
CERENKOV PULSE HEIGHT
200
100
0
1.0
1.2
1.4
1.6
π's
K's
MOMENTUM (GeV/c)
HADRONS ONLY

Figure 3

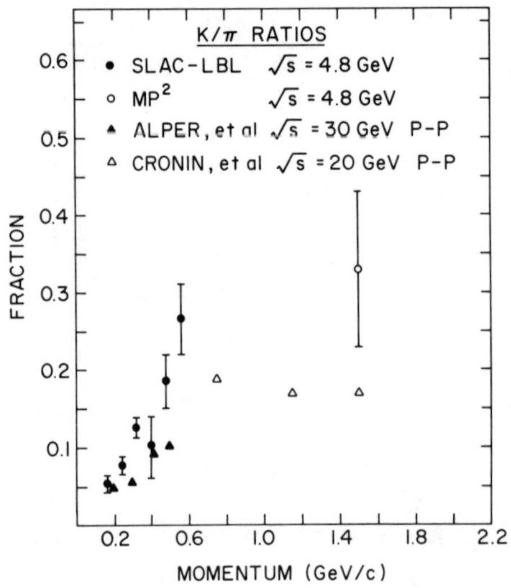
K/π RATIOS
SLAC-LBL √s = 4.8 GeV
MP² √s = 4.8 GeV
ALPER, et al √s = 30 GeV P-P
CRONIN, et al √s = 20 GeV P-P
FRACTION
0.6
0.5
0.4
0.3
0.2
0.1
0.2
0.6
1.0
1.4
1.8
2.2
MOMENTUM (GeV/c)

Figure 4

results and the high energy p-p results of Alper[2], et al., and Cronin[3], et al. The p-p and e^+-e^- results look very similar at lower values of momenta, but at higher momenta there seem to be relatively more kaons produced in e^+-e^- interactions than in p-p.

Figure 5 shows the invariant cross sections of π's, K's, and p's versus energy at $\sqrt{S}$ = 4.8 GeV. The lower energy points of the SLAC-LBL experiment seem to indicate that all three types of particles fall on a universal exponential as in a Maxwell-Boltzmann distribution. Our higher energy pions and kaons are above the extrapolated line, indicating that this simple relationship works only for low momenta. Since we found no protons in our sample, the proton cross section might well fit the extrapolated curve out to higher energies.

Figure 6 shows the invariant cross section for hadrons versus momentum for the SLAC-LBL and MP[2] experiments. The general agreement between the two experiments is reasonably good. Both show that the slope of the part between 1.0 and 2.0 GeV/c is less than that found by SLAC-LBL below 1.0 GeV/c, and the SLAC-LBL data shows that the invariant cross section is rather independent of S.

Figure 7 shows a scatter plot of the multiplicity for charged particles measured by our central detection versus the momentum of the hadron in the spectrometer. In the momentum region above 1.2 GeV/c the spectrometer kaons and pions are labeled with crosses and dots respectively. This plot indicates that the multiplicity of the event decreases as the momentum of one particle increases. This is probably expected if one merely says that if one particle has a lot of energy there is little left to use in the creation of other particles.

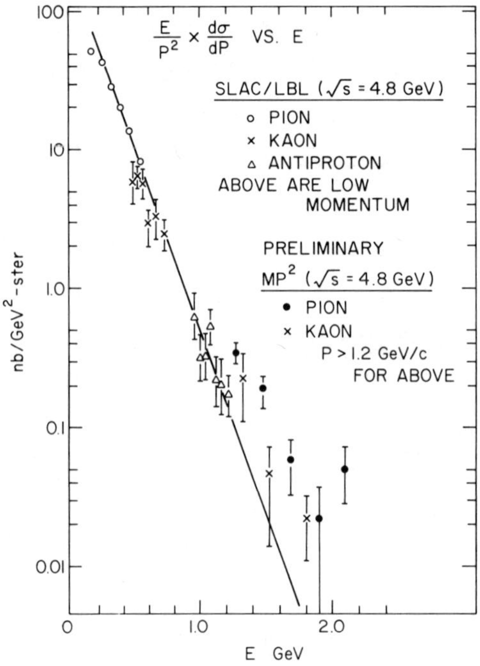
$\frac{E}{P^2} \times \frac{d\sigma}{dP}$ VS. E
SLAC/LBL ($\sqrt{s}$ = 4.8 GeV)
o PION
× KAON
△ ANTIPROTON
ABOVE ARE LOW MOMENTUM
PRELIMINARY
MP^2 ($\sqrt{s}$ = 4.8 GeV)
• PION
× KAON
P > 1.2 GeV/c FOR ABOVE
nb/GeV^2-ster
100
10
1.0
0.1
0.01
0
1.0
2.0
E GeV

Figure 5

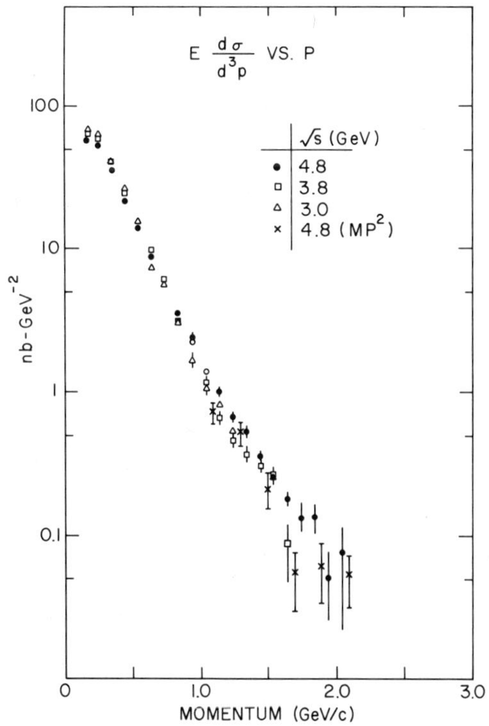

$E \frac{d\sigma}{d^3p}$ VS. P
$\sqrt{s}$ (GeV)
4.8
3.8
3.0
4.8 (MP^2)
100
10
1
0.1
$nb\text{-}GeV^{-2}$
0
1.0
2.0
3.0
MOMENTUM (GeV/c)

Figure 6

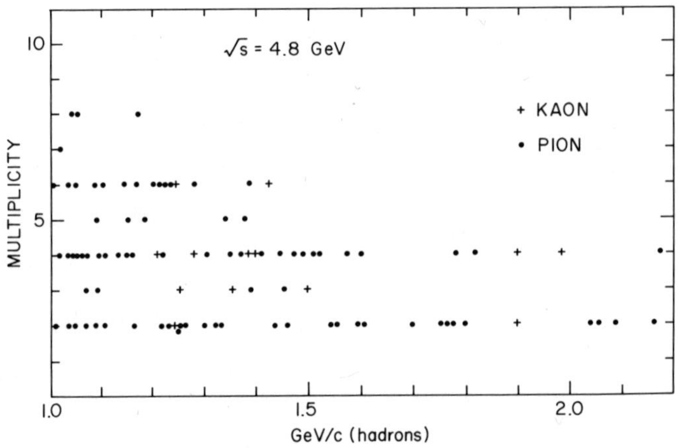

Figure 7

Since the central detector subtends nearly the entire solid angle all events should have an even number of charged particles. The few events which have an odd number are thought to be due predominately to γ-ray conversions in the vacuum pipe and central detector with the produced e^+-e^- pair appearing to be one particle, and, to a lesser extent, to cases where some particle is not detected because of an inefficiency in the PWC's, probably near the support wires.

The mean multiplicity for the events in Figure 7 is 3.7, but one should not confuse this multiplicity with that observed by experiments like SLAC-LBL. Our inclusive trigger requires a high momentum particle and will, for example, observe an event configuration containing two high momentum particles twice as often as a configuration containing only one high momentum particle. Thus, the fact that the mean multiplicity observed in our events is similar to that observed by non-inclusive experiments might be considered somewhat fortuitous.

Allow me now to address a question which I glossed over in my earlier discussion of the hadron spectra, namely the normalization of these curves. This was done by comparing the hadron rates in our apparatus to the μ^+-μ^- rate, with the $e^+ e^- \rightarrow \mu^+ \mu^-$ cross section being calculable from QED. In this regard it is very important that one be sure that his μ^+-μ^- events have the momentum and angular distributions predicted by QED.

Figure 8 shows the momentum of the spectrometer particle versus the real space non-collinearity for events which have a particle penetrating each of the hadron filters when $\sqrt{S}$ = 4.8 GeV. The quite striking

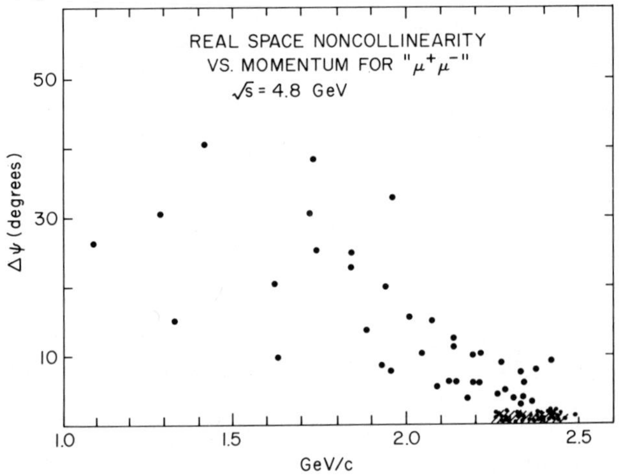
REAL SPACE NONCOLLINEARITY
VS. MOMENTUM FOR "$\mu^+\mu^-$"
$\sqrt{s}$ = 4.8 GeV
50
30
10
Δψ (degrees)
1.0
1.5
2.0
2.5
GeV/c

Figure 8

effect seen in this figure is that as the momentum of the particle decreases the non-collinearity becomes quite large. We have made detailed studies of this distribution using the computer programs encompassing the QED calculations of Berends, Gaemers, and Gastmans[4] to see if it is consistent with QED radiative corrections. Our conclusion is that QED does explain the distribution, so that there is no problem in using $e^+ e^- \to \mu^+ \mu^-$ for normalization of the hadron spectra.

As a final comment I would like to point out that this experiment has been approved for running at SPEAR at $\sqrt{S} \simeq 7 \to 8$ GeV during the autumn of 1975.

REFERENCES

1. B. Richter, XVII International Conference on High Energy Physics, London, 1974.
2. B. Alper, H. Boggild, P. Booth, F. Bulos, L. J. Carroll, G. Von Dardel, G. Domgaard, B. Duff, F. Heymann, J. N. Jackson, G. Jarlskog, L. Jonsson, A. Klovning, L. Leistam, E. Lillethun, G. Lynch, M. Prentice, D. Quarrie, and J. M. Weiss, Phys. Lett. 47B, 275 (1973).
3. J. W. Cronin, H. J. Frisch, M. J. Shochet, J. P. Boymond, P. A. Piroue, and R. L. Sumner, Phys. Rev. Lett. 31, 1426 (1973).
4. F. A. Berends, K. J. F. Gaemers, and R. Gastmans, Nucl. Phys. B57, 381 (1973). We particularly thank Dr. Gaemers for visiting Maryland and installing their program in the Maryland computer so that we could make calculations appropriate to our own selection criteria.

ON THE CONSEQUENCES OF NON-LINEARITY IN A UNIFIED THEORY OF FUNDAMENTAL INTERACTIONS*

Behram Kursunoglu

Center for Theoretical Studies

University of Miami, Coral Gables, Fla. 33124

ABSTRACT

The coupling strength between the field and particle is found to be described by $\frac{Q_n^2}{\hbar c}$ $(= \frac{e^2}{\hbar c} + \frac{g_n^2}{\hbar c})$, $n=0,1,2,\ldots$, where the partial magnetic charges g_n generate short range fields only and where $g_n \to 0$ for $n \to \infty$ or $r \to \frac{\hbar}{Mc}$. The sign of the total magnetic charge g_o $(\sum_{n=o}^{\infty} g_n = (-1)^s g_o)$ correlates with the spin direction, where s=0 and s=1 correspond to spin up and spin down states, respectively. At short distances a strongly interacting particle-antiparticle system with anti-parallel spins becomes, via single spin flip, a weakly interacting system in which the spins are parallel. The infinite spectrum of "bare fundamental lengths"

---

*The mathematical part of this paper concerning non-linear equations was in part sponsored by the Army Research Office, Department of the Army, Durham, North Carolina, under Grant No. DAHCO 4-71-0050.

$r_{on} = \frac{\sqrt{(2G)}}{c^2}\sqrt{(e^2+g_n^2)} \sim (10^{-33}\text{cm})$ measure the deviation of the theory from general relativity plus classical electrodynamics and induce a structure of stratified layers of magnetic charges, g_n, of alternating signs, within a particle. The solutions of the field equations, as a result of the non-linearity and general covariance, produce an indeterminacy in the localizability of the neutral surfaces (and therefore in the g_n) separating magnetic charge densities of opposite signs in the stratified layers. The size of the magnetic structure is of the order of $\frac{\hbar}{Mc}$. For e = 0 the corresponding solutions break the symmetries of charge conjugation and parity and lead to the prediction of two massive neutrinos with different masses. The equations of motion are derived and the results lead to mass relations for the four massive fundamental particles p, e, ν_e, ν_μ and their anti-particles as half the difference of the "bare gravitational mass" $m[\sim \sqrt{(\frac{\hbar c}{2G})}]$ and their finite self-energies. Based on the extremum value properties of the vacuum magnetic field (generated by g_o) it is conjectured that the p-e and ν_μ-ν_e mass ratios are equal. All elementary particles can be constructed as sub-nuclear bound or resonance states of the fundamental particles p, e, ν_e, ν_μ and $\bar{p}$, e^+, $\bar{\nu}_e$, $\bar{\nu}_\mu$. It is further shown that the mass and charge appearing in the Nordström solution of general relativity correspond, for an elementary particle, to the bare gravitational mass and the observed electric charge and therefore they do not refer to either the bare or observed particles.

1. INTRODUCTION

The storage ring experiments on electron-positron annihilation at center of mass energies in the many BeV range, experiments concerning the observation of weak neutral currents, and the most recent Stanford Accelerator - Brookhaven National Laboratory announcement[(6)] disclosing the discovery of slowly decaying neutral particles (the ψ or J) do, inter alia, indicate decided deviations from currently favored models. These deviations indicate that the present classification of elementary particles as well as the rather well established classification of fundamental interactions into four basic couplings of strong, electromagnetic, weak and gravitational types must be reexamined. The ratio of the crossection for the production of hadrons to the production of leptons has, so far, shown a rate of increase with energy that is not explainable in terms of quarks, partons etc. or any reasonable combination of these models. The storage ring experiments at current energies in the many BeV range seems to throw some doubts on the assumed basic differences, from the strong interaction point of view, between leptons and hadrons. These experiments have for the first time allowed the leptons to essentially manifest strong interactions. Thus the present classification of elementary particles into leptons and hadrons may, with further experiments, prove to be the result of observations which depend strongly on energy.

The absence of neutral weak currents in the V-A theory of weak interactions could be a consequence of the assumption that neutrinos are massless particles and therefore have no structure. The presence of weak neutral currents in gauge theories unifying weak and electromagnetic interactions will not be discussed here. The various theories which appeared recently in the literature to "fit" or to "explain" the weakly decaying particles Ψ_1 and Ψ_2 have helped to clarify their classification but have also raised interesting questions on the probable nature of these particles. In light of the known experimental observations and various theoretical models a trend towards unification of all fundamental interactions is emerging.

In this paper we propose a unified theory of fundamental interactions based on the premises of an older approach that differs, in detail as well as in substance, from the current favorites. However the results derived from it, besides being in complete accord with the well established principles of the quantum field theory, throw new light on such things as particle structure, what constitutes a fundamental particle, the nature of electric charge, spin, the intrinsic parity of elementary particles, the breaking of space-time symmetries, bound and resonance states of elementary particles and other structural considerations.

This paper is a sequel to an earlier one[1] hereafter to be referred to as (A). The paper (A) contains the author's version (versus the Einstein[2] and Schrödinger[3] theories) of the nonsymmetric generalization of general relativity, proposed over 20 years ago. In (A) we were able, for the first time, to obtain some of the spherically symmetric solutions of the field equations. These solutions are regular everywhere. It was furthermore found that all fundamental particles, in addition to their usual electromagnetic properties, carry a net magnetic charge g_0 (with different magnitudes for different particles) associated with a short range field. The short range character of the field is due to magnetic charge screening arising from the distribution of magnetic charge density in an infinite sequence of stratified layers of magnetic charge densities, the signs of which alternate (see Fig. 1). The magnetic charge predicted by this theory is in no way related to the magnetic monopole theory of Dirac[4] producing a long range field and quantized according to $ge = \frac{1}{2}n\hbar c$, or to

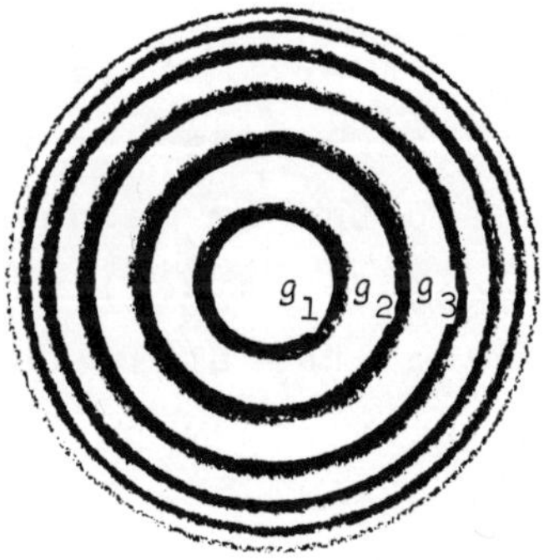

Fig. 1. The partial magnetic charges $|g_{n-1}| > |g_n|$ are distributed with alternating signs in the stratified layers n=0,1,2,... which have the total magnetic charge value $\sum_{n=0}^{\infty} g_n = (-1)^s |g_o|$. The values s=0, s=1, or positive and negative signs of the total magnetic charge g_o correlate with spin up (or down) and spin down (or up) states, respectively. The shaded bands describe the uncertainties in the partial charges g_n or the uncertainties in the location of the neutral magnetic surfaces. The distribution extends to distances of the order of $r_c \sim \frac{\hbar}{Mc}$, where r_c is the indeterminate distance of the "magnetic horizon" from the particle's center.

the magnetic charge theories of Schwinger[5] for the structure of elementary particles. The new magnetic charge g is carried by all elementary particles and anti-particles as described above. The charge g has an infinite spectrum of values g_n, n=1,2,3,.... which correspond to the amounts of magnetic charge contained in each of the stratified layers along with their alternating signs.

In view of the predicted uncertainty in the location of magnetically neutral surfaces (arising from the change of sign of magnetic charge densities from layer to layer) there is also an uncertainty in the g-values contained in a specified layer. It is conceivable that this <u>g-indeterminacy</u> can be related to the energy widths in particle-antiparticle bound or resonance states. The <u>indeterminacy</u> of the g-values as well as of the neutral surfaces is related also to the ultimate boundary (or <u>magnetic horizon</u>) of an elementary particle "located" at the limiting surface where $\lim_{n\to\infty} g_n = 0$. The indeterminacies in the boundary surface at $r=r_c$ for an extended object as well as of the interior neutral surfaces is due to the requirement of general covariance of the theory and the resulting non-linearity. The total magnetic charge carried by an elementary particle is given as the sum of the <u>partial magnetic charges</u> g_n in the form

$$\sum_{0}^{\infty} g_n = g_o(-1)^s \quad ,$$

where, as will be shown, s=0 and s=1 correspond to spin up and spin down states, respectively.

In (A) it was shown that for $g_o = 0$ or $g_n = 0$ the solutions, at distances large compared to the fundamental length r_{on}, reduce to the solutions of general relativity and classical electrodynamics and that they are no longer regular everywhere. Thus using a "magnetic" basis of matter in terms of the new magnetic charge g_o with the properties described above and in (A) we can hope to establish a new approach to elementary particle physics without the need for adapting the renormalizability of an interaction as the criterion for its acceptance or rejection. The study of a theory without any singularities and divergencies should enable us to understand the basic reasons for the success of the renormalization scheme in quantum electrodynamics. Despite its phenomenal success renormalization theory concealed the fundamental properties (unity of all interactions, actual structure of elementary particles) of elementary particles arising from the very nature of their extended structure versus the point description assumed in the renormalizable quantum electrodynamics.

In this series of papers we shall discuss these interesting consequences for the fundamental interactions of elementary particles associated with the finiteness of the self-energy. It is pleasing to see that a theory without any infinities does, in fact, provide a unification of all fundamental interactions. The magnetic charge of this theory is the novel idea which was missing in conventional theories. However the present theory deviates from Einstein's 1916 general relativity in the way quantum theory deviates from classical theory. The degree of deviation of this theory from general relativity plus classical electrodynamics is measured by the size of a fundamental length r_o which is a function of the electric and magnetic charges. In (A) the length r_o was shown to be an infinite spectrum of lengths given by

$$r_{on}^2 = \surd(\ell_{on}^4 + \lambda_{on}^4) \ , \tag{1.1}$$

where

$$\ell_{on}^2 = \frac{2G}{c^4} |g_n| \surd(e^2+g_n^2) \ , \ n=1,2,3,... \ , \tag{1.2}$$

$$\lambda_{on}^2 = \frac{2G}{c^4} |e| \surd(e^2+g_n^2) \ , \tag{1.3}$$

G is the gravitational constant, e and c represent the unit of electric charge and speed of light, respectively. As n tends to infinity g_n tends to zero, r_{on} tends to a smaller limiting value

$$r_{on} \to \frac{2G}{c^4} e^2 \ ,$$

and the field equations approach the field equations of general relativity. In fact for distances $r \gg r_{on}$ the generalized theory of gravitation reduces exactly to the field equations of general relativity and classical electrodynamics of free fields.

Both the lengths ℓ_o and λ_o in (1.1) were obtained in (A) as constants of integration. Thus the existence of a correspondence principle (i.e. the r_o=0 limit yields general relativity plus the electromagnetic fields) provides a powerful basis for the unique and unambigous physical interpretation of the theory (see Fig. 2). The four fundamental conserved currents j_e^μ (charged electromagnetic current vector density), j_o^μ (neutral electromagnetic current vector density), s^μ (charged intrinsic magnetic axial current density), ζ^μ (neutral intrinsic magnetic axial current density) play a crucial role in the physical interpretation of the theory. These

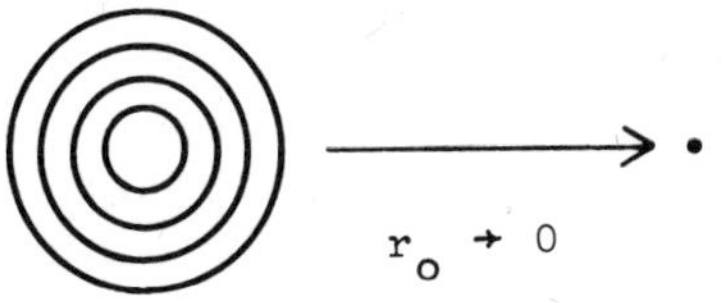

Fig. 2. In the correspondence limit $r_o=0$ the magnetic structure collapses to a point representing a classical particle.

currents are derived from the field equations and can be determined only if we know the solutions of the field equations. The currents cannot be prescribed arbitrarily. The neutral electric and magnetic currents j_o^μ and ζ^μ and their corresponding fields describe the <u>vacuum pairs</u> associated with the field. The theory predicts only four massive particles (and their antiparticles) which hopefully will be identified as proton, electron and two chargeless (i.e. e=0) particles. The latter two have the same symmetry properties as the two neutrinos ν_e and ν_μ. The current experimental measurements have provided upper limits for ν_e and ν_μ masses but did not rule out the possibility of the neutrinos having finite rest masses. The restrictions on the four currents mentioned above applies also to the total energy density of the field since it is also determined in terms of the solutions of the field equations. A further important result concerns the concept of the spin of an elementary particle. We shall demonstrate in the next section that the $\frac{1}{2}$ and $-\frac{1}{2}$ values of spin is a consequence of stratified distribution of the magnetic charge in an elementary particle.

We shall also derive the equations of motion of

particles from an action principle of the field. The motion of the particles results from varying the extremum action function obtained by substituting the field equations in the action function of the field. This new way of obtaining the equations of motion from varying the extremum action function is a consequence of the regularity of the fields everywhere since the latter property leads after the volume integration to the appearance of the particle mass in the action function. The particles move along with the extremal points of the field. However, because of the indeterminacy or spread in the particle boundary the resulting trajectory cannot be defined as sharply as in classical theory. This spread in the particle trajectory is a quantum like behavior though in the present case it results from effect of the requirement of relativistic invariance on an object extended in space and time. In general relativity and in electrodynamics the particles move along the points where the field assumes an infinite value.

The concept of field quantization for the generalized theory of gravitation, because of the nonlinearity of the theory, can only be applied beyond the magnetic horizon or the asymptotic region, where the laws of classical electrodynamics hold. A linearization of any form would be quite useless since none of the results of this paper and the previous paper (A) could have been obtained without an exact treatment of the field equations. At this time the possible role of magnetic charge in any possible quantization scheme and the ultimate fate of renormalization is not known. We do not consider this problem an urgent one, but the applicability of quantization or an equivalent procedure may hold the key for testing the ultimate validity of the generalized theory of gravitation.

2. SYMMETRIES OF THE FIELD EQUATIONS

The special case of time independent spherically symmetric field equations contains a wealth of information on the physics of the generalized theory of gravitation. They were derived in (A) in the form of equations (4.13)-(4.16). These equations can readily be further simplified into the form

$$\frac{1}{2}r_o^2 f[fS\ \exp(\rho)\Phi']' = R^2\cos\Phi + (-1)^s \ell_o^2 \sin\Phi \quad , \qquad (2.1)$$

$$\frac{1}{2}r_o^2 f[fS\ \exp(\rho)\rho']' = -R^2\sin\Phi + (-1)^s \ell_o^2 \cos\Phi + \exp(\rho) \quad , \qquad (2.2)$$

$$\frac{1}{2}r_o^2 f[f\ \exp(\rho)S']' = \left(1 - \frac{\sin\Phi}{\cosh\Gamma}\right)\exp(\rho) \quad , \qquad (2.3)$$

$$\rho'' + \rho'\ \frac{f'}{f} + \frac{1}{2}\left(\rho'^2 + \Phi'^2\right) = 0 \quad , \qquad (2.4)$$

where prime indicates differentiation with respect to r and where

$$f = \upsilon\ \cosh\Gamma \quad , \quad S = \frac{\exp(u)}{\cosh^2\Gamma} \quad ,$$

$$\ell_o^2 = q^{-1}|g| \quad , \quad \lambda_o^2 = q^{-1}|e| \quad , \quad \exp(\rho) = \surd(r^4 + \ell_o^4) \quad , \qquad (2.5)$$

$$\cosh\Gamma = (R^2 + r_o^2)\exp(-\rho) \quad , \quad R^2 + r_o^2 = \surd(r^4 + r_o^4) .$$

The fundamental length r_o was calculated in (A) in terms of the constants of integration λ_o and ℓ_o as

$$r_o^2 = \surd(\ell_o^4 + \lambda_o^4) = \frac{2G}{c^4}\left(e^2 + g^2\right) \quad , \qquad (2.6)$$

where

$$\ell_o^2 = q^{-1}|g| = \frac{2G}{c^4}|g|\sqrt{(e^2+g^2)} , \qquad (2.7)$$

$$\lambda_o^2 = q^{-1}|e| = \frac{2G}{c^4}|e|\sqrt{(e^2+g^2)} . \qquad (2.8)$$

The field equations (2.1)-(2.3), through the factor $(-1)^s\ell_o^2$, depend on the sign of the magnetic charge g. Now, by using the results (4.18), (4.19) of (A) the explicit dependence of the field equations on $(-1)^s$ can be represented as a new degree of freedom of the field. Thus, by using the new set of angle functions

$$\Phi_{ns}(r) = \pm (2n+s)\pi+(-1)^s\Phi(r) , \qquad (2.9)$$

where $s=0,1$ and $n=0,1,2,\ldots$., we can rewrite the first three of the field equations in the form

$$\frac{1}{2}r_o^2 f[fS \exp(\rho)\Phi'_{ns}]' = R^2\cos\Phi_{ns} + \ell_o^2\sin\Phi_{ns} , \qquad (2.10)$$

$$\frac{1}{2}r_o^2 f[fS \exp(\rho)\rho']' = -R^2\sin\Phi_{ns} + \ell_o^2\cos\Phi_{ns}+\exp(\rho) , \qquad (2.11)$$

$$\frac{1}{2}r_o^2 f[f \exp(\rho)S']' = (1 - \frac{\sin\Phi_{ns}}{\cosh\Gamma}) \exp(\rho) , \qquad (2.12)$$

where now Φ_{ns} represent the ∞^2 distinct solutions of the field equations and where we have used the relations

$$\sin\Phi = \sin\Phi_{ns} , \quad \cos\Phi=(-1)^s\cos\Phi_{ns} , \quad \Phi'=(-1)^s\Phi'_{ns} .$$

It was pointed out in (A) that compatibility with the light cone partition of space-time events requires that all the solutions of the field equations must fulfill the condition

$$\sin \Phi \geq 0 \quad , \tag{2.13}$$

in order to insure positivity of the coefficients

$$- g_{22} = \exp(\rho)\sin\Phi \quad , \quad g_{33} = g_{22} \sin^2\theta \tag{2.14}$$

of the metric tensor $g_{\mu\nu}$. The fulfillment of the condition (2.13) confines all the solutions to the upper half of the Φ-plane where Φ is measured in the counter-clockwise direction. Indeed, as was shown in (A), all the solutions satisfy (2.13) and there exist no solutions violating condition (2.13) provided only that the positive square root of $\exp(\rho) = \sqrt{(r^4+\ell_o^4)}$ is admitted. However, if negative square root of $\exp(\rho)$ is included then the condition (2.13) can be replaced by

$$\exp(\rho)\sin\Phi \geq 0 \ , \tag{2.15}$$

and in the Φ-plane, for the negative square root of $\exp(\rho)$, the angle function Φ can also be measured in the clockwise direction. In this case we obtain ∞^4 distinct solutions satisfying (2.15), and no others exist. Thus the new sets of solutions are of the form

$$\Phi_{ns\tau} = \pm (2n+s+\tau)\pi+(-1)^s\Phi \ , \ \rho\pm(2n+\tau)i\pi = \rho_{n\tau} \ , \tag{2.16}$$

where

$$\tau = 0,1 \quad ,$$

and where now

$$\sin\Phi=(-1)^{\tau}\sin\Phi_{ns\tau} \;,\; \cos\Phi=(-1)^{s+\tau}\cos\Phi_{ns\tau} \;,\; e^{\rho}=(-1)^{\tau}\exp(\rho_{n\tau}), \tag{2.17}$$

so that

$$\exp(\rho)\sin\Phi = \exp(\rho_{n\tau})\sin\Phi_{ns\tau} \quad ,$$

remains unchanged. Furthermore the field equations (2.1)-(2.4) can be expressed as a function of a "charge variable" y where

$$r = \surd(\frac{2G}{c^4})y \tag{2.17'}$$

and where y has the dimensions of a charge. The field equations remain unchanged under the transformation (2.17') and do not, explicitly, contain the constant $\surd(\frac{2G}{c^4})$. We may thus study the field equations in a "charge space" specified by the transformation (2.17'). By using the results (2.16), (2.17) and (2.17') we obtain the equations (2.1)-(2.4) in the form

$$\frac{1}{2} Q_n^2 \; f[fS\exp(\rho_{cn\tau})\Phi'_{ns\tau}]' = Y_n^2 \cos\Phi_{ns\tau} + |g_n|Q_n\sin\Phi_{ns\tau}, \tag{2.18}$$

$$\frac{1}{2} Q_n^2 \; f[fS\exp(\rho_{cn\tau})\rho'_{cn\tau}]'=-Y_n^2 \sin\Phi_{ns\tau}+|g_n|Q_n\cos\Phi_{ns\tau} + \exp(\rho_{cn\tau}), \tag{2.19}$$

$$\frac{1}{2} Q_n^2 \; f[f\exp(\rho_{cn\tau})S']' = (1 - \frac{\sin\Phi_{ns\tau}}{\cosh\Gamma_{cn\tau}})\exp(\rho_{cn\tau}), \tag{2.20}$$

$$\rho''_{cn\tau} + \rho'_{cn\tau}\frac{\upsilon'}{\upsilon} + \frac{1}{2}(\rho'^2_{cn\tau} + \Phi'^2_{ns\tau}) = \rho'^2_{cn\tau}\tanh^2\Gamma_{cn\tau} \;, \tag{2.21}$$

where

$$R^2=\frac{2G}{c^4}\,Y_n^2\ ,\quad Y_n^2=\sqrt{(y^4+Q_n^4)}-Q_n^2\ ,\quad Q_n^2=e^2+g_n^2\ ,\quad \exp(\rho)=\frac{2G}{c^4}\exp(\rho_c)\,,$$

$$\exp(\rho_c) = \sqrt{(y^4+g_n^2Q_n^2)}\ ,\quad \cosh\Gamma_{cn\tau} = \sqrt{\left[\frac{y^4+Q_n^4}{y^4+g_n^2Q_n^2}\right]}\quad .$$

In this case the prime in (2.18)-(2.21) indicates differentiation with respect to y. Because of the non-linearity of the equations the solutions for n=0,1,2,..., are non-trivial discrete solutions corresponding to the stratified layers carrying positive or negative magnetic charges g_n , n=0,1,2... . Beyond n=∞ the solutions are the continuum solutions which are without magnetic charge content and at distances large compared to r_c they reduce to the Nordström solutions of general relativity.

Now, the field equations (2.18)-(2.21) are independent of the sign of the electric charge and therefore the solutions (2.16) refer to both positive and negative electric charge irrespective of the positive and the negative energy states. There are thus two signs for electric charges for a particle as well as for an antiparticle. Furthermore, as seen from (9.2) of (A) the energy density has a linear dependence on υ and therefore it changes sign under the transformation

$$\upsilon \rightarrow -\upsilon\ , \qquad (2.22)$$

under which the field equations are unchanged. Hence the field equations have both positive and negative energy solutions for particles with positive as well as with negative sign of electric charge.

The spherically symmetric fields and the

corresponding electric and magnetic charge densities are given by

$$E_e = \frac{q}{\upsilon} \tanh\Gamma = \frac{\pm e}{\upsilon(R^2+r_o^2)} \quad , \qquad (2.23)$$

for the charged electric field,

$$E_o = q\, r_o^2\, \upsilon \cosh\Gamma \sinh\Gamma\, \rho' S' \quad , \qquad (2.24)$$

for the neutral electric field, and

$$B_g = q\, e^{\rho} \cos\Phi \sin\theta \quad , \qquad (2.25)$$

for the charged magnetic field,

$$H_o = \frac{q}{\upsilon} \frac{\cos\Phi}{\cosh\Gamma} \quad , \qquad (2.26)$$

for the neutral magnetic field. The corresponding charge densities† are

$$j_e^4 = \frac{q}{4\pi} (e^{\rho}\tanh\Gamma\sin\Phi)'\sin\theta = \frac{\pm e}{4\pi} \left(\frac{\sin\Phi}{\cosh\Gamma}\right)' \sin\theta \quad , \qquad (2.27)$$

$$j_o^4 = \frac{\pm e r_o^2}{4\pi} (\upsilon^2\cosh\Gamma\sin\Phi\, \rho' S')'\sin\theta \quad , \qquad (2.28)$$

for the electric charge densities, and

$$s^4 = \frac{q}{4\pi} (e^{\rho}\cos\Phi)' \sin\theta \quad , \qquad (2.29)$$

---

†Due to an oversight the magnetic current densities s^{μ}, ζ^{μ} and the corresponding magnetic fields B_g and H_o were interchanged in (A). This error did not affect the results of the paper.

$$\zeta^4 = \frac{g}{4\pi}\left(\frac{e^{\rho}\cos\Phi\sin\Phi}{\cosh\Gamma}\right)' \sin\theta \quad , \tag{2.30}$$

for the magnetic charge densities, where

$$\int j_e^4 \, dr d\theta d\phi = \pm e \;, \quad \int j_o^4 \, dr d\theta d\phi = 0 \quad , \tag{2.31}$$

and

$$\int s^4 dr d\theta d\phi = (-1)^s g_o \;, \quad \int \zeta^4 dr d\theta d\phi = 0 \;. \tag{2.32}$$

We note that the r-integration in (2.32) is carried out over the interval $(0,r_c)$ where r_c represents the indeterminate distance of the magnetic horizon from the origin. In this case, for the functions $\Phi(r)$ and $\rho(r)$, we have the relations

$$\Phi(r_c) = \tfrac{1}{2}\pi(-1)^s \pm (2n+s+\tau)\pi \quad , \tag{2.33}$$

$$\rho(r_c) = \ln r_c^2 \pm i(2n+\tau)\pi \;, \; n=0,1,2,\ldots \quad . \tag{2.34}$$

The invariance of the field equations under the transformation

$$\Gamma \to -\Gamma \tag{2.35}$$

implies charge conjugation invariance which leaves B_g, H_o, s^4, and ζ^4 unchanged and reverses the signs of E_e, E_o, j_e^4, j_o^4. The sign change of energy under (2.22) leads to the change of signs of E_e and E_o. Hence, because of $\upsilon \to -\upsilon$ invariance, it follows that particles and antiparticles carry equal and opposite signs of electric charge. However, under (2.22) the charged magnetic field B_g and magnetic charge density s^4

remain unchanged, and therefore particles and antiparticles can have the same sign of net magnetic charge.

Now, if the transformations (2.22) and (2.35) are followed by a change of magnetic charge sign (spin inversion) and parity inversion (i.e. $(-1)^{\tau}$) then we obtain the results

$$E_e \to (-1)^{J+\varepsilon} E_e \ , \quad E_o \to (-1)^{J+\varepsilon+\tau} E_o \ , \tag{2.36}$$

$$B_g \to (-1)^{s} B_g \ , \quad H_o \to (-1)^{\varepsilon+s} H_o \ ,$$

and

$$j_e^4 \to (-1)^J j_e^4 \ , \quad j_o^4 \to (-1)^J j_o \ , \tag{2.37}$$

$$s^4 \to (-1)^s s^4 \ , \quad \zeta^4 \to (-1)^s \zeta^4 \ ,$$

where J=0, 1 select positive and negative charge. Note that none of the spherically symmetric fields, except E_o, change sign under the parity operation $(-1)^{\tau}$. The fields E_o and H_o represent the electric and magnetic fields of the vacuum pairs. The vacuum charge densities j_o^4 and ζ_o^4 change signs under charge conjugation and spin inversion, respectively. The latter statement applies also to the charge densities j_e^4 and s^4.

3. SPIN AND MAGNETIC CHARGE

The non-linearity of the field equations does not preclude their invariance under the 2-dimensional unitary transformations of the group SU(2).

The right hand sides of the field equations (2.18)-(2.20) contain a rotation by an angle $\Phi_{ns\tau}$ around the "3-direction" of the "vector"

$$|V\rangle = \begin{bmatrix} Y_n^2 \\ |g_n| Q_n \\ \exp(\rho_{cn\tau}) \end{bmatrix} , \tag{3.1}$$

where the rotation matrix is given by

$$A = \begin{bmatrix} \cos\Phi_{ns\tau} & \sin\Phi_{ns\tau} & 0 \\ -\sin\Phi_{ns\tau} & \cos\Phi_{ns\tau} & 0 \\ 0 & 0 & 1 \end{bmatrix} . \tag{3.2}$$

The real orthogonal transformations

$$|V'\rangle = A|V\rangle , \tag{3.3}$$

can be represented by a stereographic projection of the unit sphere on to the equatorial plane, the south pole of the sphere being the Center of projection. Thus if the point (a',b',o) is the image on the plane of the point (a,b,d) on the sphere and we write $\xi = a'+i\,b'$, then the relations for the projection are

$$a+ib = \frac{2\xi}{1+\bar{\xi}\xi} , \quad a-ib = \frac{2\bar{\xi}}{1+\bar{\xi}\xi} , \quad d = \frac{1-\bar{\xi}\xi}{1+\bar{\xi}\xi} , \tag{3.4}$$

where

$$a^2+b^2+d^2 = 1$$

and

$$a = \frac{Y_n^2}{V^2} , \quad b = \frac{g_n Q_n}{V^2} , \quad d = \frac{\exp(\rho_{cn\tau})}{V^2} , \tag{3.5}$$

$$V^2 = \sqrt{[Y_n^4 + g_n^2 Q_n^2 + \exp(2\rho_{cn\tau})]} \quad . \tag{3.6}$$

Hence the radius of the "charge sphere" can be written as

$$V = 2^{\frac{1}{4}}[y^4 + Q_n^4 - Q_n^2\sqrt{(y^4+Q_n^4)} + g_n^2 Q_n^2]^{\frac{1}{4}} \quad . \tag{3.7}$$

The minimum value

$$V_{Min.} = 2^{\frac{1}{4}} g_n (1 + \frac{e^2}{g_n^2})^{\frac{1}{4}} \quad ,$$

of V occurs at the point y=0. For g_n=0 we obtain $V_{Min.}$ =0.

In order to include the south pole of the sphere in the stereographic projection we use the homogeneous representation

$$\xi = \frac{u_1}{u_2} \quad .$$

Hence the relations (3.4) yield for the right hand sides of equations (2.18)-(2.20) the results

$$Y_n^2 \cos\Phi_{ns\tau} + |g_n| Q_n \sin\Phi_{ns\tau} = \langle v_{ns\tau}|\sigma_1|v_{ns\tau}\rangle \quad , \tag{3.8}$$

$$-Y_n^2 \sin\Phi_{ns\tau} + |g_n| Q_n \cos\Phi_{ns\tau} = \langle v_{ns\tau}|\sigma_2|v_{ns\tau}\rangle \quad , \tag{3.9}$$

$$\exp(\rho_{cn\tau}) = - v_{ns\tau}|\sigma_3|v_{ns\tau}\rangle \quad , \tag{3.10}$$

where σ_j(j=1,2,3) are the usual Pauli spin matrices, and where

$$|v_{ns\tau}\rangle = V \exp(-\tfrac{1}{2} i\sigma_3 \Phi_{ns\tau})|u\rangle \quad , \tag{3.11}$$

$$\langle u|u\rangle = 1 \quad , \quad |u\rangle = \begin{bmatrix} u_1 \\ u_2 \end{bmatrix} .$$

Thus the rotations of the "charge sphere" of radius V ($\sim r_c$) are, for given s and τ, completely represented by the unitary transformations (3.11) which cover the double-valued representations of the proper rotation group.

From the definition of $\Phi_{ns\tau}$ by (2.16) it follows that the unitary transformations (3.11) can be expressed as

$$|v_n\!\uparrow^+\rangle = (-1)^n \; V \; \exp(-\tfrac{1}{2}i\sigma_3\Phi)|u\rangle \; , \qquad (3.12)$$

for spin up (s=0), even parity (τ=0) ,

$$|v_n\!\downarrow^-\rangle = -(-1)^n \; V \; \exp(\tfrac{1}{2}i\sigma_3\Phi)|u\rangle \; , \qquad (3.13)$$

for spin down (s=1), odd parity (τ=1) ,

$$|v_n\!\uparrow^-\rangle = -i(-1)^n\sigma_3 \; V \; \exp(-\tfrac{1}{2}i\sigma_3\Phi)|u\rangle \; , \qquad (3.14)$$

for spin up (s=0), odd parity (τ=1) ,

$$|v_n\!\downarrow^+\rangle = +i(-1)^n \; \sigma_3 \; V \; \exp(\tfrac{1}{2}i\sigma_3\Phi)|u\rangle \; , \qquad (3.15)$$

for spin down (s=1), even parity (τ=0) states, respectively. The phase factor $(-1)^n$ describes change of sign in the transition through the stratified layers of magnetic charges. The factor $\frac{1}{2}$ on the left hand sides of the field equations (2.18)-(2.20) can now be interpreted as the spin of an elementary particle provided the spectrum of fundamental lengths r_{on} or charges Q_n have an appropriate $\hbar$-dependence. A simple approach is to assume the relation

$$g_n^2 = \gamma_n \hbar c \quad , \tag{3.16}$$

where the numerical coefficients γ_n which satisfy

$$\lim_{n\to\infty} \gamma_n = 0 \quad , \tag{3.17}$$

correspond to the solutions of the field equations (2.18)-(2.20) in the magnetic layers. Thus with the assumption (3.16) we obtain

$$r_{on}^2 = \hbar \frac{2G}{c^3} \left(\frac{e^2}{\hbar c} + \gamma_n\right) , \quad \frac{Q_n^2}{\hbar c} = \frac{e^2}{\hbar c} + \frac{g_n^2}{\hbar c} \quad . \tag{3.18}$$

The spin degree of freedom of an elementary particle is due to its magnetic charge structure as described here and in (A). Thus when the sign of the magnetic charges g_n is changed, the net magnetic charge

$$\sum_{n=o}^{\infty} g_n = (-1)^s |g_o| \tag{3.19}$$

changes its sign and the particle spin reverses its direction. From the above results we see that the spin of an elementary particle arising from its magnetic content assumes a new physical status. The direction of the spin is determined by the sign of its net magnetic charge g_o. This result implies that in the coupling of particles and antiparticles at high energies with parallel spins and opposite parities, because of the equality of their net magnetic charges, the annihilation process must slow down (see Figs. 3, 4 and 5). In the case of antiparallel spins, because of the opposite

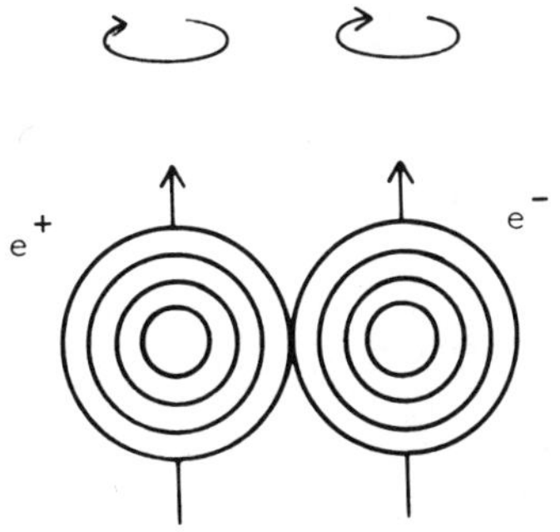

Fig. 3. Parallel spins or equal signs of magnetic charges correspond to a magnetic repulsion of two "magnetic spheres" rotating in the same direction. The magnetic repulsion at short distances is partly counterbalanced by the electrical attraction.

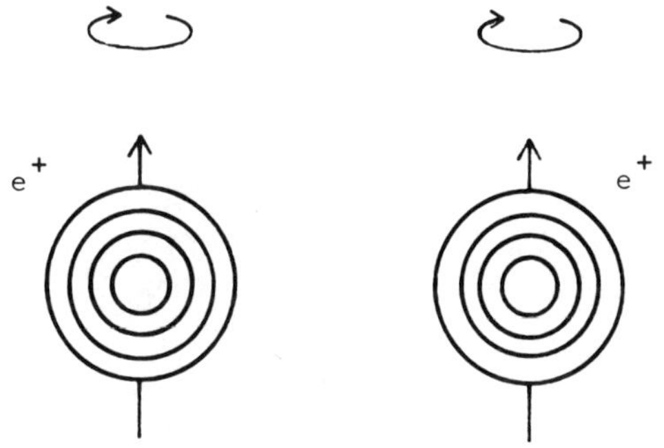

Fig. 4. Parallel spins or equal signs of magnetic charges correspond to a magnetic repulsion of two "magnetic spheres" rotating in the same direction. The magnetic repulsion at short distances is further enhanced by the electrical repulsion.

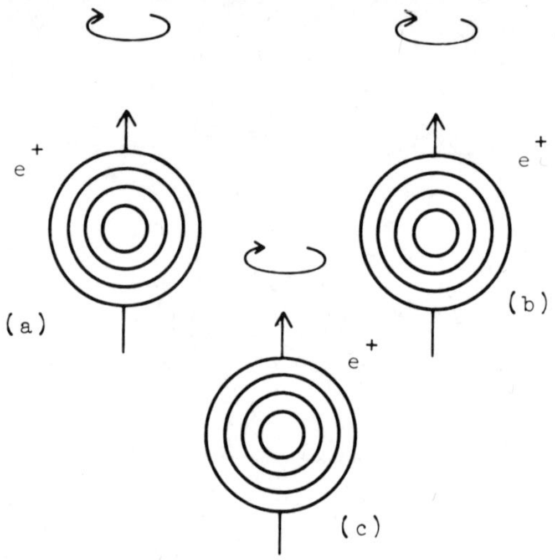

Fig. 5. Three parallel spins (equal signs of magnetic charges) of three "magnetic spheres" rotating in the same direction. The magnetic repulsions of the spheres a, b, and c are further enhanced by their electrical repulsions.

signs of their net magnetic charges, the annihilation process is faster than in the previous case. Thus, the strongly bound magnetic layers or magnetic levels of an elementary particle with its anti-particle in a parallel spin state (i.e. same signs of their net magnetic charges) results in bound states of a new particle of spin 1 and negative parity. The energy levels of the new particle are determined by electromagnetic, strong, weak (and even gravitational) interactions at short distances. For such systems (e.g. proton + anti-proton) the slow annihilation could lead to a discrete spectrum of photons. In fact the observed Ψ_n (n=1,2,3 so far) or J particles could well be due to the formation of such bound states of particles and anti-particles. The uncertainties associated with the partial magnetic charges g_n, pointed out earlier, may be related to the discrete energy widths of the two body system.

From (3.18) we see that the term $g_n^2/\hbar c$ represents the magnetic coupling between the n-th layer of the particle and the field. Thus in the range of $(0,r_c)$ corresponding to each magnetic layer (n=0,1,2,...) there exists an infinite number of couplings between the field and the particle, the strength of which decreases as $n\to\infty$. Beyond $n\to\infty$ (i.e. beyond $r=r_c$) the coupling between the field and the particle is measured by the fine structure constant alone.

The above symmetries may now be depicted in the Φ-diagram below.

4. SYMMETRIES OF CHARGELESS PARTICLES

The case where the constant of integration $\ell_o^2 = q^{-1}g$ is set equal to zero was discussed in (A). The solutions describe the field beyond the magnetic horizon. Now, the case where the constant of integration $\lambda_o^2 = q^{-1}e$ is set equal to zero has been solved in (A) only for the special situation of zero magnetic charge density leading to the infinite sequence of stratified magnetic structure of a chargeless particle. It is of great interest to study the effect of the absence of electric charge on space time symmetries discussed in the previous section.

In the limit

$$\lambda_o^2 = q^{-1}e = 0 \quad ,$$

the field equations (2.1)-(2.4) reduce to

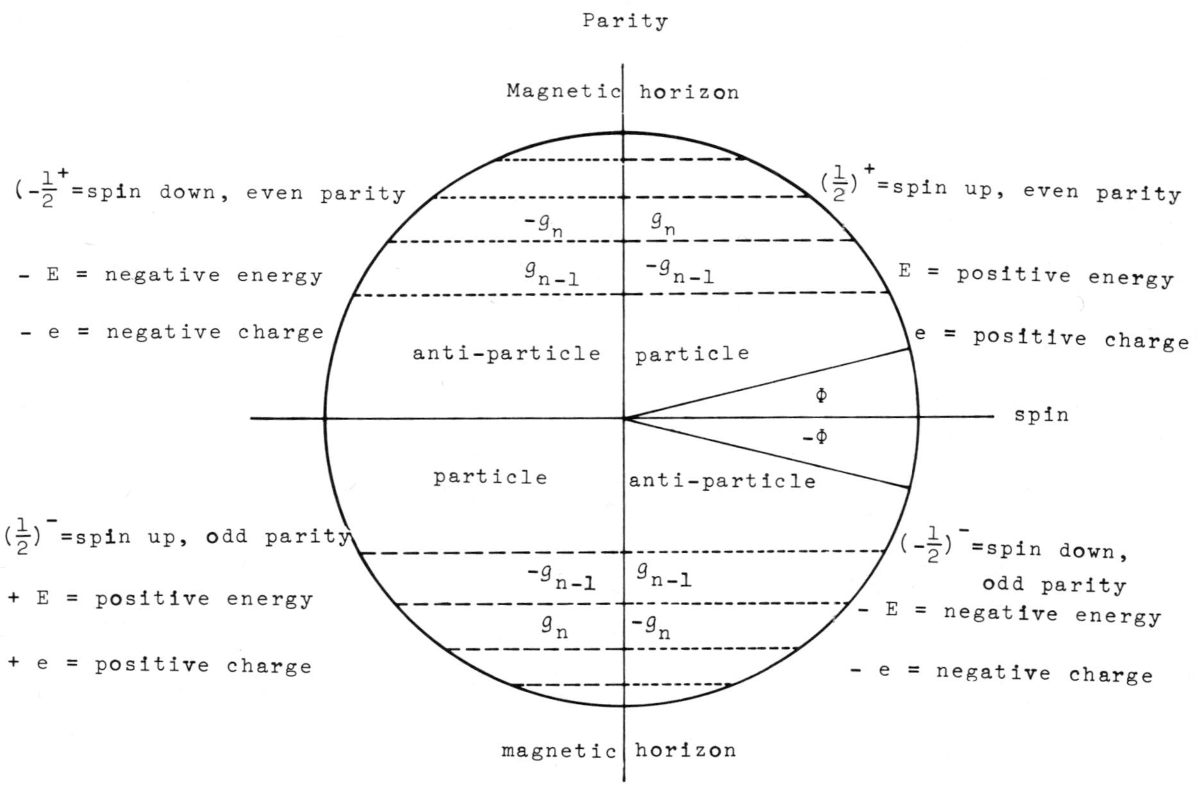

Fig. 6. Spin, Parity and Magnetic Charge States
The first and third quadrants for particle, and the second and fourth for the corresponding antiparticle, describe the four possible states discussed in the text. The magnetic layers illustrate magnetic charge and spin reversals whenever the angle Φ crosses the parity and spin axes in clockwise and counter clockwise directions.

$$\frac{1}{2}\ell_o^2\upsilon(\upsilon e^{u+\rho}\Phi')' = (e^\rho-\ell_o^2)\cos\Phi+(-1)^s\ell_o^2\sin\Phi \quad , \tag{4.1}$$

$$\frac{1}{2}\ell_o^2\upsilon(\upsilon e^{u+\rho}\rho')' = -(e^\rho-\ell_o^2)\sin\Phi+(-1)^s\ell_o^2\cos\Phi+e^\rho \quad , \tag{4.2}$$

$$\frac{1}{2}\ell_o^2\upsilon(\upsilon e^{u+\rho}u')' = e^\rho(1 - \sin\Phi) \quad , \tag{4.3}$$

$$\rho'' + \rho'\frac{\upsilon'}{\upsilon} + \frac{1}{2}(\rho'^2+\Phi'^2) = 0 \quad , \tag{4.4}$$

where the last equation, as in the general case, is a consequence of the first three equations. In this case the solutions (2.16) involving both spin and parity do not satisfy the field equations (4.1)-(4.4). However, the solutions (2.9) without the parity quantum number do satisfy the field equations (4.1)-(4.4) and therefore they can be replaced by

$$\frac{1}{2}\ell_o^2\upsilon[\upsilon\exp(u+\rho)\Phi'_{ns}]' = (e^\rho-\ell_o^2)\cos\Phi_{ns} + \ell_o^2\sin\Phi_{ns} \quad , \tag{4.5}$$

$$\frac{1}{2}\ell_o^2\upsilon[\upsilon\exp(u+\rho)\rho']'=-(e^\rho-\ell_o^2)\sin\Phi_{ns}+\ell_o^2\cos\Phi_{ns}+\exp(\rho), \tag{4.6}$$

$$\frac{1}{2}\ell_o^2\upsilon[\upsilon\exp(u+\rho)u']' = e^\rho(1-\sin\Phi_{ns}) \quad , \tag{4.7}$$

where, as before, the discrete indices n,s for the functions υ, u, ρ and for the ℓ_o have been suppressed and where

$$\Phi_{ns} = \pm(2n+s)\pi+(-1)^s\Phi, \quad n=0,1,2,\ldots . \tag{4.8}$$

Thus the solutions of the equations (4.5)-(4.7) do not contain parity and <u>charge conjugate</u> states. In this case we have only ∞^2 distinct solutions. Because of the invariance under $\upsilon \to -\upsilon$ we still have particle-antiparticle solutions, each with two spin states s=0 and 1. These particles have no electromagnetic interactions and they couple through the magnetic charge alone. The absence of parity and charge conjugation symmetries for e=0 imply that these symmetries are of electromagnetic origin. Conversely, intrinsic parity and charge conjugation are space-time symmetries induced by electric charge. The chargeless particles have no continuum solutions occuring beyond the magnetic horizon since for $g_n = 0$ ($\ell_o=0$) the equations (4.5)-(4.7), as a consequence of the relations $\lim_{\ell_o \to 0} \cos\Phi_{ns} = 0$, $\lim_{\ell_o \to 0} \sin\Phi_{ns} = 1$, are empty. Thus chargeless particles have short range interactions only, where the range of the force is $g_n^2/M_\nu c^2$ which, of course, has an indeterminacy specified by g_n. The chargeless massive particles predicted by this theory have the same symmetry properties as the two neutrinos ν_e and ν_μ.

The fields of the particles and the corresponding magnetic charge densities are given by

$$B_g = q\, e^\rho \cos\Phi \sin\theta \ , \quad H_o = \frac{q}{\upsilon} \cos\Phi \ , \tag{4.9}$$

$$s^4 = \frac{q}{4\pi} (e^\rho \cos\Phi)' \sin\theta \ , \quad \zeta^4 = \frac{q}{4\pi} (e^\rho \cos\Phi \sin\Phi)' \sin\theta . \tag{4.10}$$

The extremum values of the magnetically charged field, as follows from (8.7) of (A), are given by

$$B_n = (-1)^s g_n \sin\theta \ . \tag{4.11}$$

For the extremum values of the neutral field H_o, using (4.4), we obtain the equations

$$\frac{1}{\upsilon} \cos\Phi = 0 \ , \quad \Phi \neq \frac{\pi}{2} \ , \qquad (4.12)$$

and

$$\frac{d\Phi}{d\rho} \cot\Phi = 1 \pm \sqrt{(1 - \frac{3\ell_o^4}{r^4} \cot^2\Phi)} \ , \qquad (4.13)$$

where in (4.12) for $\frac{1}{\upsilon} = 0$ we obtain the point r=0 as the point where $H_o(0)=0$ takes its minimum value. Another minimum, as follows from (4.13), occurs for $\Phi = \frac{\pi}{2}$ or at $r = r_c$. However the equations (4.13) imply that there exist two sets of maximal values for the neutral field H_o. This result, in conjunction with the field equations (4.5)-(4.7), implies two different chargeless particles possessing the same symmetry properties but different masses.

The equation (4.13) is also obtained for the field of the charged particles, so that the condition for the maximal values of the vacuum field H_o do not depend on the electric charge. In the charged case also we shall interpret this result as implying the existence of two charged different massive particles. For the charged electric field

$$E_e = \frac{q}{\upsilon} \tanh\Gamma \ ,$$

the minimum value $E_e=0$ occurs at r=0. For the maximal values of E_e using the equation (2.12) and the result

$$\frac{1}{\upsilon} = \pm (\exp\tfrac{1}{2}\rho)' \exp(F) \cosh\Gamma \ , \qquad (4.14)$$

we obtain the maxima

$$E_{max} = \frac{q}{A} \ ,$$

where A is a dimensionless constant. We have used here the results

$$F = \frac{1}{2}\int \frac{\Phi'^2}{\rho'}\, dr = Ln\left[\frac{2\exp(\frac{1}{2}\rho)}{B\rho'}\right] , \quad e^F = \frac{2\exp(\frac{1}{2}\rho)}{B\rho'}$$

$$\Phi'^2 = \rho'^2 - 2\rho'' = \frac{4r^2(2r^4-3\ell_o^2)}{(r^4+\ell_o^4)^2} \quad . \tag{4.15}$$

Hence, by using the substitution

$$r^2 = \sqrt{(\tfrac{3}{2})}\ \ell_o^2 \cosh\gamma \quad ,$$

the equation

$$\Phi' = \pm \frac{2r\ \sqrt{(2r^4-3\ell_o^4)}}{r^4 + \ell_o^4} \quad , \tag{4.16}$$

can be integrated to

$$\Phi = D \pm \sqrt{2}\left[\tanh^{-1}\left|\sqrt{(1-3\ell_o^4/2r^4)}\right| - \sqrt{(\tfrac{5}{2})}\tanh^{-1}\left|\sqrt{(\tfrac{5}{2})}(1-3\ell_o^4/2r^4)^{-\frac{1}{2}}\right|\right], \tag{4.17}$$

where D is a constant of integration and where

$$r > (\tfrac{3}{2})^{\frac{1}{4}}\ell_o \quad .$$

Thus for the maximal values of electric field also the angle function Φ is independent of the electric charge and assumes two different sets of values.

5. ENERGY-MOMENTUM TENSOR

The field equations, derived in (A), are given by

$$R_{\{\mu\nu\}} = \frac{1}{2}\kappa^2(b_{\mu\nu}-g_{\mu\nu}) \quad , \tag{5.1}$$

$$R_{[\mu\nu\rho]} = -\frac{1}{2}\kappa^2 I_{\mu\nu\rho} \quad , \tag{5.2}$$

$$\hat{g}^{[\mu\nu]}{}_{,\nu} = 0 \quad , \tag{5.3}$$

where the triple subscript $[\mu\nu\rho]$ implies cyclic derivatives of $R_{[\mu\nu]}$, and where the non-symmetric curvature tensor $R_{\mu\nu}$ is given by

$$R_{\mu\nu} = -\Gamma^{\rho}_{\mu\nu,\rho} + \Gamma^{\rho}_{\mu\rho,\nu} + \Gamma^{\rho}_{\mu\sigma}\Gamma^{\sigma}_{\rho\nu} - \Gamma^{\rho}_{\mu\nu}\Gamma^{\sigma}_{\rho\sigma} \quad . \tag{5.4}$$

The affine connections are obtained as the algebraic solutions of the "transposition invariant" equations

$$\hat{g}_{\mu\nu;\rho} = \hat{g}_{\mu\nu,\rho} - \hat{g}_{\sigma\nu}\Gamma^{\sigma}_{\mu\rho} - \hat{g}_{\mu\sigma}\Gamma^{\sigma}_{\rho\nu} = 0 \quad . \tag{5.5}$$

The equations (5.5), because of (5.3), yield the results

$$\hat{g}^{\mu\nu}{}_{;\rho} = 0 \; , \; \Gamma^{\rho}_{[\mu\rho]} = 0 \quad , \tag{5.6}$$

where

$$\hat{g}^{\mu\nu} = \surd(-\hat{g})\hat{g}^{\mu\nu} \quad , \quad \hat{g}^{\mu\rho}\hat{g}_{\nu\rho} = \delta^{\mu}_{\nu} \; , \; \hat{g} = \mathrm{Det}(\hat{g}_{\mu\nu}) \quad , \tag{5.7}$$

$$\hat{g}_{\mu\nu} = g_{\mu\nu} + q^{-1}\,\Phi_{\mu\nu} \quad .$$

By separating out symmetric and antisymmetric parts of the equations (5.5) and by solving formally the resulting equations we obtain the results

$$\Gamma^{\rho}_{\mu\nu} = \{^{\rho}_{\mu\nu}\} + S^{\rho}_{\mu\nu} + \Gamma^{\rho}_{[\mu\nu]} \quad , \tag{5.8}$$

$$g_{\mu\sigma}\Gamma^{\sigma}_{[\nu\rho]} + g_{\nu\sigma}\Gamma^{\sigma}_{[\rho\mu]} + g_{\rho\sigma}\Gamma^{\sigma}_{[\mu\nu]} = -\frac{1}{2} I_{\mu\nu\rho} \quad , \tag{5.9}$$

$$g_{\mu\sigma}S^{\sigma}_{\nu\rho} + g_{\nu\sigma}S^{\sigma}_{\rho\mu} + g_{\rho\sigma}S^{\sigma}_{\mu\nu} = 0 \quad , \tag{5.10}$$

where the tensor $S^{\rho}_{\mu\nu} (= S^{\rho}_{\nu\mu})$ and the fully anti-symmetric tensor $I_{\mu\nu\rho}$ are given by

$$S^{\rho}_{\mu\nu} = g^{\rho\sigma}[\Phi_{\mu\alpha}\Gamma^{\alpha}_{[\sigma\nu]} + \Phi_{\nu\alpha}\Gamma^{\alpha}_{[\sigma\mu]}] \quad , \tag{5.11}$$

$$I_{\mu\nu\rho} = \Phi_{\mu\nu,\rho} + \Phi_{\nu\rho,\mu} + \Phi_{\rho\mu,\nu} \quad , \tag{5.12}$$

and where $I_{\mu\nu\rho} = -4\pi\,\varepsilon_{\mu\nu\rho\sigma}s^{\sigma}$ represents charged magnetic current density. The metric tensor $g_{\mu\nu}$ and its inverse $g^{\mu\nu}$ are related by

$$g^{\mu\rho}g_{\nu\rho} = \delta^{\mu}_{\nu} \quad .$$

Furthermore, the tensor $b^{\mu\nu}$, which will be shown to be part of the energy tensor, is defined by

$$b^{\mu\nu} = \frac{1}{\sqrt{(-g)}}\,\hat{g}^{\{\mu\nu\}} = \frac{g^{\mu\nu}(1+\frac{1}{2}\Omega)+T^{\mu\nu}}{\sqrt{(1+\Omega-\Lambda^2)}} \tag{5.13}$$

and its inverse by

$$b_{\mu\nu} = \frac{g_{\mu\nu}(1+\frac{1}{2}\Omega)-T_{\mu\nu}}{\sqrt{(1+\Omega-\Lambda^2)}} \quad , \tag{5.14}$$

where

$$T_{\mu\nu}=\tfrac{1}{2}g_{\mu\nu}\Omega-\Phi_{\mu\rho}\Phi_{\nu}{}^{\rho} \quad , \quad \Omega=\tfrac{1}{2}\Phi^{\mu\nu}\Phi_{\mu\nu} \quad , \quad \Lambda=\tfrac{1}{4}f^{\mu\nu}\Phi_{\mu\nu} \quad , \tag{5.15}$$

$$f^{\mu\nu} = \frac{1}{2\sqrt{(-g)}}\,\varepsilon^{\mu\nu\rho\sigma}\,\Phi_{\rho\sigma} \quad ,$$

and

$$b^{\mu\rho}b_{\nu\rho} = \delta^{\mu}_{\nu} \quad .$$

If we set $\Gamma^{\rho}_{[\mu\nu]} = 0$ we obtain, following from (5.9), $I_{\mu\nu\rho} = 0$. Therefore the antisymmetric part $\Gamma^{\rho}_{[\mu\nu]}$ of the affine connection $\Gamma^{\rho}_{\mu\nu}$ can be interpreted as the structure tensor giving rise to magnetic charge content of an elementary particle and hence to its spin. In terms of $\Gamma^{\rho}_{[\mu\nu]}$ the charged magnetic current s^{μ} can be expressed as

$$s^{\mu} = \varepsilon^{\mu\nu\rho\sigma}\,\Gamma_{[\nu\rho]\sigma} \quad , \tag{5.16}$$

where

$$\Gamma_{[\nu\rho]\sigma} = g_{\sigma\alpha}\,\Gamma^{\alpha}_{[\nu\rho]} \quad .$$

Furthermore, as shown in (2.53) and (8.5) of (A), the field equations (5.2) have the linearized asymptotic form

$$(\nabla^2 - \frac{\partial^2}{c^2\partial t^2} + \kappa^2)s^{\mu} = 0 \quad , \tag{5.17}$$

implying the confinement of the magnetic current density s^{μ} to distances of the order of r_c $(\sim\frac{\hbar}{mc})$ since beyond r_c

$$\kappa = \frac{2}{r_o^2} \sim 10^{33}\ \text{cm}^{-1} \tag{5.18}$$

tends to infinity and s^{μ} vanishes. Thus the presence of a net magnetic charge $(-1)^s|g_o|$ for an elementary particle does not change the short range character of the forces, which arise from the screening in the stratified layered structure of the elementary particle. It must be noted, as pointed out earlier, that r_o is not the range of the magnetic charge distribution but, as a function of the partial magnetic charges g_n, it measures the degree of deviation of this theory from general relativity and classical electrodynamics.

Now, the gravitational field is described in terms of the curvature of space and, therefore it is necessary to know all the interaction energy densities which act as the source of the gravitational field. The generalized theory provides a complete microscopic basis for calculating, uniquely, the energy momentum tensor as the source of the gravitational field. Thus by using the definition (5.4) and the result (5.8), the field equations (5.1) can be written as

$$G_\mu^\nu - \frac{1}{2}\,\delta_\mu^\nu G = \frac{8\pi G_o}{c^4}\,T_\mu^\nu\ , \tag{5.19}$$

where the subscript (o) of G_o for the gravitational constant on the right hand side differentiates it from the scalar curvature G. In the derivation of (5.19) we used the relations

$$R_{\{\mu\nu\}} = -\,G_{\mu\nu} + S_{\mu\nu} + \Gamma^\rho_{[\mu\sigma]}\Gamma^\sigma_{[\rho\nu]} = \frac{1}{2}\,\kappa^2(b_{\mu\nu}-g_{\mu\nu})\ , \tag{5.20}$$

where

$$S_{\mu\nu} = -\,S^\rho_{\mu\nu|\rho} + S^\rho_{\mu\rho|\nu} + S^\rho_{\mu\sigma}S^\sigma_{\rho\nu} - S^\rho_{\mu\nu}S^\sigma_{\rho\sigma}\ , \tag{5.21}$$

$$S^\rho_{\mu\rho} = \frac{\partial}{\partial x^\mu}\,[\,Ln\sqrt{(1+\Omega-\Lambda^2)}\,] = -\frac{1}{2}\,g_{\mu\nu}g^{\rho\sigma}S^\nu_{\rho\sigma}\ , \tag{5.22}$$

$$G_{\mu\nu} = \left\{{\rho \atop \mu\nu}\right\}_{,\rho} - \left\{{\rho \atop \mu\rho}\right\}_{,\nu} + \left\{{\rho \atop \mu\nu}\right\}\left\{{\sigma \atop \rho\sigma}\right\} - \left\{{\rho \atop \mu\sigma}\right\}\left\{{\sigma \atop \rho\nu}\right\}\ , \tag{5.23}$$

and where the symbol (|) signifies the covariant derivative with respect to the metric tensor $g_{\mu\nu}$.

Because of the known properties of the left hand

side of the equations (5.19), the symmetric energy momentum tensor $T_{\mu\nu}$ satisfies the covariant conservation laws

$$[\sqrt{(-g)}T^{\nu}_{\mu}]_{|\nu} = 0 \quad , \tag{5.24}$$

where the energy tensor T^{ν}_{μ} is given by

$$4\pi\ T_{\mu\nu}=q^2[(\tfrac{1}{2}b^{\rho}_{\rho}-1)g_{\mu\nu}-b_{\mu\nu}]+r_o^2\ \text{trace}[S_{\mu|\nu}-\tfrac{3}{2}g_{\mu\nu}S^{\rho}_{|\rho}$$
$$+S_{\mu}S_{\nu}-\tfrac{1}{2}g_{\mu\nu}S^{\rho}S_{\rho}-\Gamma_{\mu}\Gamma_{\nu}$$
$$+\tfrac{1}{2}g_{\mu\nu}\Gamma^{\rho}\Gamma_{\rho}]-r_o^2[(S_{\mu})^{\rho}{}_{\nu|\rho}+(S_{\mu})^{\rho}_{\nu}\ \text{trace}\ S_{\rho}+g_{\mu\nu}\ \text{trace}\ S^{\rho}\ \times$$
$$\text{trace}\ S_{\rho}], \tag{5.25}$$

and where the 4×4 matrices S_{μ} and Γ_{μ} are defined by

$$(S_{\mu})^{\rho}_{\nu} = S^{\rho}_{\mu\nu} = (S_{\nu})^{\rho}_{\mu}\ ,\ (\Gamma_{\mu})^{\rho}_{\nu} = \Gamma^{\rho}_{[\mu\nu]} = -\ (\Gamma_{\nu})^{\rho}_{\mu}\ . \tag{5.26}$$

These transform according to

$$S'_{\mu} = \frac{\partial x^{\rho}}{\partial x'^{\mu}}\ US_{\rho}\ U^{-1}\ ,\ \Gamma'_{\mu} = \frac{\partial x^{\rho}}{\partial x'^{\mu}}\ U\Gamma_{\rho}U^{-1}\quad ,$$

where U is the 4×4 matrix

$$U = [\frac{\partial x'}{\partial x}]\ ,\ U^{-1} = [\frac{\partial x}{\partial x'}]\quad .$$

Thus

$$\text{trace}\ S_{\mu} = (S_{\mu})^{\rho}_{\rho} = S^{\rho}_{\mu\rho} = \partial_{\mu}[\mathit{Ln}\sqrt{(1+\Omega-\Lambda^2)}]\quad ,$$

$$\text{trace}\ \Gamma_{\mu} = (\Gamma_{\mu})^{\rho}_{\rho} = \Gamma^{\rho}_{[\mu\rho]} = 0\quad .$$

In terms of the matrices S_μ and Γ_μ the neutral field $R_{[\mu\nu]}$ can be written as

$$R_{[\mu\nu]}=-(\Gamma_\mu)^\rho_{\nu|\rho}-(\Gamma_\mu)^\rho_\nu \text{ trace } S_\rho + \text{trace } (\Gamma_\mu S_\nu-\Gamma_\nu S_\mu).\quad(5.27)$$

The trace of the energy tensor is given by

$$4\pi\, \mathcal{T}=4\pi\, \mathcal{T}^\rho_\rho=q^2(b^\rho_\rho-4)+r_o^2 \text{ trace } [\Gamma^\rho\Gamma_\rho-3\, S^\rho_{|\rho}-S^\rho S_\rho-2S^\rho \times \text{trace } S_\rho]\ . \quad (5.28)$$

In the energy tensor $\mathcal{T}_{\mu\nu}$ in the limit $r_o = 0$ the first term tends to the energy tensor

$$T_{\mu\nu} = \frac{1}{2} g_{\mu\nu}\, \Omega - \Phi_{\mu\rho}\, \Phi_\nu{}^\rho \quad (5.29)$$

of the pure radiation field since in this case $\Phi_{\mu\nu} = \partial_\mu A_\nu - \partial_\nu A_\mu$. In the limit $r_o = 0$ the remaining terms vanish. Thus, they evidently refer to the short range interaction energy density of the field and the associated particles. We note that for the limit $r_o = 0$ we have used the relation

$$r_o^2\, q^2 = \frac{c^4}{2G}\ . \quad (5.30)$$

At this point it is interesting to note that the presence of a short range interaction energy density in a theory obtained from the unification of two long range fields like electromagnetic and gravitational fields may seem quite surprising. There are at least two reasons for this result: (i) The antisymmetric tensor $\Phi_{\mu\nu}$, not being derivable from a potential, led to the existence of magnetic charges of the field; (ii) If in primeval times the field consisted of free magnetic charge units g_n ($n = 0,1,2,...$) then through the gravitational attraction of this "primordial field" a gravitational condensation, occurring over the enormous times available to nature, could have placed all these units g_n into their most stable states, that of stratified layers and thus give rise to the birth of elementary particles and hence to their short range interactions.

The fundamental constant r_o, which measures the degree of deviation from the conventional theory, in the energy tensor $T_{\mu\nu}$ also couples the field and its particles at short distances, where the strength of the coupling is measured by $\frac{Q_n^2}{\hbar c}$. We can now rewrite the tensor $T_{\mu\nu}$ in the form

$$4\pi\, T_{\mu\nu} = \Lambda_{\mu\nu} + W_{\mu\nu} \tag{5.31}$$

where the first term

$$\Lambda_{\mu\nu} = q^2 \left[\left(\tfrac{1}{2} b^\rho_\rho - 1\right) g_{\mu\nu} - b_{\mu\nu} \right]$$

represents total electromagnetic energy density as well as magnetic energy density throughout space time which is divided into the three regions $0 \leqq r \leqq r_c$, $r \geqq r_c$ and $r >> r_c$. The indeterminate surface $r=r_c$ contains, in the rest frame, an amount of energy Mc^2 and therefore we may quantify r_c by assuming that $Mc\, r_c \sim \hbar$ or

$$r_c \sim \frac{\hbar}{Mc} \quad . \tag{5.32}$$

Thus at distances

$$r \geqq \frac{\hbar}{Mc}$$

we have only an electromagnetic interaction between the particle and the radiation field and in this region of space time the fundamental constant r_o has the small value

$$r_o^2 = \frac{2G}{c^4} e^2 \quad .$$

Therefore at these distances the deviation from the conventional theory is still smaller. For distances

$$r >> r_c$$

the constant $r_o = 0$ and we have only the radiation energy density.

We see that the larger r_o (approaching inner regions of magnetic structure) the greater is the deviation of this theory from electrodynamics and general relativity. In the first region $(0 \leqq r \leqq r_c)$ of space time the electromagnetic energy density is a function of the magnetic charge and hence of mass also. Therefore this portion of the electromagnetic energy density exists also in the rest frame of the particles.

The $W_{\mu\nu}$ part of the energy tensor, which refers to terms of $T_{\mu\nu}$ containing r_o^2 explicitly, contributes only in the regions $0 \leqq r \leqq r_c$ and $r_c \leqq r < r$ (radiation) since for $r >> r_c$, we can set $r_o = 0$ and the short range energy density vanishes. The contribution of $W_{\mu\nu}$ to the energy density in $r_c \leqq r$ (radiation) is purely electromagnetic because $g_n = 0$. Thus the fundamental constant r_o, from the point of view of the energy density, partitions space time into three regions specified by the values

$$r_{on}^2 = \frac{2G}{c^4} (e^2 + g_n^2) \ , \ r_{o\infty}^2 = \frac{2G}{c^4} e^2 \ , \ r_o^2 = 0 \quad .(5.33)$$

The maximum value of r_o^2, which occurs at r=0, is given by

$$r_{oo}^2 = \frac{2G}{c^4}(e^2+g_o^2) \quad , \qquad (5.34)$$

where g_o is the net magnetic charge of an elementary particle. Hence in addition to the deviations from classical behavior due to the existence of Planck's constant $\hbar$ (i.e. quantum mechanics) we have here an additional change measured by the discrete values of the constant r_o. The new modification of the classical theory arises from finite description of the structure of elementary particles.

It will be shown that the energy tensor $T_{\mu\nu}$, as discussed here briefly, and its conservation laws (5.24) contains the laws of motion of particles in the field, including that of the chargeless particles or neutrino like particles. For the motion of neutrinos the coupling is given by $\frac{g_n^2}{\hbar c}$ and the motion will be confined to short range interaction region where $r < r_c$. However, the neutrino magnetic horizon

$$r_c(\text{neutrino}) = \frac{\hbar}{M_\nu c}$$

can be expected to be much larger than that of electron and proton. Therefore a massive neutrino has more uncertainty in its localizability when compared to that of the electron and proton.

The inertial properties of the energy momentum tensor (5.25) can be studied in terms of the time independent spherically symmetric field. By using the results of (A), it is easily shown that

$$\frac{c^4}{4\pi G_o}\sqrt{(-g)}G_4^4=\sqrt{(-g)}(T_4^4-T_1^1-T_2^2-T_3^3)=\frac{c^4}{8\pi G_o}[\upsilon\ \exp(u+\rho)u'\sin\Phi]'\sin\theta. \tag{5.35}$$

The volume integral of G_4^4 yields the interesting result

$$\int\sqrt{(-g)}(T_4^4-T_1^1-T_2^2-T_3^3)drd\theta\ d\phi = \pm\ mc^2\ , \tag{5.36}$$

where $\pm$ signs signify the presence of positive and negative energy states. The mass m appearing in (5.36) is the "bare gravitational mass" which is, because of principle of equivalence, equal to the "bare inertial mass". The gravitational force does not distinguish between different masses. Therefore any mass splitting must have a nongravitational origin. In the present theory the electron and proton mass ratio will have to arise from the extremum values of the intrinsic fields (i.e. the field strength inside the region $0 \leqq r \leqq r_c$).

In order to complete the discussion of the energy-momentum tensor we must also consider the use of the conservation laws

$$\mathfrak{T}^{\nu}_{\mu,\nu} = 0 \tag{5.37}$$

where the non-symmetrized pseudo energy tensor $\mathfrak{T}^{\nu}_{\mu}$ is given by

$$-4\pi q^{-2}\kappa^2\mathfrak{T}^{\nu}_{\mu}=\hat{g}^{\nu\rho}\ R_{\mu\rho}+\hat{g}^{\rho\nu}\ R_{\rho\mu}-\delta^{\nu}_{\mu}\hat{g}^{\rho\sigma}\ R_{\rho\sigma}+\hat{g}^{\rho\sigma}{}_{,\mu}\ B^{\nu}_{\rho\sigma}-\delta^{\nu}_{\mu}B, \tag{5.38}$$

and where, because of the field equations (5.3), we have

$$B^{\rho}_{\mu\nu}=\frac{1}{2}(\delta^{\rho}_{\mu}\ \Gamma^{\sigma}_{\nu\sigma}+\delta^{\rho}_{\nu}\ \Gamma^{\sigma}_{\mu\sigma})-\Gamma^{\rho}_{\mu\nu}\ ,\quad B=\hat{g}^{\mu\nu}(\Gamma^{\sigma}_{\mu\sigma}\ \Gamma^{\sigma}_{\rho\nu}-\Gamma^{\rho}_{\mu\nu}\ \Gamma^{\sigma}_{\rho\sigma}). \tag{5.39}$$

The quantities $\mathcal{E}_\mu^\nu$, except in flat space time, do not, under general coordinate transformations, behave as components of a tensor. Therefore the somewhat undecided status of $\mathcal{E}_\mu^\nu$ as an energy tensor is carried over from general relativity. However the conservation laws (5.37), with the application of Gauss' theorem, enable us, formally, to define a "4-momentum vector" by

$$P_\mu = \int \mathcal{E}_\mu^\nu \, d\sigma_\nu \quad . \tag{5.40}$$

We shall treat $\mathcal{E}_\mu^\nu$, at least in the rest frame of a spherically symmetric system, as a respectable physical quantity to define and discuss the self-energy and the binding energy of an elementary particle.

6. SELF-ENERGY

In (A) the self-energy was calculated for the special case e=0. In this paper we shall derive the most general form of the self-energy where $e \neq 0$. This can readily be done by multiplying the field equation (2.3) by $\cosh^2\Gamma$ and rewriting it in the form

$$[\upsilon\, S'\exp(\rho)\cosh^3\Gamma]' = \kappa^2 \frac{\cosh\Gamma}{\upsilon}\left(1-\frac{\sin\Phi}{\cosh\Gamma}\right)\exp(\rho) - 2R_{[41]} \times \sinh\Gamma\, \exp(\rho) \tag{6.1}$$

where

$$R_{[41]} = \upsilon\, \rho' S' \cosh\Gamma \sinh\Gamma \quad .$$

If we define the binding energy density of an elementary particle (using the field equations in 5.38) by

$$\mathcal{E}_4^4 - \mathcal{E}_1^1 - \mathcal{E}_2^2 - \mathcal{E}_3^3 = \frac{g^2}{2\pi}[\sqrt{(-\hat{g})} - \sqrt{(-g)}] - \frac{g^2}{2\pi}\hat{g}^{[41]} F_{41} \quad , \tag{6.2}$$

where

$$F_{41} = \Phi_{41}+r_o^2\, R_{[41]}, \quad \Phi_{41}=-\frac{1}{\upsilon}\tanh\Gamma, \quad \hat{g}^{[41]}=\exp(\rho)\sinh\Gamma\, \sin\theta,$$

we obtain

$$\mathfrak{T}_4^4-\mathfrak{T}_1^1-\mathfrak{T}_2^2-\mathfrak{T}_3^3=\frac{q^2}{2\pi}\, [\frac{\cosh\Gamma}{\upsilon}\, (1-\frac{\sin\Phi}{\cosh\Gamma})\exp(\rho)-r_o^2\exp(\rho)\sinh\Gamma \times$$

$$R_{[41]}]\sin\theta = \frac{r_o^2 q^2}{4\pi}\, [\upsilon\, S'\, \exp(\rho)\cosh^3\Gamma]'\sin\theta\ .$$

Hence

$$\Delta E = \int (\mathfrak{T}_4^4-\mathfrak{T}_1^1-\mathfrak{T}_2^2-\mathfrak{T}_3^3)\, dr\, d\theta\, d\phi =$$

$$r_o^2\, q^2\, \frac{2mG}{c^4} - r_o^2\, q^2\, [\upsilon\, \exp(\rho)S'\, \cosh^3\Gamma]_{r=0}\ .$$

On using the asymptotic expressions (5.23)-(5.33) of (A) we obtain the result

$$\Delta E = mc^2 - \frac{2Q_o^2}{\ell_{oo}}\, Z(\beta_o)\quad , \tag{6.3}$$

where

$$Q_o^2 = e^2+g_o^2\ , \quad \ell_{oo}^2 = \frac{2G}{c^4}\, |g_o|\surd(e^2+g_o^2)\quad , \tag{6.4}$$

$$\tan\beta_o = |\frac{e}{g_o}|\ , \quad g_o = \text{total magnetic charge}\ ,$$

and

$$Z(\beta_o) = \frac{1}{\cos^2\beta_o} + 2\, \sin^2\beta_o\, (\frac{1}{\cos^4\beta_o} + \cos\beta_o)\ . \tag{6.5}$$

The factor 2 in the self-energy

$$E_S = \frac{2Q_o^2}{\ell_{oo}} Z(\beta_o) \tag{6.6}$$

is due to the two spin states of the particle (or two possible signs of magnetic charge).

For a neutrino-like particle (e=0) the binding energy (6.3) reduces to

$$\Delta E_\nu = mc^2 - \frac{2g_o^2}{\ell_{oo}} , \tag{6.7}$$

which was calculated in (A). For the limit $g_o = 0$ the self-energy of a charged particle is infinite and that of the neutrino-like particle, due to the absence of long range interactions, vanishes.

Now, in order to compare the energy tensors T_μ^ν and $\mathfrak{T}_\mu^\nu$ let us consider the pseudo tensor $\mathfrak{T}_\mu^\nu$ of the gravitational field alone i.e. we construct $\mathfrak{T}_\mu^\nu$ in terms of the $g_{\mu\nu}$ of this theory. The tensor $\mathfrak{T}_\mu^\nu$ can be obtained in terms of $g_{\mu\nu}$ by setting $\Phi_{\mu\nu} = 0$ in the $\mathfrak{T}_\mu^\nu$ of the nonsymmetric theory. Thus using the relations

$$\mathfrak{T}_\mu^\nu = \frac{c^4}{16\pi G} \frac{\partial}{\partial x^\rho} (S_\mu^{\nu\rho}) , \quad \mathfrak{T} = \mathfrak{T}_\rho^\rho = \frac{\partial U^\rho}{\partial x^\rho} , \tag{6.8}$$

with

$$U^\rho = \frac{c^4}{8\pi G} \frac{1}{\sqrt{(-\hat{g})}} \frac{\partial}{\partial x^\sigma} [(-\hat{g})\hat{g}^{\rho\sigma}] , \tag{6.9}$$

$$S_\mu^{\nu\rho} = \hat{g}^{\nu\sigma} B_{\mu\sigma}^\rho + \hat{g}^{\sigma\nu} B_{\sigma\mu}^\rho - \delta_\mu^\nu \hat{g}^{\alpha\beta} B_{\alpha\beta}^\rho , \tag{6.10}$$

for the nonsymmetric theory and setting $\Phi_{\mu\nu} = 0$ we can obtain the corresponding results for the pure gravitational field. Hence for the gravitational part alone we have

$$\overset{\circ}{\mathfrak{T}}{}^{4}_{4} = \frac{c^4}{8\pi G}\frac{\sin\theta}{\upsilon} - \frac{c^4 \sin\theta}{8\pi G}[\upsilon \exp(u+\rho)(\rho'+\Phi'\cot\Phi)\sin\Phi]' , \tag{6.11}$$

$$\overset{\circ}{\mathfrak{T}} = \frac{c^4}{4\pi G}\frac{\sin\theta}{\upsilon} - \frac{c^4}{4\pi G}[\upsilon \exp(u+\rho)(\rho'+\Phi'\cot\Phi)\sin\Phi + \frac{1}{2} u'\exp(u+\rho) \sin\Phi]' . \tag{6.12}$$

Hence we obtain

$$\overset{\circ}{\mathfrak{T}}{}^{4}_{4} - \overset{\circ}{\mathfrak{T}}{}^{1}_{1} - \overset{\circ}{\mathfrak{T}}{}^{2}_{2} - \overset{\circ}{\mathfrak{T}}{}^{3}_{3} = \frac{c^4}{8\pi G}[\upsilon\, u' \exp(u+\rho)\sin\Phi]' , \tag{6.13}$$

and

$$\int (\overset{\circ}{\mathfrak{T}}{}^{4}_{4} - \overset{\circ}{\mathfrak{T}}{}^{1}_{1} - \overset{\circ}{\mathfrak{T}}{}^{2}_{2} - \overset{\circ}{\mathfrak{T}}{}^{3}_{3})\, dr\, d\theta\, d\phi = \pm\, mc^2 , \tag{6.14}$$

yielding the same result obtained in (5.36) for the energy tensor T_μ^ν. In both of these calculations the self-energy term does not appear.

7. THE FOUR FUNDAMENTAL CURRENTS

Some of the properties of elementary particles and their interactions can be expressed and analyzed in terms of their currents. The currents of the generalized theory of gravitation can be defined in a unique manner. One of the basic premises of the theory lies in the fact that the antisymmetric part $\Phi_{\mu\nu}$ of the fundamental field variables $\hat{g}_{\mu\nu} = g_{\mu\nu} + q^{-1}\Phi_{\mu\nu}$, is not derivable from a potential viz.,

$$\Phi_{\mu\nu} \neq \partial_\mu A_\nu - \partial_\nu A_\mu ,$$

and therefore, as discussed in (A), its cyclic derivatives

$$\Phi_{\mu\nu,\rho} + \Phi_{\nu\rho,\mu} + \Phi_{\rho\mu,\nu} \; (\equiv I_{\mu\nu\rho})$$

can be used to define a conserved magnetic current density by

$$\mathscr{s}^{\mu} = \frac{1}{4\pi} \frac{\partial}{\partial x^{\nu}} [\sqrt{(-g)} f^{\mu\nu}] \quad , \tag{7.1}$$

where

$$I_{\mu\nu\rho} = -4\pi \, \varepsilon_{\mu\nu\rho\sigma} \, \mathscr{s}^{\sigma} \; , \; \mathscr{s}^{\mu} = \sqrt{(-g)} s^{\mu} \quad , \tag{7.2}$$

and where $f^{\mu\nu}$ was defined by (5.15). It is clear that if $\Phi_{\mu\nu}$ were derivable from a potential then the current $\mathscr{s}^{\mu}$ would vanish. The integral of (7.1) which is conveniently evaluated in its spherically symmetric rest frame, is given by

$$\int \mathscr{s}^{\mu} \, d\sigma_{\mu} = (-1)^{s} |g_{o}| \quad , \tag{7.3}$$

where s = 0,1 corresponds to the two spin states.

Now from the field equations

$$\Psi_{\mu\nu,\rho} + \Psi_{\nu\rho,\mu} + \Psi_{\rho\mu,\nu} = 0 \quad , \tag{7.4}$$

we can derive another (axial) conserved magnetic current, where

$$\Psi_{\mu\nu} = \frac{1}{2} \varepsilon_{\mu\nu\rho\sigma} \, \hat{g}^{[\rho\sigma]} \; , \; \hat{g}^{[\mu\nu]}{}_{,\nu} = 0 \quad , \tag{7.5}$$

$$\Psi_{\mu\nu} = \partial_{\mu} B_{\nu} - \partial_{\nu} B_{\mu} \; , \; \hat{g}^{[\mu\nu]} = \hat{g}^{[\mu\nu\rho]}{}_{,\rho} \quad , \tag{7.6}$$

$$\hat{g}^{[\mu\nu\rho]} = \varepsilon^{\mu\nu\rho\sigma} B_{\sigma} \quad .$$

A neutral magnetic current can now be defined by

$$\zeta^{\mu} = \frac{1}{4\pi} \frac{\partial}{\partial x^{\nu}} [\surd(-g)\Psi^{\mu\nu}] \quad , \tag{7.7}$$

where, as before we use its spherically symmetric rest frame for convenience and obtain

$$\int \zeta^{\mu} \, d\sigma_{\mu} = 0 \quad . \tag{7.8}$$

The conserved current ζ^{μ} will be interpreted as the magnetic "vacuum current" where the vacuum contains distributions of equal amounts of net positive and negative magnetic charges (e.g. particles and anti-particles with anti-parallel spins).

The two electric currents can be derived from the field equations

$$F_{\mu\nu,\rho} + F_{\nu\rho,\mu} + F_{\rho\mu,\nu} = 0 \quad . \tag{7.9}$$

Thus the generalized conserved electric current can be defined by

$$J^{\mu} = \frac{1}{4\pi} \frac{\partial}{\partial x^{\nu}} [\surd(-g)F^{\mu\nu}] \quad , \tag{7.10}$$

where in accordance with the field equations (4.2) we have

$$F_{\mu\nu} = \Phi_{\mu\nu} + r_o^2 \, R_{[\mu\nu]} = \partial_{\mu}A_{\nu} - \partial_{\nu}A_{\mu} \quad . \tag{7.11}$$

Hence

$$J^{\mu} = j_e^{\mu} + j_o^{\mu} \quad , \tag{7.12}$$

where

$$j_e^\mu = \frac{1}{4\pi} \frac{\partial}{\partial x^\nu} [\sqrt{(-g)}\Phi^{\mu\nu}] \quad , \tag{7.13}$$

represents charged electric current, and

$$j_o^\mu = \frac{r_o^2}{4\pi} \frac{\partial}{\partial x^\nu} [\sqrt{(-g)}R^{[\mu\nu]}] \quad , \tag{7.14}$$

represents the neutral electric current. Their integrals are given by

$$\int j_e^\mu \, d\sigma_\mu = \pm e \; , \int j_o^\mu \, d\sigma_\mu = 0 \quad . \tag{7.15}$$

The neutral currents ζ^μ, j_o^μ together with the corresponding fields $\Psi_{\mu\nu}$, $R_{[\mu\nu]}$, respectively, describe the properties of the vacuum where there are equal amounts of positive and negative electric charges residing on particles and anti-particles. It is clear from the above definitions that the four currents s^μ, ζ^μ, j_e^μ, j_o^μ are obtained from the solutions of the field equations, contrary to classical electrodynamics where one assumes distributions of currents and then calculates the fields they generate.

In (A) it was found that the neutral charge density j_o^4 and the corresponding field E_o fall off as $1/r^5$ and they, therefore, have short range character. But both of these quantities, like their charged counterparts j_e^4, E_e, vanish at the origin. Furthermore, both j_o^4 and E_o, through their dependence in magnetic charge, have mass dependence. Therefore all four currents because of their dependence on ℓ_o^2 have an indirect functional relationship to mass. The four currents j_e^μ, j_o^μ, s^μ, ζ^μ represent either the proton (anti-proton) or the electron (positron) currents depending on the extremum values of their fields. In conventional theories extremum values of the fields are infinite and therefore one has no method for differentiating between electron and proton currents. Furthermore, currents in classical theories are prescribed to generate fields and not vice versa. For zero electric charge the only surviving currents are s_o^μ and ζ_o^μ, where subscript o is used to distinguish them from those belonging to charged particles. In this case the two currents s_o^μ and ζ_o^μ together represent either ν_e-like or ν_μ-like particle currents.

Based on the above premises we can construct an energy density representing the coupling of two particles and their fields. From the definition (5.25) of the energy we see that the short range coupling between the field and particle is measured by r_o^2. It is, therefore, quite natural to expect a similar coupling between different particles for which the total energy density can be written as

$$H = \frac{4\pi R_{on}^2}{\sqrt{(-g)}} \sum_{\lambda=1}^{4} g_{\mu\nu}\, j_\lambda^\mu\, j_\lambda^\nu \quad , \tag{7.16}$$

where we have represented all four currents according to

$$j_1^\mu = j_e^\mu,\; j_2^\mu = j_o^\mu,\; j_3^\mu = s^\mu,\; j_4^\mu = \zeta^\mu \quad ,$$

and where

$$R_{on}^2 = \sqrt{(r_c^4 + r_{on}^4)} - r_{on}^2 \quad .$$

There are 4 current-current terms representing

interaction energy densities for scattering, annihilation and bound states in the processes (e^-e^-), (e^+e^+), (e^+e^-), (pp), $(\bar{p}\bar{p})$, $(\bar{p}p)$, (e^-p), (e^+p), $(e^+\bar{p})$, $(\bar{e}\bar{p})$. The validity of the above formal statements does depend very much on actual calculations say, for example, the proton-anti-proton bound state (the 1^-state), and its slow decay into γ-rays. For this we shall need equations of motion and the time-dependent solutions of the field equations.

8. FOUNDATIONS OF ELEMENTARY PARTICLE SPECTRUM

Based on the physical interpretation of the generalized theory of gravitation we shall give a qualitative description of the elementary particle spectrum. From the maximum and minimum values of the electric and magnetic fields of charged and chargeless particles (see section 4) it was deduced that there exist four massive particles two of which carry positive and negative electric charge and two of which are chargeless (i.e. e=0, no magnetic moment either). All four particles have the magnetic structure (stratified magnetic layers with alternating sign of magnetic charges) described here and in paper (A). The chargeless particles, as shown in section 4, have the same symmetries as the neutrinos ν_e and ν_μ (and the corresponding anti-particles). However the predicted neutrino-like particles are massive (but light) chargeless particles. In this paper we shall assume that neutrinos, however small, are massive (but light) particles. The two charged particles (and their anti-particles) of the theory, subject to a later proof, (i.e. actual calculation of their mass ratios) will be assumed to represent proton and electron (and the corresponding anti-particles $\bar{p}$ and e^+). Thus all in all we have eight fundamental massive particles p,e,ν_e, ν_μ (plus $\bar{p}$,e^+,$\bar{\nu}_e$,$\bar{\nu}_\mu$) from which to construct all other particles. The magnetic structure of these fundamental particles provides a basis for the coupling (with the strength $\frac{Q_n^2}{\hbar c} = \frac{e^2}{\hbar c} + \frac{g_n^2}{\hbar c}$) of these particles and their anti-particles to create new states or "sub-nuclear atoms". The corresponding "energy levels" of these "atoms" would be in the range of hundreds, thousands or millions of Mev. Such energy levels could have either narrow widths (bound states with long life times) or large widths (broad resonance states of short duration).

Construction of bound or resonance states of these four fundamental particles and their anti-particles can be based on the three basic predictions and symmetries of the theory.

(i) Spin

For each fundamental particle the sign of the net magnetic charge and the direction of its spin are correlated. A reversal of spin direction corresponds to a change of sign of the magnetic charge and vice versa; the change in the sign of magnetic charge flips the spin. This implies that the short range interactions of particles depend on the directions of their spins. Thus an encounter in which the spins are parallel implies a magnetic repulsion. In particular in a particle and anti-particle interaction the electromagnetic attraction is depressed by the magnetic repulsion. The latter together with the electric attraction leads to a weakly coupled particle-anti-particle state.

(ii) Electric and Magnetic Currents

The charged particles e,p (and e^+,$\bar{p}$) each carry charged conserved currents j_e^μ (electric), s^μ(magnetic) and the neutral conserved currents (vacuum currents) j_o^μ (electric), ζ^μ (magnetic). For the chargeless particles ν_e, ν_μ (and $\bar{\nu}_e$, $\bar{\nu}_\mu$) only the magnetic currents s_o^μ and ζ_o^μ exist. Thus for the neutrinos ν_e, ν_μ there are no associated vector currents, like j_e^μ, j_o^μ, unless they interact with other particles. The vacuum charge densities j_o^4 and ζ^4 change sign under charge conjugation and spin reversal, respectively. The vacuum currents, as shown in the previous section, are derived from the short range vacuum fields.

(iii) New Vacuum

The existence of neutral currents and their corresponding fields imply the existence of vacuum pairs of zero magnetic charge, and therefore zero spin, zero electric charge, as well as of zero energy. Thus around each fundamental particle there exists a cloud of vacuum pairs of the type

$$(\underset{\rightarrow\leftarrow}{\bar{p}p}),\ (\underset{\rightarrow\ \leftarrow}{e^+e^-}),\ (\underset{\rightarrow\leftarrow}{\bar{\nu}_e\nu_e}),\ (\underset{\rightarrow\leftarrow}{\bar{\nu}_\mu\nu_\mu})\quad, \tag{8.1}$$

and their conjugate pairs resulting from electric and magnetic charge conjugation (spin reversal),

$$(\underset{\leftarrow\rightarrow}{p\bar{p}}),\ (\underset{\leftarrow\ \rightarrow}{e^-e^+}),\ (\underset{\leftarrow\rightarrow}{\nu_e\bar{\nu}_e}),\ (\underset{\leftarrow\rightarrow}{\nu_\mu\bar{\nu}_\mu})\quad, \tag{8.2}$$

where arrows indicate spin directions of the respective particles. There are magnetic and electric attractions associated with the vacuum pairs $(\underset{\rightarrow\leftarrow}{\bar{p}p})$, $(\underset{\rightarrow\ \leftarrow}{e^+e^-})$ and only magnetic attraction associated with the vacuum pairs $(\underset{\rightarrow}{\bar{\nu}}_e \underset{\leftarrow}{\nu}_e)$, $(\underset{\rightarrow}{\bar{\nu}}_\mu \underset{\leftarrow}{\nu}_\mu)$. Thus the vacuum of this theory differs from that of quantum field theory in a fundamental way. The vacuum here consists of pairs with zero energy and there is no infinite sea of negative energy electrons. Pair production proceeds by imparting sufficient energy to the vacuum pair.

For a qualitative application of the above concepts let us consider a collision of e^+ and e^- where sufficient energy exists for these particles to probe each others' magnetic structure. In this collision the e^+ and e^- can acquire from the vacuum the pair with the lightest constituents i.e. $(\underset{\rightarrow}{\bar{\nu}}_e \underset{\leftarrow}{\nu}_e)$ with greater ease than, for example, the pairs $(\underset{\rightarrow}{\bar{\nu}}_\mu \underset{\leftarrow}{\nu}_\mu)$ and $(\underset{\rightarrow}{e}^+ \underset{\leftarrow}{e}^-)$, since in the latter case the $e^+ + e^-$ system must transfer larger momentum to the pair than would be the case with $(\underset{\rightarrow}{\bar{\nu}}_e \underset{\leftarrow}{\nu}_e)$. Thus at threshold energies the most likely reaction would proceed according to

$$e^+ + e^- \rightarrow (\underset{\rightarrow}{e}^+ \underset{\leftarrow}{e}^-) + (\underset{\rightarrow}{\bar{\nu}}_e \underset{\leftarrow}{\nu}_e) \rightarrow (\underset{\rightarrow}{e}^+ \underset{\leftarrow}{\nu}_e) + (\underset{\leftarrow}{e}^- \underset{\rightarrow}{\bar{\nu}}_e) = \pi^+ + \pi^- \quad , \quad (8.3)$$

where

$$\pi^+ = (\underset{\rightarrow}{e}^+ \underset{\leftarrow}{\nu}_e) \; , \; \pi^- = (\underset{\leftarrow}{e}^- \underset{\rightarrow}{\nu}_e) \qquad (8.4)$$

represent the "ground states" of "π-atoms" as bound states of the indicated particles. In the reactions (8.4) the "effective masses" of the electrons and neutrinos are, of course, much higher than their respective rest masses. The $\pi^\pm$ systems are bound by their magnetic attractions alone and therefore the absence of the electric attraction at short distances should yield only a weak coupling for the ground states

(8.4). Hence they can weakly decay according to

$$\pi^+ \to \underset{\rightarrow}{e^+} + \underset{\leftarrow}{\nu_e} \;, \quad \pi^- \to \underset{\leftarrow}{e^-} + \underset{\rightarrow}{\bar{\nu}_e} \;. \tag{8.5}$$

Now if the center of mass energy of e^+e^--system (of the storage ring experiments) is less than the threshold energy for $\pi^\pm$ production but greater or equal to the threshold energy for π^0-production then the most likely reaction in the <u>magnetic encounter</u> of e^+ and e^- could lead to the reaction

$$\pi^0 = (\underset{\rightarrow}{e^+}\underset{\leftarrow}{e^-}) \tag{8.6}$$

where both magnetic and electric attractions lead to strong and electromagnetic interactions alone and the π^0 decays according to

$$\pi^0 \to \underset{\leftarrow}{\gamma} + \underset{\rightarrow}{\gamma} \;, \tag{8.7}$$

a pair of left and right circularly polarized photons.

At energies higher than threshold production of $\pi^\pm$ the e^+ and e^- encounter can acquire both of the vacuum pairs $(\underset{\rightarrow}{\bar{\nu}_e}\underset{\leftarrow}{\nu_e})$, $(\underset{\leftarrow}{\bar{\nu}_\mu}\underset{\rightarrow}{\nu_\mu})$ to yield the reaction

$$\begin{aligned} e^+ + e^- &\to (\underset{\rightarrow}{e^+}\underset{\leftarrow}{e^-}) + (\underset{\rightarrow}{\bar{\nu}_e}\underset{\leftarrow}{\nu_e}) + (\underset{\leftarrow}{\bar{\nu}_\mu}\underset{\rightarrow}{\nu_\mu}) \to \\ &(\underset{\rightarrow}{e^+}\underset{\leftarrow}{\nu_e}) + (\underset{\leftarrow}{e^-}\underset{\rightarrow}{\bar{\nu}_e}) + (\underset{\leftarrow}{\bar{\nu}_\mu}\underset{\rightarrow}{\nu_\mu}) \to \\ &(\underset{\rightarrow}{e^+}\underset{\leftarrow}{\nu_e}\underset{\leftarrow}{\bar{\nu}_\mu}) + (\underset{\leftarrow}{e^-}\underset{\rightarrow}{\bar{\nu}_e}\underset{\rightarrow}{\nu_\mu}) = \underset{\leftarrow}{\mu^+} + \underset{\rightarrow}{\mu^-} \;, \end{aligned} \tag{8.8}$$

where the muon is obtained as a magnetically bound three-body state weakly decaying according to

$$\mu^- = (\underset{\leftarrow}{e^-}\underset{\rightarrow}{\bar{\nu}_e}\underset{\rightarrow}{\nu_\mu}) \to \underset{\leftarrow}{e^-} + \underset{\rightarrow}{\bar{\nu}_e} + \underset{\rightarrow}{\nu_\mu} \quad . \tag{8.9}$$

Because $\nu_e \neq \nu_\mu$ the vacuum exchange possibility $(\underset{\rightarrow}{\bar{\nu}_e}\underset{\leftarrow}{\nu_e}) \to (\underset{\rightarrow}{e^+}\underset{\leftarrow}{e^-})$ is absent and therefore the reaction $\mu \to e+\gamma$ cannot occur. We observe that the magnetic repulsion between $\bar{\nu}_e$ and ν_μ and magnetic attraction between e^- and the two neutrinos $\bar{\nu}_e$ and ν_μ together with the absence of any electric attraction to counteract the magnetic effects leads to the observed μ weak decay. The magnetic bound state in (8.9), because of the absence of an electromagnetic force, implies, except for their mass differences, the same electromagnetic properties for the electron and muon. Furthermore from the above discussion of the reactions (8.3) and (8.8) we obtain the qualitative result that in the $e^+ + e^-$ experiment the ratio of cross-sections for hadron pair production to lepton pair production is greater than 1.

Another possible process in the $e^+ + e^-$ experiment could be the capture of the vacuum pair $(\underset{\rightarrow}{e^+}\underset{\leftarrow}{e^-})$ leading to

$$e^+ + e^- \to (\underset{\rightarrow}{e^+}\underset{\leftarrow}{e^-}) + (\underset{\rightarrow}{e^+}\underset{\leftarrow}{e^-}) \to \pi^o + \pi^o \quad . \tag{8.10}$$

The results (8.3) and (8.10) may be interpreted as yielding one and the same particle i.e. the short lived component K^o_s of K^o. In view of the lesser energy required in the process (8.3) we can conclude that K^o_s could decay much more frequently into $\pi^+ + \pi^-$ than into $\pi^o + \pi^o$ pairs.

A not forbidden but less likely process is that a π^-, for example, by itself can excite the vacuum pair $(\underset{\rightarrow}{e^+}\underset{\leftarrow}{e^-})$ to yield the decay process

$$\pi^- = [(\underset{\rightarrow}{e^-}\underset{\leftarrow}{\bar{\nu}_e})+(\underset{\rightarrow}{e^+}\underset{\leftarrow}{e^-})] \rightarrow [(\underset{\leftarrow}{e^-}\underset{\leftarrow}{\bar{\nu}_e})+(\underset{\rightarrow}{e^+}\underset{\rightarrow}{e^-})] \rightarrow \underset{\leftarrow}{e^-}+\underset{\leftarrow}{\bar{\nu}_e}+\underset{\rightarrow}{\gamma} \quad ,(8.11)$$

where the electrons have been exchanged to yield magnetic repulsion between e^- and $\bar{\nu}_e$ and between e^+ and e^-. A much easier process for the π^- is to capture the vacuum pair $(\underset{\rightarrow}{\bar{\nu}_\mu}\underset{\leftarrow}{\nu_\mu})$ to induce the reaction

$$\pi^- = [(\underset{\rightarrow}{e^-}\underset{\leftarrow}{\bar{\nu}_e})+(\underset{\rightarrow}{\bar{\nu}_\mu}\underset{\leftarrow}{\nu_\mu})] \rightarrow [(\underset{\rightarrow}{e^-}\underset{\leftarrow}{\bar{\nu}_e}\underset{\leftarrow}{\nu_\mu})+\underset{\rightarrow}{\bar{\nu}_\mu}] \rightarrow \underset{\leftarrow}{\mu^-} + \underset{\rightarrow}{\bar{\nu}_\mu} \quad , (8.12)$$

which is the most frequent decay of the π^-. A process of electron exchange, corresponding to the case (8.11), can also occur when the π^o acquires the conjugate pair $(\underset{\leftarrow}{e^+}\underset{\rightarrow}{e^-})$. Thus we have

$$\pi^o = [(\underset{\rightarrow}{e^+}\underset{\leftarrow}{e^-})+(\underset{\leftarrow}{e^+}\underset{\rightarrow}{e^-})] = (\underset{\rightarrow}{e^+}\underset{\rightarrow}{e^-})+(\underset{\leftarrow}{e^+}\underset{\leftarrow}{e^-}) \rightarrow e^++e^-+e^++e^- \quad , \qquad (8.13)$$

which can also decay as

$$\pi^o \rightarrow \underset{\rightarrow}{e^+}+\underset{\rightarrow}{e^-}+\underset{\leftarrow}{\gamma} \qquad (8.14)$$

where γ is circularly polarized. The reaction (8.13) implies the absence of $\gamma\gamma\gamma$ decay of π^o. The occurence of (8.13) and (8.14), though rather infrequent, are due to the magnetic repulsions between the parallel spin e^+ and e^- pairs.

In the processes (8.3) and (8.10) the colliding pair could, at a slightly higher energy, have exited an additional vacuum pair $(\underset{\rightarrow}{e^+}\underset{\leftarrow}{e^-})$ and yield the decays

$$K^o_L \rightarrow \pi^++\pi^-+\pi^o \quad , \quad K^o_L \rightarrow \pi^o+\pi^o+\pi^o \quad , \qquad (8.15)$$

respectively. Many other possible decays of K^o_L can be

obtained by analogous methods.

At energies much higher than that required in π-pair production different channels in the e^+e^- experiment can be opened and the resulting excited state can correspond to the pair $K^{\pm}$ as well as other hadrons, still higher energies could lead to the proton, anti-proton pair production

$$e^+ + e^- \rightarrow \bar{p} + p \tag{8.16}$$

which in turn can easily excite the vacuum pairs (e^+e^-) and $(\bar{\nu}_e\nu_e)$ together to conserve the lepton number in the reaction

$$e^+ + e^- \rightarrow [(\underset{\rightarrow}{\bar{p}}\underset{\leftarrow}{p}) + (\underset{\rightarrow}{e^+}\underset{\leftarrow}{e^-}) + (\underset{\rightarrow}{\nu_e}\underset{\leftarrow}{\nu_e})] \rightarrow \tag{8.17}$$

$$[(\underset{\rightarrow}{\bar{p}}\ \underset{\rightarrow}{e^+}\underset{\leftarrow}{\nu_e}) + (\underset{\leftarrow}{p}\ \underset{\leftarrow}{e^-}\underset{\rightarrow}{\bar{\nu}_e})] \rightarrow \bar{n} + n$$

where the neutron n and anti-neutron $\bar{n}$, in view of the depression of the electric attractions at short distances by the magnetic repulsion (parallel spin) of p, e^- and $\bar{p}$, e^+, respectively, (see Fig. 7) undergo weak decays

$$n \rightarrow \underset{\leftarrow}{p} + \underset{\leftarrow}{e^-} + \underset{\rightarrow}{\bar{\nu}_e} \quad , \quad \bar{n} \rightarrow \underset{\rightarrow}{\bar{p}} + \underset{\rightarrow}{e^+} + \underset{\leftarrow}{\nu_e} \quad . \tag{8.18}$$

A neutron can experience, when in a bound state with a proton, a strong decay like $(p+n) = [p+(\underset{\leftarrow}{p}\ \underset{\leftarrow}{e^-}\underset{\rightarrow}{\bar{\nu}_e})] = (p+\pi^-+p) \rightarrow (n+p)$ which may describe a nuclear force in the deuteron ground state. Furthermore from (8.18) it is clear that magnetic moment of the neutron is negative. The reaction (8.16) offers two other possibilities (for the case of $\frac{1}{2}$ spin) where in one case the conjugate pair $(\underset{\leftarrow}{e^+}\underset{\rightarrow}{e^-})$ together with the pair $(\underset{\rightarrow}{\bar{\nu}_e}\underset{\leftarrow}{\nu_e})$ are

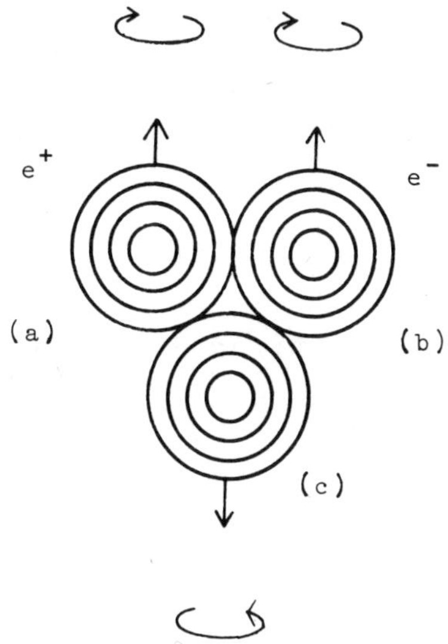

Fig. 7. The two spheres a and b with parallel spins exert a magnetic attraction on the sphere c whose spin is antiparallel (opposite sign of magnetic charge) to that of a and b. The magnetic repulsion of a and b is counterbalanced by their electrical attraction.

excited. Thus we have

$$e^+ + e^- \rightarrow [(\underset{\rightarrow}{\bar{p}}\ \underset{\leftarrow}{e^+}\ \underset{\leftarrow}{\nu_e}) + (\underset{\leftarrow}{p}\ \underset{\rightarrow}{e^-}\ \underset{\rightarrow}{\bar{\nu}_e})] \rightarrow \bar{\Sigma}_o + \Sigma_o \quad . \tag{8.19}$$

The other state refers to the excitation of both conjugate pairs $(\underset{\leftarrow}{e^+}\underset{\rightarrow}{e^-})$, $(\underset{\leftarrow}{\bar{\nu}_e}\underset{\rightarrow}{\nu_e})$ to yield

$$e^+ + e^- \rightarrow [(\underset{\rightarrow}{\bar{p}}\ \underset{\leftarrow}{e^+}\ \underset{\rightarrow}{\nu_e}) + (\underset{\leftarrow}{p}\ \underset{\rightarrow}{e^-}\ \underset{\leftarrow}{\bar{\nu}_e})] \rightarrow \bar{\Lambda} + \Lambda \quad . \tag{8.20}$$

Thus the two states

$$\Sigma_o = (\underset{\leftarrow}{p}\ \underset{\rightarrow}{e^-}\underset{\rightarrow}{\bar{\nu}_e}) \ , \ \Lambda = (\underset{\leftarrow}{p}\ \underset{\rightarrow}{e^-}\underset{\leftarrow}{\bar{\nu}_e}) \ , \tag{8.21}$$

differ only in their magnetic couplings of $\bar{\nu}_e$. The much shorter life times of Λ and Σ_o compared to the neutron are due mainly to the magnetic attraction (anti-parallel spins) of their proton and electron constituents. The magnetic attraction of e^- and $\bar{\nu}_e$ in Λ together with the magnetic repulsion between p and $\bar{\nu}_e$ lead to the decay into strongly interacting particles

$$\Lambda = p + \pi^- \tag{8.22}$$

and also a smaller probability of a weak decay

$$\Lambda = \underset{\leftarrow}{p} + \underset{\rightarrow}{e^-} + \underset{\leftarrow}{\bar{\nu}_e} \ . \tag{8.23}$$

The above procedure can be extended to other spin $\frac{1}{2}\hbar$ states. It is realized that the validity of the above qualitative discussion will ultimately depend on the actual calculation of these processes and their branching ratios. However, because of the plausibility of the above interpretation of the theory, we must also consider the experiment where e^+ and e^- couple with parallel spins (i.e. direct weak coupling). In this case the electric attraction of e^+ and e^- is depressed by their magnetic repulsion and thereby what was a strong and electromagnetic interaction at short distance has now been changed into a weak interaction. Thus the simplest and easiest acquisition from the vacuum is the $(\underset{\rightarrow}{\nu_e}\underset{\leftarrow}{\nu_e})$ pair which yield the reaction

$$\begin{aligned} e^+ + e^- &= (\underset{\rightarrow}{e^+}\underset{\rightarrow}{e^-}) \rightarrow (\underset{\rightarrow}{e^+}\underset{\rightarrow}{e^-}) + (\underset{\rightarrow}{\bar{\nu}_e}\underset{\leftarrow}{\nu_e}) \\ &\rightarrow (\underset{\rightarrow}{e^+}\underset{\leftarrow}{\nu_e}) + (\underset{\rightarrow}{e^-}\underset{\rightarrow}{\bar{\nu}_e}) \rightarrow \pi^+ + \underset{\rightarrow}{e^-} + \underset{\rightarrow}{\bar{\nu}_e} \end{aligned} \tag{8.24}$$

and decays weakly. If for higher energy the excited pair is $(\underset{\rightarrow}{e^+}\underset{\leftarrow}{e^-})$ then the resulting reaction

$$e^+ + e^- = (\underset{\rightarrow}{e^+}\underset{\rightarrow}{e^-}) \rightarrow (\underset{\rightarrow}{e^+}\underset{\rightarrow}{e^-}) + (\underset{\leftarrow}{e^+}\underset{\rightarrow}{e^-}) \quad ,$$

can decay according to

$$e^+ + e^- \rightarrow \underset{\rightarrow}{\Psi} + \underset{\rightarrow}{\gamma} + \underset{\leftarrow}{\gamma} \quad , \tag{8.25}$$

yielding the pair of left and right circularly polarized γ's along with a weak 1^- particle Ψ. This process can be continued and many other states and their strong, weak and electromagnetic decay products can be predicted.

The basic premises of the above qualitative results lie in the prediction that at short distance (or at very high energies) particles must interact in a state where their spins are either parallel (magnetic repulsion) or anti-parallel (magnetic attraction)(see Fig. 8).

9. EQUATIONS OF MOTION

A) Action Principle Derivation of the Equations of Motion

One of the most important tests of the unified field theories has always been the fundamental requirement that the field equations must yield the laws of motion of the particles. In this section we shall demonstrate that the generalized theory of gravitation does, in a straightforward way, yield the equations of motion of a particle (anti-particle) in an external field as well as the action of the self-field on the particle (anti-particle) itself. We shall give two equivalent methods for the derivations of the equations of motion,

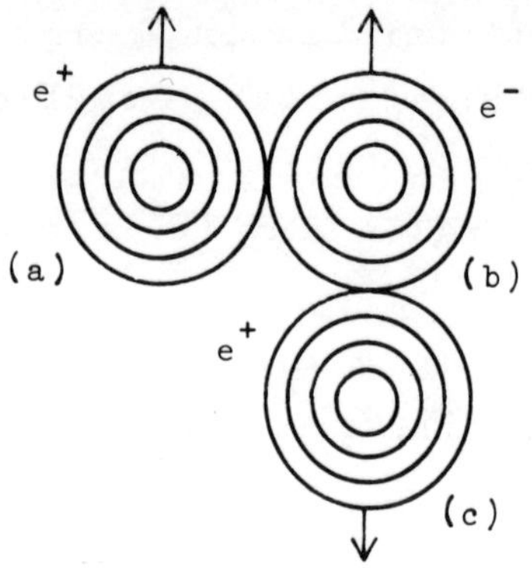

Fig. 8. The magnetic repulsion of a and b is counter-balanced by their electrical attraction while the magnetic attraction of b and c is partly compensated by the electrical repulsion of a and c. The magnetic attraction of b and c is further enhanced by their electrical attractions.

where the action principle derivation is, of course, more general than the other method, which is based, as in general relativity, on the existence of Bianchi identities. We may begin by obtaining, from the field equations (5.1)-(5.3), the most general decomposition of the field $\Phi_{\mu\nu}$. The field equations (7.4) and (7.9), which follow from (5.3) and (5.2), respectively, are satisfied not only by $\Psi_{\mu\nu}$, $F_{\mu\nu}$, but also by $\Psi_{\mu\nu} + f_{1\mu\nu}$ and $F_{\mu\nu} + \Phi_{1\mu\nu}$, where $\Phi_{1\mu\nu}$ and $f_{1\mu\nu}$ obey the field equations

$$\Phi_{1\mu\nu,\rho}+\Phi_{1\nu\rho,\mu}+\Phi_{1\rho\mu,\nu} = 0 \ , \quad \frac{\partial}{\partial x^{\nu}} [\sqrt{(-g)}\Phi_1^{\mu\nu}] = 0 \ , \tag{9.1}$$

$$f_{1\mu\nu,\rho}+f_{1\nu\rho,\mu}+f_{1\rho\mu,\nu} = 0 \ , \quad \frac{\partial}{\partial x^{\nu}} [\sqrt{(-g)}f_1^{\mu\nu}] = 0 \ , \tag{9.2}$$

and where

$$f_1^{\mu\nu} = \frac{1}{2\sqrt{(-g)}} \varepsilon^{\mu\nu\rho\sigma} \Phi_{1\rho\sigma} \quad . \tag{9.3}$$

Thus $\Phi_{1\mu\nu}$ represents radiative solutions of the field equations (5.2) and (5.3). Hence the most general decomposition of the field variables can be represented by

$$\Phi_{\mu\nu} = \Phi_{o\mu\nu} + \Phi_{1\mu\nu} \quad , \tag{9.4}$$

$$f_{\mu\nu} = f_{o\mu\nu} + f_{1\mu\nu} \quad , \tag{9.5}$$

where

$$\frac{1}{4\pi} \frac{\partial}{\partial x^\nu} [\sqrt{(-g)}\Phi_o^{\mu\nu}] = j_e^\mu \quad , \quad \frac{1}{4\pi} \frac{\partial}{\partial x^\nu} [\sqrt{(-g)} f_o^{\mu\nu}] = s^\mu . \tag{9.6}$$

By using (9.4) and (9.5) we obtain decomposition of Ω and Λ, defined by (5.15), in the form

$$\Omega = \Omega_o + \Omega_1 + \Omega_I \quad , \quad \Lambda = \Lambda_o + \Lambda_1 + \Lambda_I \quad , \tag{9.7}$$

where

$$\Omega_o = \frac{1}{2} \Phi_o^{\mu\nu} \Phi_{o\mu\nu} \; , \quad \Omega_1 = \frac{1}{2} \Phi_1^{\mu\nu} \Phi_{1\mu\nu} \; , \quad \Omega_I = \Phi_o^{\mu\nu} \Phi_{1\mu\nu} , \tag{9.8}$$

and

$$\Lambda_o = \frac{1}{4} f_o^{\mu\nu} \Phi_{o\mu\nu} \; , \quad \Lambda_1 = \frac{1}{4} f_1^{\mu\nu} \Phi_{1\mu\nu} \; , \quad \Lambda_I = \frac{1}{4}(f_o^{\mu\nu}\Phi_{1\mu\nu} + f_1^{\mu\nu}\Phi_{o\mu\nu}) . \tag{9.9}$$

The Maxwell energy tensor T_μ^ν, defined by (5.15), becomes

$$T^{\nu}_{\mu} = T^{\nu}_{o\mu} + T^{\nu}_{1\mu} + T^{\nu}_{I\mu} \quad , \qquad (9.10)$$

where

$$T^{\nu}_{o\mu} = \frac{1}{2}\,\delta^{\nu}_{\mu}\,\Omega_o - \Phi_{o\mu\rho}\Phi^{\nu\rho}_{o} \quad , \quad T^{\nu}_{1\mu} = \frac{1}{2}\,\delta^{\nu}_{\mu}\,\Omega_1 - \Phi_{1\mu\rho}\Phi^{\nu\rho}_{1} \quad , \qquad (9.11)$$

$$T^{\nu}_{I\mu} = \frac{1}{2}\,\delta^{\nu}_{\mu}\,\Omega_I - (\Phi_{o\mu\rho}\Phi^{\nu\rho}_{1} + \Phi_{1\mu\rho}\Phi^{\nu\rho}_{o}) \quad .$$

Hence, we obtain the results

$$[\surd(-g)T^{\nu}_{1\mu}]_{|\nu} = 0 \quad , \quad \frac{1}{4\pi}\,[\surd(-g)T^{\nu}_{o\mu}]_{|\nu} = \Phi_{o\mu\rho}j^{\rho}_{e} + f_{o\mu\rho}\,s^{\rho} \quad ,$$

$$\frac{1}{4\pi}\,[\surd(-g)T^{\nu}_{I\mu}]_{|\nu} = \Phi_{1\mu\rho}j^{\rho}_{e} + f_{1\mu\rho}\,s^{\rho} \quad , \qquad (9.12)$$

which, as will be seen, represent force densities corresponding to the interactions between the radiation and current densities j^{μ}_{e}, s^{μ} and also between the self-fields and their corresponding currents.

The square root term which appears in the action integral of the theory can now be written as

$$(1+q^{-2}\Omega-q^{-4}\Lambda^2)=\surd(1+q^{-2}\Omega_o-q^{-4}\Lambda_o^2)[1+\frac{q^{-2}(\Omega_1+\Omega_I)}{1+q^{-2}\Omega_o-q^{-4}\Lambda_o^2}$$

$$- q^{-4}\,\frac{\Lambda_1^2+\Lambda_I^2 +2(\Lambda_o\Lambda_1+\Lambda_o\Lambda_I+\Lambda_1\Lambda_I)}{1+q^{-2}\Omega_o-q^{-4}\Lambda_o^2}]^{\frac{1}{2}} \quad . \qquad (9.13)$$

In order to expand (9.13) in powers of q^{-2} we shall use the dimensionless constants

$$\alpha_n = \frac{e^2}{g_n^2} = \frac{1}{\gamma_n}\,\frac{e^2}{\hbar c} \quad , \quad n=0,1,2,\ldots \qquad (9.14)$$

in the limits of small and large n. Thus, with $r_c \sim \frac{\hbar}{Mc}$ we have the following four possibilities:

(i) In the region $r < r_c$ for large n (i.e. small g_n) from

$$q_n = \frac{\sqrt{(e^2+g_n^2)}}{r_{on}^2} = \frac{c^4}{2G}(e^2+g_n^2)^{-\frac{1}{2}} ,$$

we obtain the result

$$q_n^{-1} \sim \frac{2G}{c^4} e(1 + \frac{1}{2}\alpha_n^{-1}) , \qquad (9.15)$$

which is of the order of 10^{-58} (esu)$^{-1}$. The effect of the small q^{-2} is, of course, offset by the factor q^2 appearing in the energy tensor (5.25) as well as in the action function itself.

(ii) In the region $r < r_c$ for $\alpha_n \ll 1$ (i.e. large g_n) we obtain

$$q_n^{-1} \sim \frac{2G}{c^4} |g_n|(1 + \frac{1}{2}\alpha_n) , \qquad (9.16)$$

which, for reasonable values of g_n with smaller n, would still be a small quantity but somewhat larger than in the case of (i).

(iii) In the region $r > r_c$ we have $g_n = 0$ and

$$q^{-1} = \frac{2G}{c^4} e , \qquad (9.17)$$

a value that is smaller than the values obtained for q^{-1} in the cases of (i) and (ii).

(iv) In the region where $r \gg r_c$ we have $q \to \infty$ (or $r_o \to o$) and in this case the theory reduces to general relativity plus classical electromagnetic field in the absence of electric charges.

Hence to order q^{-2}, in the regions (i) and (ii) where $r < r_c$, we obtain

$$\sqrt{(1+q^{-2}\Omega-q^{-4}\Lambda^2)} \sim \sqrt{(1+q^{-2}\Omega_o-q^{-4}\Lambda_o^2)} + \frac{1}{2}q^{-2}(\Omega_1+\Omega_I)(1+q^{-2}\Omega_o - q^{-4}\Lambda_o^2)^{-\frac{1}{2}} ,$$

$$(1+q^{-2}\Omega-q^{-4}\Lambda^2)^{-\frac{1}{2}} \sim (1+q^{-2}\Omega_o-q^{-4}\Lambda_o^2)^{-\frac{1}{2}} - \frac{1}{2}q^{-2}(\Omega_1+\Omega_I)(1+q^{-2}\Omega_o-q^{-4}\Lambda_o^2)^{-\frac{3}{2}} .$$

For the region (iii) the corresponding expansions are given by

$$\sqrt{(1+q^{-2}\Omega-q^{-4}\Lambda^2)} \sim \sqrt{(1+q^{-2}\Omega_o-q^{-4}\Lambda_o^2)} + \frac{1}{2} q^{-2}(\Omega_1+\Omega_I) , \tag{9.18}$$

$$(1+q^{-2}\Omega-q^{-4}\Lambda^2)^{-\frac{1}{2}} \sim (1+q^{-2}\Omega_o-q^{-4}\Lambda_o^2)^{-\frac{1}{2}} - \frac{1}{2} q^{-2}(\Omega_1+\Omega_I) . \tag{9.19}$$

The increasing values of q (i.e. $n\to\infty$) correspond to increasing distances from the origin of the particle where the self-fields are small compared to q, and therefore in region (iv) we have the approximate values

$$\sqrt{(1+q^{-2}\Omega-q^{-4}\Lambda^2)} \sim 1 + \frac{1}{2} q^{-2}(\Omega_o+\Omega_1+\Omega_I) , \tag{9.20}$$

$$(1+q^{-2}\Omega-q^{-4}\Lambda^2)^{-\frac{1}{2}} \sim 1 - \frac{1}{2} q^{-2}(\Omega_o+\Omega_1+\Omega_I) . \tag{9.21}$$

In this theory particles (anti-particles) are represented by the <u>magnetic</u> regions (generated by the magnetic charge) of the field. The action principle of the theory yields the field equations which are valid everywhere, including the magnetic regions of the field.

In order to study the time dependent behavior of the magnetic regions under the influence of an external field (i.e. the space-time trajectories of magnetic regions), as well as under the action of their self-field, we must minimize (by displacing each point on the world-line of the particle's center by an infintesimal amount) the action function which was obtained by substituting the field equations back into the original action function, which yielded the field equations as a result of the variation of the field variables $\hat{g}_{\mu\nu} = g_{\mu\nu} + q^{-1}\,\Phi_{\mu\nu}$. The action principle for the field equations (5.1)-(5.3) is based on the variation of the action function

$$S = \frac{q^2 r_o^2}{8\pi c} \int \{\hat{g}^{\mu\nu} R_{\mu\nu} + \kappa^2[\sqrt{(-\hat{g})} - \sqrt{(-g)}]\} d^4x \ , \qquad (9.22)$$

where

$$\hat{g}^{[\mu\nu]} = g^{[\mu\nu]}{}_{,\rho} \quad (\text{i.e. } \hat{g}^{[\mu\nu]}{}_{,\nu} = 0)$$

and where, as shown in (A), the variation of S with respect to $\hat{g}^{\{\mu\nu\}}$ and $g^{[\mu\nu\rho]}$ yields the field equations (5.1)-(5.3).

On substituting the field equations (5.1)-(5.3) in (9.22) and dropping the divergence term, we obtain the extremum value of the action function S in the form

$$S_o = -\frac{q^2}{4\pi} \int [\sqrt{(-\hat{g})} - \sqrt{(-g)}] d^4x \ , \qquad (9.23)$$

where now the integrand is a function of the solutions $\hat{g}_{\mu\nu}$ of the field equations (5.1)-(5.3). Thus whenever the field equations (5.1)-(5.3) are solved, of which particles are prescribed as a special spectrum of values of $\hat{g}_{\mu\nu}$, the value of the action function S_o for these solutions can be minimized to obtain the equations of motion. Such equations of motion would then describe all interactions between particles and fields (external as well as self-fields). In this way the evolution of the particle aspects of the field are separated out, leading, under the variation of the appropriate variables, to the actual trajectories of these particles. The simplest application of this method is to consider the motion of a massive neutrino in the gravitational field. In this case the action function (9.23) in the rest frame of a spherically symmetric neutrino, using (3.18) of (A), becomes

$$S_o = -\frac{q^2}{c}\int \frac{\exp(\rho)}{\upsilon}(1-\sin\Phi)dr\, dx^4 \quad , \qquad (9.24)$$

where the r-integration extends from o to r_c (of neutrino). From the solution (7.7) of (A), setting $\lambda_o^2 = 0$, it is seen that for the neutrino metric the function $\exp(u)$ at $r = r_c$ is given by

$$\exp(u) = 1 - \frac{2mG}{c^2 r_c} \quad ,$$

and also

$$\upsilon = \pm 1 \; , \; \exp(\rho) = r^2 \quad .$$

Hence the results (9.2), (9.3) of (A) yield the rest frame value

$$S_o = -(\pm M_\nu c)\int dx^4 \quad , \qquad (9.25)$$

where the observed neutrino mass M_ν is related to the

"bare gravitational mass" m by

$$M_\nu = m + \delta m \quad , \tag{9.26}$$

and where

$$\delta m = -\frac{1}{2}m - \frac{g_o^2}{c^2 \ell_{oo}} \tag{9.27}$$

is related to the neutrino binding energy. The flat space-time generalization of (9.25) to a moving frame of reference is of the form

$$S_o = -(\pm M_\nu c)\int v_\mu dx^\mu \quad ,$$

where

$$v^\mu = \frac{dx^\mu}{ds} \quad , \quad v^\mu v_\mu = 1 \ , \ dx^\mu = v^\mu ds$$

is the velocity vector of the moving frame of reference. In the rest frame of a flat space-time we have $v^4 = 1$, $v_j = 0$, $(j=1,2,3)$ and we regain (9.25). Therefore (because of the principle of equivalence) in a moving frame of reference of a curved space-time we obtain the action function (9.25) in the form

$$S_o = -(\pm M_\nu c)\int ds \tag{9.28}$$

where now

$$ds^2 = g_{\mu\nu}\, dx^\mu\, dx^\nu \tag{9.29}$$

and where x^μ represents the coordinates of the "neutrino's center". Thus, in the gravitational field of the bare mass m, the center of a neutrino moves along a geodesic world-line (obtained from variation of S_o) spanning the space-time region of a tube comprised of a bundle of world-lines of an extended particle (with spatial dimension $r_c \sim \frac{\hbar}{M_\nu c}$).

For the more general case of a charged particle we may decompose the action function S_o of (9.24) in the form

$$S_o \cong S_{oo} + S_{1I} + S_{2I} \quad , \tag{9.30}$$

where

$$S_{oo} = -\frac{q^2}{4\pi c}\int [\sqrt{(1+q^{-2}\Omega_o - q^{-4}\Lambda_o^2)} - 1]\sqrt{(-g)}\,d^4x \; , \tag{9.31}$$

$$S_{1I} = -\frac{1}{8\pi c}\int_{r<r_c} \frac{(\Omega_1+\Omega_I)\sqrt{(-g)}\,d^4x}{\sqrt{(1+q^{-2}\Omega_o - q^{-4}\Lambda_o^2)}} \quad , \tag{9.32}$$

$$S_{2I} = -\frac{1}{8\pi c}\int_{r\geqq r_c} (\Omega_1+\Omega_I)\sqrt{(-g)}\,d^4x \quad . \tag{9.33}$$

In the rest frame of the particle the action function S_{oo} for a spherically symmetric field becomes

$$S_{oo} = -\frac{q^2}{c}\int \frac{\exp(\rho)}{\upsilon}\left(\frac{1}{\cosh\Gamma} - \sin\Phi\right)dr\,dx^4 \quad , \tag{9.34}$$

where we used the results (3.16) and (3.18) of (A), and where the integration over r extends from 0 to ∞. The interval (0,∞) for the range of r can be subdivided into the intervals $(0,r_c)$ and (r_c,∞). The contributions to the action function in (r_c,∞) are due to the presence of the long range tails of gravitational and Coulomb forces. However in the interval $(0,r_c)$ all the forces contribute. Most of the contributions to the integral (9.34) come from the integration over the interval $(0, r_c)$. Thus we may regard the particle as confined to a region of dimension r_c. The integral (9.34) in a moving coordinate system using the self-energy result (6.3), can be written as

$$S_{oo} = -(\pm Mc)\int ds \quad , \tag{9.35}$$

where now the observed mass M is related to the "bare gravitational mass" m according to (see 6.3)

$$M = m + \delta m \quad , \quad \delta m = -\frac{1}{2} m - \frac{Q_o^2}{c^2 \ell_{oo}} Z(\beta_o) \; . \tag{9.36}$$

For $g_o = 0$ we obtain $S_{oo} = \infty$ and therefore in this case the particle cannot move (unless we use the method of infinite renormalization of mass). In (9.35) ds refers to the line element of the particle's center with the space time coordinates z^μ. Thus the motion of the particle spans a world tube whose spatial dimensions are of the order of $r_c \sim \frac{\hbar}{Mc}$.

The action function S_{2I} can be brought to the conventional form by writing

$$\Omega_I \sqrt{(-g)} = \Phi_o^{\mu\nu} \Phi_{1\mu\nu} \sqrt{(-g)} = 2 \frac{\partial}{\partial x^\mu} [\Phi_o^{\mu\nu} A_\nu \sqrt{(-g)}] - 2A_\nu [\frac{\partial}{\partial x^\mu} [\sqrt{(-g)} \Phi_o^{\mu\nu}]] = 8\pi A_\mu j_e^\mu \quad ,$$

where the divergence term has been dropped. Hence the total action function (9.30) can be written as

$$S_o = S_{1I} - (\pm Mc)\int ds - \frac{1}{c}\int [\int_\sigma A_\mu j^\mu d\sigma] ds - \frac{1}{16\pi c}\int \Phi_1^{\mu\nu} \Phi_{1\mu\nu} \sqrt{(-g)} d^4x , \tag{9.37}$$

where

$$d\sigma = v^{\mu} d\sigma_{\mu} \quad , \quad v^{\mu} = \frac{dz^{\mu}}{ds} \quad , \quad v^{\mu} v_{\mu} = 1 \quad ,$$

and

$$\sqrt{(-g)}\, d^4x \rightarrow d\sigma\, ds \quad , \quad j^{\mu} = \frac{1}{\sqrt{(-g)}}\, j_e^{\mu} \quad .$$

In the result (9.37) the last three terms are the same as the classical action function for a charged particle moving according to Lorentz's equations of motion in an external electromagnetic field. The last term in (9.37), because of the field equations (9.1), does not contribute to the action principle. The action S_{1I} defined by (9.32) contains the effects of the particle's own fields on its motion in the external field $\Phi_{\mu\nu}$. The term S_{1I} will not be discussed in this paper.

It is interesting to observe that in Einstein's(2) as well as in Schrödinger's(3) versions of the generalized theory of gravitation the action function S_o defined by (9.23) vanishes, and that therefore these theories cannot yield equations of motion.

B) Derivation of the Equations of Motion From the Bianchi Identities

The field equations (5.19), via Bianchi identities, imply the covariant conservation laws

$$[\sqrt{(-g)}\, T_{\mu}^{\nu}]_{|\nu} = 0 \quad , \tag{9.38}$$

where the energy momentum tensor T_{μ}^{ν} can be decomposed in the form

$$T_{\mu}^{\nu} = T_{o\mu}^{\nu} + T_{1\mu}^{\nu} + T_{I\mu}^{\nu} \quad , \tag{9.39}$$

and where $T^{\nu}_{o\mu}$ is constructed in terms of $\Phi_{o\mu\nu}$ of (9.4) in the form given by (5.25) and has the linearized form (see appendix 1)

$$T^{\mu\nu}_{o} = \frac{1}{4\pi} T^{\mu\nu}_{o} + 4\pi r_o^2 [\tfrac{1}{2}(s^{\mu}s^{\nu} + \tfrac{1}{2}g^{\mu\nu}s^{\rho}s_{\rho}) + j^{\mu}j^{\nu} + \tfrac{1}{2} g^{\mu\nu} j_{\rho} j^{\rho}] +$$

$$\frac{1}{2} r_o^2 (f^{\mu}_{o\rho} s^{\rho\nu} + f^{\nu}_{o\rho} s^{\rho\mu}) \quad . \tag{9.40}$$

The tensor $T^{\mu\nu}_{o}$ vanishes on the tubular surface (dimensions $r_c \sim \frac{\hbar}{Mc}$) generated during the motion of the particle. The remaining two terms in (9.39) are given by (9.11) and

$$T^{\mu\nu}_{I} = \frac{1}{4\pi} T^{\mu\nu}_{I} + \frac{1}{2} r_o^2 (f^{\mu}_{1\rho} s^{\rho\nu} + f^{\nu}_{1\rho} s^{\rho\mu}) \quad . \tag{9.41}$$

By using the relations

$$g^{\rho\sigma}(s^{\mu}{}_{|\rho\sigma}) = \kappa^2 s^{\mu} \; , \quad (s^{\nu|\rho})_{|\nu} \cong 0 \quad , \tag{9.42}$$

we obtain

$$T^{\mu\nu}_{I\,|\nu} = \Phi^{\mu}_{1\rho} j^{\rho} - \frac{1}{4} (g^{\mu\sigma} f^{\rho\alpha}_{1} s_{\rho\alpha})_{|\sigma} \quad ,$$

where

$$\frac{1}{2} (g^{\mu\sigma} f^{\rho\alpha}_{1} s_{\rho\alpha})_{|\sigma} = (g^{\mu\sigma} f^{\rho\alpha}_{1} s_{\alpha})_{|\rho\sigma} \quad ,$$

and where the first equation of (9.42) follows from linearization of the field equations (5.2). Hence

$$T^{\mu\nu}_{I\,|\nu} = \Phi^{\mu}_{1\rho} j^{\rho} \quad , \tag{9.43}$$

where the last term has been dropped since its

contribution to the energy integral vanishes (see Appendix 1). For the divergence of $T^{\mu\nu}_{o}$ we obtain

$$T^{\mu\nu}_{o}{}_{|\nu} = \Phi^{\mu}_{\ o\rho}\, j^{\rho} + 4\,\pi\, r_{o}^{2}\,(j^{\rho} j^{\mu}{}_{|\rho} + j_{\rho} j^{\rho|\mu}) \;. \qquad (9.44)$$

In terms of a hydrodynamic picture we can introduce a velocity vector field to describe a continuous flow of matter. The density and flow of electric and magnetic charges can be described in terms of the electric and magnetic current densities by defining them in the form

$$j^{\mu} = c\, v^{\mu} \quad , \quad s^{\mu} = m\, v^{\mu} \quad , \qquad (9.45)$$

so that c, m and v^{μ} are not independent variables. The scalar c and pseudo-scalar m determine the electric and magnetic charge densities. The conservation laws,

$$j^{\mu}{}_{|\mu} = 0 \quad , \quad s^{\mu}{}_{|\mu} = 0 \quad , \qquad (9.46)$$

lead to the relation

$$\frac{1}{m}\frac{dm}{ds} = \frac{1}{c}\frac{dc}{ds}$$

or

$$c = \surd(\alpha_{n})\, m_{n} \quad , \qquad (9.47)$$

where the α_n were defined by (9.14). By using the above definitions the internal part of the energy density can be written as

$$T^{\mu\nu}_{o} = (\varepsilon_{n} + P_{n}) v^{\mu} v^{\nu} + P_{n}\, g^{\mu\nu} + \tfrac{1}{2} r_{o}^{2}(f^{\mu}_{\ o\rho}\, s^{\rho\nu} + f^{\nu}_{\ o\rho}\, s^{\mu\rho}) - \tfrac{1}{4\pi}\, \Phi^{\mu}_{\ o\rho}\, \Phi^{\nu\rho}_{o} , \qquad (9.48)$$

where the energy density ε_n and the isotopic pressure P_n are defined by

$$\varepsilon_n = 2\,\pi\, r_{on}^2\, m_n^2 \left(\frac{1}{2} + \frac{e^2}{\hbar c}\frac{1}{\gamma_n}\right) - \frac{1}{8\pi}\,\Omega_o \quad , \tag{9.49}$$

$$P_n = 2\,\pi\, r_{on}^2\, m_n^2 \left(\frac{1}{2} + \frac{e^2}{hc}\frac{1}{\gamma_n}\right) + \frac{1}{8\pi}\,\Omega_o \quad . \tag{9.50}$$

The remaining terms in (9.48) represent self-couplings of the field and the particle. In the result (9.48) the subscript n of $T_o^{\mu\nu}$ has been suppressed, but in fact it describes the energy densities in each magnetic layer specified by n=0,1,2,... .

Let us now rewrite the conservation law (9.38) in the form

$$[\sqrt{(-g)}\,T_o^{\mu\nu}]_{|\nu} + \Phi^{\mu}_{1\rho}\, j_o^{\rho} = 0 \quad , \tag{9.51}$$

where the first term will be treated exactly and therefore the linearized form will not be used in (9.51). The integration of (9.51) over a four-dimensional tubular region spanned by the motion of the extended particle can be written as

$$\int_T \sqrt{(-g)}\,T_o^{\mu\nu}\, d\sigma_\nu + \int \sqrt{(-g)}\,T_o^{\rho\sigma}\, \{^{\mu}_{\rho\sigma}\}\, d^4x + \int \Phi^{\mu}_{1\rho}\, j_e^{\rho}\, d^4x = 0 \ , \tag{9.52}$$

where in the first integral we used Gauss' theorem and where T represents a region bounded by the hypersurfaces at the instants $x^4 = \sigma_1$ and $x^4 = \sigma_2$ (where $\sigma_1 < \sigma_2$) and by the tubular region between these hypersurfaces. The total energy in the tubular region consists of an influx of energy at the instant σ_1 and an efflux of energy at the instant σ_2 plus the energy on the surface of the tubular region spanned during the motion of the particle from σ_1 to σ_2. Hence the first integral in (9.52) can be written as

$$\int \sqrt{(-g)}\, T_o^{\mu\nu}\, d\sigma_\nu = P^\mu(\sigma_1) - P^\mu(\sigma_2) + P^\mu(\text{tubular}) \;, \qquad (9.53)$$

where

$$P^\mu(\sigma_1) = \int_{\sigma_1} \sqrt{(-g)}\, T_o^{\mu\nu}\, d\sigma_\nu \;, \quad P^\mu(\sigma_2) = \int_{\sigma_2} \sqrt{(-g)}\, T_o^{\mu\nu}\, d\sigma_\nu \;, \qquad (9.54)$$

and where the term P^μ (tubular), as seen from the linearized form (9.48), vanishes.

Now the integral (5.36) of the energy tensor, because of its time independence, can be taken to refer to either of the instants σ_1 and σ_2. We can write (5.36) as

$$\int \sqrt{(-g)}\, (T_{o\nu}^4 - \tfrac{1}{2}\, \delta_\nu^4\, T_o)\, d\sigma^\nu = \pm \tfrac{1}{2}\, mc^2 \;,$$

or as

$$\int \sqrt{(-g)}\, T_{o\nu}^4\, d\sigma^\nu = \pm \tfrac{1}{2}\, mc^2 + \tfrac{1}{2} \int \sqrt{(-g)}\, T_o\, \delta_\nu^4\, d\sigma^\nu = P^4(\sigma) \;, \qquad (9.55)$$

where

$$T_o = T_{o\mu}^\mu \;.$$

In a moving frame of reference the equation (9.55) can be replaced by the equation (9.54), where, as in the action principle derivation, the observed particle mass is defined by

$$M = m + \delta m \quad ,$$

$$\delta m = -\frac{1}{2} m + \frac{1}{2}\int \sqrt{(-g)}\; T_o \; d\sigma \quad . \qquad (9.56)$$

In the limit $\sigma_2 \to \sigma_1$ the integral (9.52) can be replaced by

$$\int_{\sigma_1}^{\sigma_2} Mc^2 \frac{dv^\mu}{ds}\, ds + \int_{\sigma_1}^{\sigma_2} \left[\int T_o^{\rho\sigma} \{^{\mu}_{\rho\sigma}\} d\sigma\right] ds + \int_{\sigma_1}^{\sigma_2} \left[\int \Phi^{\mu}_{1\rho}\, j^{\rho}\, d\sigma\right] ds = 0 \ , \qquad (9.57)$$

which, in view of the arbitrariness of σ_1 and σ_2, implies the equations motion

$$Mc^2 \frac{dv^\mu}{ds} + \int T_o^{\rho\sigma} \{^{\mu}_{\rho\sigma}\} d\sigma + \int \Phi^{\mu}_{1\rho}\, j^{\rho}\, d\sigma = 0 \quad . \qquad (9.58)$$

The velocity vector v^μ of the particle's center is the same vector which defines the current vector in the form $j^\mu = cv^\mu$. It was shown in (A) that at the origin the electric and magnetic field (of the magnetic charge) vanish. If we wish we can use the linearized energy tensor (9.48) in the second term of (9.58) and calculate it in the approximation where in the magnetic core of the particle self-couplings and pressure vanish. In this case the equations of motion (9.58) are replaced by Lorentz's equations of motion in a gravitational field,

$$Mc^2 \left[\frac{dv^\mu}{ds} + \{^{\mu}_{\rho\sigma}\} v^\rho v^\sigma\right] + \int \Phi^{\mu}_{1\rho}\; j^{\rho}\; d\sigma = 0 \ . \qquad (9.59)$$

The derivation of the equations of motion as a consequence of the Bianchi identities, as can be seen from the result (9.58), is less general than the derivation based on action principle. This can, for example, be seen from the self-interaction effects contained in

(9.37) which are absent in the present derivation. However, Bianchi identities are of great physical significance for the generalized theory of gravitation. In fact the original derivation of the field equations (5.1)-(5.3) was based on the Bianchi identities of the nonsymmetric theory (see Appendix, 2).

In a purely gravitational field the equations of motion, in accordance with the principle of equivalence, are independent of mass. In any other field the equations of motion depend on the mass, and, since the motion perturbs the vacuum, the observed mass has a definite dependence on the total electric and magnetic charges. The mass of an elementary particle appears in the laws of motion as a function of the bare gravitational mass m which was obtained as a constant of integration. Thus the role of the gravitational field in the physics of the elementary particle is first manifested by the size of the bare gravitational mass m. From the definition (9.36) or (9.56) of the observed particle mass we infer that the bare gravitational mass m must assume a value of the order of $(\sim \frac{g_n^2}{\ell_{oo}})10^{20}$ Mev to counter-balance the self-energy or binding energy term and to yield the observed particle mass M. A possible fixed value for m can be taken as

$$m \cong \sqrt{(\frac{\hbar c}{2G})} \quad , \tag{9.60}$$

which has the right order of magnitude provided the total magnetic charge g_o is of the order of

$$g_o \sim \frac{\mp 1}{2} \sqrt{(\hbar c)} \quad . \tag{9.61}$$

Thus the physics of an elementary particle in the

generalized theory of gravitation begins with the identification of the three constants of integration (i) e as the electric charge, (ii) m as the maximum value of gravitational mass (9.60) which determines the observed mass of an elementary particle by

$$M \cong \frac{1}{2}\sqrt{\left(\frac{\hbar c}{2G}\right)} - \frac{Q_o^2}{c^2 \ell_{oo}} Z(\beta_o) \quad , \tag{9.62}$$

where the remaining constant of integration (iii) g_o is, as implied by (9.61), of the order of 10^{-9} esu. In principle the masses of the four fundamental particles P, e^-, ν_μ, ν_e are to be determined through the mass formula (9.62) as a function of g_o. The masses M_{ν_μ} and M_{ν_e} are independent of the electric charge but M_P and M_e both depend on the electric charge e^2 and magnetic charge g_o^2. For $g_o = 0$ the masses M_P and M_e become infinite and those of M_{ν_μ} and M_{ν_e} increase to the bare gravitational mass m. Actually the theory predicts a mass separation through a fundamental property of the vacuum magnetic field H_o (generated by g_o). This fact is manifested in the stationary values of the vacuum magnetic field H_o. The conditions for the two stationary values of H_o, as seen by (4.13), are independent of the electric charge and thus it is rather tempting to expect a fundamental relationship of mass ratios where

$$\frac{M_P}{M_e} = \frac{M_{\nu_\mu}}{M_{\nu_e}} \quad . \tag{9.63}$$

This expectation is based on the assumption that mass separation due to the electric charge (i.e. M_P, M_e versus M_{ν_μ}, M_{ν_e}) does not effect the equality of mass ratios.

The expression (4.13) because of the small size of ℓ_o which implies that for fixed Φ the second term in the square root will be small, entails a large mass separation of the corresponding particles. This fact has some interesting consequences. Let us write (4.13) in the form

$$\dot{\Phi} \cot\Phi = 1 + \tau_o \surd \left[1 - \frac{3\ell_o^4 \cot^2\Phi}{\exp(2\rho)-\ell_o^4}\right] , \qquad (9.64)$$

where $\tau_o = 1$ and $\tau_o = -1$ correspond to the conditions for the vacuum magnetic field which yield stationary values for P, ν_μ and e, ν_e, respectively, and where

$$\dot{\Phi} = \frac{d\Phi}{d\rho} , \quad \exp(\rho) = \surd(r^4+\ell_o^4) \quad .$$

The solutions $\Phi(r,\tau_o)$ of the equation (9.64) yield the angle function $\Phi(r,1)$ for P and ν_μ and $\Phi(r,-1)$ for e^- and ν_e for the respective extremum values of their vacuum magnetic field H_o. The corresponding electric field for proton and electron is given by

$$E_e(r,\tau_o) = \left(\frac{|e|\tau_o}{R^2+r_o^2}\right) \frac{1}{\upsilon(r,\tau)} , \qquad (9.65)$$

where $\tau_o = -1$ for electron and $\tau_o = 1$ for proton and where

$$\frac{1}{\upsilon(r,\tau_o)} = \varepsilon[\exp(\tfrac{1}{2}\rho)]'\exp[F(r,\tau_o)]\cosh\Gamma \quad . \qquad (9.66)$$

The values $\varepsilon = +1$ and $\varepsilon = -1$ correspond to particle, anti-particle charge conjugation and the function F is defined by

$$F(r,\tau_o) = \frac{1}{2}\int \dot{\Phi}^2 \, d\rho$$

$$= \frac{1}{2}\int[\tan\Phi + \tau_o\sqrt{[\tan^2\Phi - \frac{3\ell_o^4}{\exp(2\rho)-\ell_o^4}]}]^2 d\rho \quad . \quad (9.67)$$

At distances $r = r_c$ and beyond the electric field reduces to its Coulomb value

$$E_e(r,\tau) \to \frac{|e|\tau_o\varepsilon}{r^2} \quad ,$$

and, therefore, for the extremum values of the vacuum magnetic field H_o the electric fields of proton and electron assume, at distances less than r_c, different values. Thus at distances less than r_c the electric field of the proton is greater than that of electron's electric field. For neutrinos, where e = 0, the stationary values of the vacuum magnetic field are given by

$$H_o(r,\tau_o) = \frac{q\cos[\Phi(r,\tau_o)]}{\upsilon(r,\tau_o)} \quad . \qquad (9.68)$$

The stationary values of the vacuum magnetic field for the proton and electron depend on the square of the electric charge and are given by

$$H_o(r,\tau_o) = \frac{q\cos[\Phi(r,\tau_o)]}{\upsilon(r,\tau_o)\cosh\Gamma} \quad , \qquad (9.69)$$

where

$$\frac{1}{\cosh\Gamma} = \frac{\sqrt{(r^4+\ell_o^4)}}{\sqrt{(r^4+r_o^4)}} \quad .$$

The actual computation of the ratios (9.63) involves the use of the definition of observed mass

$$\varepsilon M(\tau_o,\gamma) = \int T_4^4 \; (r,\ \gamma|e|,\tau_o)\,dr\,d\theta\,d\phi \quad , \qquad (9.70)$$

where for P and e^-, $\gamma = 1$ and for ν_μ and ν_e, $\gamma = 0$. The integrals for $\gamma = 1$ and $g_o = 0$ are infinite while for $\gamma = 0$, $g_o = 0$ they assume the value εmc^2. Thus the infinite renormalization of mass, which occurs in quantum electrodynamics, cannot be used for the computation of fundamental particle masses. The field equations (5.1) -(5.3) were solved in (A) for the spherically symmetric case by taking $\Phi(r) = \frac{\pi}{2}$ (i.e. at $r = r_c$ and beyond) and also for the case of zero magnetic charge density (i.e. on the surfaces of the stratified layers of magnetic charges). In order to perform the integration (9.70) we shall need the solutions inside the stratified layers. In the absence of these solutions the validity of the conjecture (9.63) cannot be tested. In the mass formula (9.70) the $\gamma = 1$ solutions conserve the space time symmetries of charge conjugation and parity while the $\gamma = 0$ solutions violate these symmetries which distinguish between the P, e^- and ν_μ, ν_e masses.

The electric charge e appearing in the equations of motion (9.58), like the mass M, is the observed charge and is related to the bare electric charge e_o according to the relation (4.4) of (A). The constant of integration λ_o^2 in (4.3) of (A) was expressed in the form

$$\lambda_o^2 = e\,q^{-1} \quad ,$$

which can be written as

$$e = \frac{q}{q_o}\,e_o \quad , \qquad (9.71)$$

where

$$q_o = \frac{e_o}{\lambda_o^2} \quad , \tag{9.72}$$

and e_o is the "bare electric charge". In the limit $q \to \infty$ the observed charge e, like the observed mass M, tends to infinity. In the same way, which follows from (4.7) of (A), the observed total magnetic charge g_o and "the bare magnetic charge" $\bar{g}_o$ can be related according to

$$g_o = \frac{q}{\bar{q}} \bar{g}_o \quad , \tag{9.73}$$

where

$$\bar{q} = \frac{\bar{g}_o}{\ell_o^2} \quad . \tag{9.74}$$

From the above results and their interpretations it follows that the lengths λ_o, ℓ_o and therefore r_o may be regarded as "bare lengths" which lead to the existence of "observed lengths", such as, for example r_c, many orders of magnitudes greater than the bare ones. We may, for example, estimate the bare charge of a proton by observing that the ratio of the electrostatic force between two identical bare charges to the gravitational force of their bare masses should be equal to the ratio obtained from the corresponding observed quantities i.e.

$$\frac{e_o^2}{Gm^2} = \frac{e^2}{GM^2} \quad .$$

Hence

$$e_o = \frac{m}{M} e \sim 10^9 \text{ e.s.u} \quad , \tag{9.75}$$

where we have assumed that the charges e_o and e are

carried by the masses m and M, respectively. Moreover, the "electric dipole moment" of a system of two bare charges at a distance λ_o will be equal to the electric dipole moment of two observed charges provided the latter are placed at a distance r_c given by

$$e\, r_c = e_o\, \lambda_o \qquad ,$$

where now r_c, because $\lambda_o \sim 10^{-34}$ cm, is of the order of 10^{-14} cm. We thus see that all of the constants of integration λ_o, ℓ_o, m etc. refer to bare quantities out of which we build the corresponding observed quantities by means of "finite renormalizations" as obtained from the theory.

10. CONCLUSIONS

Unification of gravitational and electromagnetic forces by the non-symmetric generalization of the general theory of relativity has led to a new understanding of the nature of short range forces in the elementary particle interactions. There are two basic reasons for obtaining these results: (i) the presence of screening caused by the magnetic charge distribution with alternating signs; (ii) the field equation (5.2), which follows from its linearized form

$$\left(\nabla^2 - \frac{1}{c^2}\frac{\partial^2}{\partial t^2} + \kappa^2\right) s^\mu = 0 \quad , \qquad (10.1)$$

and the very large size of $\kappa(\sim 10^{34}\,\mathrm{cm}^{-1})$, which besides causing the stratified magnetic structure, has confined the magnetic charge distribution s^μ to a region of the field with an <u>indeterminate</u> size $r_c(\sim \frac{\hbar}{Mc})$. The role of gravitation can be understood in terms of a <u>primeval</u>

field where the gravitational condensation of free magnetic charges g_n composed the elementary particle and conserved the electric and magnetic currents.

The existence of the fundamental "bare length" r_o as a result of the Bianchi identities (see Appendix 2) of the nonsymmetric theory, laid the foundations of a correspondence principle and, furthermore, induced an extended structure ($r_c \sim \frac{\hbar}{Mc}$) for an elementary particle. Thus the length r_o ($\sim 10^{-33}$cm) which is zero in the conventional theory, measures the degree of deviation of the generalized theory of gravitation (or the nonsymmetric theory) from general relativity plus classical electrodynamics, just as Planck's constant $\hbar$ ($\sim 10^{-27}$cgs) can be thought of as measuring the degree of deviation of quantum theory from the classical theory. The effort in the paper (A) was in trying to bring the length r_o in line with the "magic" quantity 10^{-13}cm, by choosing g_o to be of the order of 10^{18}e, and was mainly due to personal prejudices accumulated over many years. It is now clear that g_o (total magnetic charge) of the theory is, at most, one or two orders of magnitude of the electric charge. Furthermore, as shown in (A) and in this paper, there exist no monopoles in this theory and that the fields produced by the magnetic charges g_n (with $\sum_{n=o}^{\infty} g_n = (-1)^s g_o$) are short range fields. In the limit $n \to \infty$ ($g_n \to 0$) the coupling between the field and the particle of strength $\frac{Q_n^2}{\hbar c}$ ($= \frac{e^2}{\hbar c} + \frac{g_n^2}{\hbar c}$) tends to $\frac{e^2}{\hbar c}$ and the interaction occurs at and beyond the distance r_c($\sim \frac{\hbar}{Mc}$). Despite the indeterminacy associated with the partial magnetic charges g_n the total magnetic charge g_o has, for a given fundamental particle, a fixed value. The quantity g_o was found to play a unique role in correlating the spin ($s = \frac{1}{2}\hbar$) direction and the sign of g_o.

Thus a parallel spin coupling at short distances between a particle and anti-particle can induce a slow annihilation process. This could be interpreted as the most likely production and decay process of the ψ-particles. The widths in a ψ energy level could originate from the uncertainties in g_n.

In the derivation of spin we found that the parity and charge conjugation symmetries are, for e = 0, broken and the corresponding two massive particles have the same symmetry properties as the two neutrinos. The two massive neutrinos of this theory and the electron and proton together with the corresponding four anti-particles can form the basis for constructing "sub-nuclear atoms". Thus all the particles so far observed can be accounted for and new particles predicted. The mass separation of the four fundamental particles has its origin in the two possible stationary values of the vacuum magnetic field. The condition for the extremum values of the vacuum magnetic field does not depend on the electric charge. On this basis it has been conjectured that the proton-electron and muon-neutrino-electron-neutrino mass ratios could be equal. If this proves to be correct then the unification of all fundamental interactions will assume an entirely new status. The vacuum, in this theory, consists of the zero energy, zero spin, zero electric and magnetic charge pairs of $(\bar{P}P)$, (e^+e^-), $(\bar{\nu}_\mu\nu_\mu)$, $(\bar{\nu}_e\nu_e)$. These pairs can be created with a threshold energy of at least $2Mc^2$.

The methods for calculating the mass ratios and fine structure constant have been formulated but, because of the so far unknown solutions of the field equations inside the stratified magnetic layers, the calculations have not been performed. The constants of integration such as the bare gravitational mass m, bare length λ_o, and bare length ℓ_o, have, together with the equations of motion, laid the foundations for an unambiguous physical interpretation of the theory and led to the discovery of the nature of the corresponding observed quantities like mass, electric charge, and magnetic charge. A most remarkable formal result refers to the fact that for $g_o = 0$ and for distances large compared to r_c the spherically symmetric time independent solutions reduce to Nordström solution of general relativity with the surprising result that the bare gravitational mass m appears along with the observed electric charge e in the same solution. Hence one obtains the hitherto, (to author's knowledge), unnoticed fact that the electric charge and mass appearing in the Nordström solution

$$\exp(u) = 1 - \frac{2mG}{c^2 r} + \frac{Ge^2}{c^4 r^2} \quad , \tag{10.2}$$

of general relativity have the wrong $\frac{e}{m}$ ratio i.e. the e and m do not belong to one another. The bare gravitational mass m and its corresponding bare electric charge e_o, as shown in section 9, are of the order of 10^{20} Mev. and 10^9 esu, respectively and are related to the corresponding observed quantities M and e according to

$$\frac{e_o}{m} = \frac{e}{M} \quad . \tag{10.3}$$

This basic result, in view of the point singularity character of a particle assumed in general relativity and also the corresponding associated infinities, could not have been obtained without the regularity of solutions in the generalized theory and the resulting consequences. The origin of this result may be found in the fact that the gravitational field, as shown in (5.35) of (A), assumes its maximum value

$$c^2\left(\frac{r_o^2}{\ell_o^2}\right) = c^2\left(1 + \frac{e^2}{g_o^2}\right)^{5/2} , \qquad (10.4)$$

at the origin whereas the electric field has its minimum value $E_e(0) = 0$. In general relativity both of these quantities are infinite and hence the discrepency of the kind discussed above. Furthermore, the mass m in eq. (10.2) is a constant of integration and was identified as the mass producing a gravitational field in the correspondence limit of the Newtonian approximation. However, there is no obvious reason to believe that the observed charge e in the eq. (10.2) should be sitting on the bare mass m.

The equations of motion based on the use of the solutions of the field equations in the original action function and the variation of the resulting extremum action function with respect to the displacement of the particle coordinates is a new and powerful method for deriving the laws of motion from the field equations. In principle this can be done in an exact way. One can then discover further consequences of a non-linear field theory describing elementary particles as "regularities" of the field. It is hoped that the extremum action function

$$S_o = -\frac{q^2}{4\pi}\int [\surd(-\hat{g})-\surd(-g)]d^4x , \qquad (10.5)$$

obtained in this manner may also be used to discuss the quantum mechanical behavior of the field. In fact the uncertainties, as a consequence of the invariance principle of the theory under general coordinate transformations, in the magnetic structure of the fundamental particles have already emerged without the use of quantum mechanical principles. In this context a further important result refers to the derivation of the spin $\frac{1}{2}\hbar$ and its new status connecting it to the sign of the magnetic charge. Moreover, the infinite renormalizations of quantum electrodynamics have become, in this theory, "finite renormalizations". They have thereby revealed themselves to be fundamental requirements for obtaining the observed mass of an elementary particle as the difference between bare gravitational mass and self energy. In this way we have justified the statement in the introduction of this paper that the infinite renormalization scheme did in fact conceal the real structure of an elementary particle.

ACKNOWLEDGEMENTS

It is a pleasure to thank Drs. A. Perlmutter and S. Mintz for a reading of the manuscript and for suggested improvements in its presentation.

APPENDIX 1

Linearization of Energy Tensor

From the equations

$$\hat{g}_{\mu\nu;\rho} = \hat{g}_{\mu\nu,\rho} - \hat{g}_{\sigma\nu}\Gamma^{\sigma}_{\mu\rho} - \hat{g}_{\mu\sigma}\Gamma^{\sigma}_{\rho\nu} = 0 \ , \qquad (1)$$

by separating out the anti-symmetric part of the affine connection $\Gamma^{\rho}_{\mu\nu}$ we can easily show that

$$\Gamma^{\rho}_{[\mu\nu]} = g^{\rho\sigma}(-\tfrac{1}{2}\, I_{\mu\nu\sigma} + \Phi_{\mu\nu o \sigma}) \ , \qquad (2)$$

where the symbol (o) implies covariant differentiation with respect to the symmetric part $\Gamma^{\rho}_{\{\mu\nu\}}$ of $\Gamma^{\rho}_{\mu\nu}$, viz.,

$$\Phi_{\mu\nu o\sigma} = \Phi_{\mu\nu,\sigma} - \Phi_{\alpha\nu}\, \Gamma^{\alpha}_{\{\mu\sigma\}} - \Phi_{\mu\alpha}\, \Gamma^{\alpha}_{\{\sigma\nu\}} \qquad (3)$$

$$= \Phi_{\mu\nu|\sigma} - \Phi_{\alpha\nu}\, S^{\alpha}_{\mu\sigma} - \Phi_{\mu\alpha}\, S^{\alpha}_{\sigma\nu} \ ,$$

where we used the relations

$$\Gamma^{\rho}_{\{\mu\nu\}} = \{^{\rho}_{\mu\nu}\} + S^{\rho}_{\mu\nu} \ , \ S^{\rho}_{\mu\nu} = S^{\rho}_{\nu\mu} \ . \qquad (4)$$

The tensor $S^{\rho}_{\mu\nu}$, as follows from (1), is given by

$$S^{\rho}_{\mu\nu} = g^{\rho\sigma}[\Phi_{\mu}{}^{\alpha}\, \Gamma_{[\sigma\nu]\alpha} + \Phi_{\nu}{}^{\alpha}\, \Gamma_{[\sigma\mu]\alpha}] \ , \qquad (5)$$

where

$$\Gamma_{[\mu\nu]\rho} = g_{\sigma\rho}\, \Gamma^{\sigma}_{[\mu\nu]} \ .$$

From the equations (2) and (3) it is clear that the tensor $\Gamma^{\rho}_{[\mu\nu]}$ can be expanded in powers of q^{-1}. Because of very large size of q ($\sim 10^{58}$ esu) it will not be necessary to retain terms beyond q^{-2} orders. Thus to q^{-2} order the equation (2), dropping (o)-covariant derivatives in favor of (|)-covariant derivatives, becomes

$$\Gamma^{\rho}_{[\mu\nu]} = g^{\rho\sigma}\left(-\frac{1}{2} I_{\mu\nu\sigma} + \Phi_{\mu\nu|\sigma}\right) . \qquad (6)$$

Hence for the tensor $S^{\rho}_{\mu\nu}$, as defined by (5), we can write

$$S^{\rho}_{\mu\nu} = (g_{\mu\beta}\Phi_{\nu\alpha}+g_{\nu\beta}\Phi_{\mu\alpha})\left(\frac{1}{2} I^{\alpha\beta\rho}+\Phi^{\rho\beta|\alpha}\right) , \qquad (7)$$

where

$$\Phi^{\alpha\beta|\rho} = g^{\rho\sigma}\Phi^{\alpha\beta}{}_{|\sigma} . \qquad (8)$$

In the linearization of the energy tensor $T_{\mu\nu}$ defined by (5.25) we shall use the following relations and definitions: From

$$f^{\mu\nu} = \frac{1}{2\surd(-g)} \varepsilon^{\mu\nu\rho\sigma}\Phi_{\rho\sigma} \qquad (9)$$

we obtain

$$\Phi_{\mu\nu} = \frac{1}{2} \surd(-g)\varepsilon_{\mu\nu\rho\sigma}f^{\rho\sigma} , \quad \Phi^{\mu\nu} = -\frac{1}{2\surd(-g)} \varepsilon^{\mu\nu\rho\sigma}f_{\rho\sigma} , \qquad (9')$$

where we used the well-known relations

$$\varepsilon_{\alpha\beta\gamma\delta}\, g^{\alpha\mu}g^{\beta\nu}g^{\gamma\rho}g^{\delta\sigma} = \frac{1}{g}\,\varepsilon^{\mu\nu\rho\sigma} ,$$

$$\varepsilon^{\mu\nu\rho\gamma}\varepsilon_{\alpha\beta\sigma\gamma} = \delta^{\mu\nu\rho}_{\alpha\beta\sigma} , \quad \delta^{\mu\nu\rho}_{\alpha\beta\rho} = 2\delta^{\mu\nu}_{\alpha\beta} = 2(\delta^{\mu}_{\rho}\delta^{\nu}_{\sigma}-\delta^{\mu}_{\sigma}\delta^{\nu}_{\rho}) . \qquad (10)$$

From the definitions

$$I_{\mu\nu\rho} = -4\pi\,\varepsilon_{\mu\nu\rho\sigma}\,\mathfrak{s}^{\sigma} \quad , \quad \mathfrak{s}^{\rho} = \sqrt{(-g)}\,s^{\rho} \; , \tag{11}$$

we obtain

$$\mathfrak{s}^{\mu} = \frac{1}{4\pi}\frac{\partial}{\partial x^{\nu}}[\sqrt{(-g)}f^{\mu\nu}] = \frac{1}{4\pi}[\sqrt{(-g)}f^{\mu\nu}]_{|\nu} \quad , \tag{12}$$

$$I^{\mu\nu\rho} = \frac{4\pi}{\sqrt{(-g)}}\,\varepsilon^{\mu\nu\rho\sigma}s_{\sigma} \quad ,$$

where

$$s^{\mu} = \frac{1}{4\pi}\,f^{\mu\nu}{}_{|\nu} \quad . \tag{13}$$

We may now express the linearized tensor $S^{\rho}_{\mu\nu}$ in the form

$$S^{\rho}_{\mu\nu} = 4\pi[-g_{\mu\nu}f^{\rho\sigma}s_{\sigma}+\tfrac{1}{2}(f_{\mu\sigma}\delta^{\rho}_{\nu}+f_{\nu\sigma}\delta^{\rho}_{\mu})s^{\sigma}-\tfrac{1}{2}(f_{\mu}{}^{\rho}s_{\nu}+f_{\nu}{}^{\rho}s_{\mu})] +$$
$$4\pi(\Phi_{\mu}{}^{\rho}j_{\nu}+\Phi_{\nu}{}^{\rho}j_{\mu})-(\Phi_{\mu}{}^{\rho}\Phi_{\nu}{}^{\sigma}+\Phi_{\nu}{}^{\rho}\Phi_{\mu}{}^{\sigma})_{|\sigma} \quad , \tag{14}$$

where the electric current density vector j_{μ} is given by

$$j^{\mu} = \frac{1}{4\pi}\,\Phi^{\mu\nu}{}_{|\nu} \quad , \tag{15}$$

which is related to the electric current vector density j^{μ}_{e} by

$$\sqrt{(-g)}\,j^{\mu} = j^{\mu}_{e} \quad . \tag{16}$$

Hence the covariant divergence of $S^{\rho}_{\mu\nu}$ can be written as

$$S^{\rho}_{\mu\nu|\rho} = 4\pi[4\pi(g_{\mu\nu}s_{\rho}s^{\rho}-s_{\mu}s_{\nu})+\tfrac{1}{2}(f_{\mu}{}^{\sigma}s_{\nu\sigma}+f_{\nu}{}^{\sigma}s_{\mu\sigma}-g_{\mu\nu}f^{\rho\sigma}s_{\rho\sigma})+$$
$$\tfrac{1}{2}(f_{\mu\sigma|\nu}+f_{\nu\sigma|\mu})s^{\sigma}]+4\pi(\Phi_{\mu}{}^{\rho}j_{\nu|\rho}+\Phi_{\nu}{}^{\rho}j_{\mu|\rho})$$
$$-(\Phi_{\mu}{}^{\rho}\Phi_{\nu}{}^{\sigma}+\Phi_{\nu}{}^{\rho}\Phi_{\mu}{}^{\sigma})_{|\sigma\rho} \quad , \tag{17}$$

where

$$s_{\rho\sigma} = s_{\sigma|\rho}-s_{\rho|\sigma} = \partial_{\rho}s_{\sigma}-\partial_{\sigma}s_{\rho} \quad . \tag{18}$$

For the bilinear term of the energy tensor we have

$$\Gamma^{\rho}_{[\mu\sigma]}\Gamma^{\sigma}_{[\rho\nu]} = 4\pi[4\pi\tfrac{1}{2}(g_{\mu\nu}s_{\rho}s^{\rho}-s_{\mu}s_{\nu})+\tfrac{1}{2}(f_{\mu\rho|\nu}+f_{\nu\rho|\mu})s^{\rho}] +$$
$$4\pi[4\pi j_{\mu}j_{\nu}+\Phi_{\mu}{}^{\rho}j_{\nu|\rho}+\Phi_{\nu}{}^{\rho}j_{\mu|\rho}]-\tfrac{1}{2}[\Phi_{\mu}{}^{\rho}\Phi_{\nu}{}^{\sigma}+\Phi_{\nu}{}^{\rho}\Phi_{\mu}{}^{\sigma}]_{|\rho\sigma}, \tag{19}$$

and

$$g^{\mu\nu}\Gamma^{\rho}_{[\mu\sigma]}\Gamma^{\sigma}_{[\rho\nu]} = 4\pi[4\pi(\tfrac{1}{2}s_{\rho}s^{\rho}+j_{\rho}j^{\rho})-\Phi^{\rho\sigma}j_{\rho\sigma}]-(\Phi^{\nu\rho}\Phi_{\nu}{}^{\sigma})_{|\rho\sigma} \quad , \tag{20}$$

where

$$j_{\mu\nu} = j_{\nu|\mu}-j_{\mu|\nu} = \partial_{\mu}j_{\nu}-\partial_{\nu}j_{\mu} \quad . \tag{21}$$

For the derivation of (19) we have used the relations

$$\Phi_{\mu}{}^{\rho}{}_{|\sigma\rho}-\Phi_{\mu}{}^{\rho}{}_{|\rho\sigma} = G_{\rho\sigma}\Phi_{\mu}{}^{\rho}+G^{\alpha}{}_{\mu\rho\sigma}\Phi_{\alpha}{}^{\rho} \quad , \tag{22}$$

where $G_{\mu\nu}$ was defined by (5.23) and where $G^{\sigma}{}_{\mu\nu\rho}$ is the corresponding curvature tensor. Hence, using the field equations (5.19) in (22), we obtain

$$\Phi_{\mu}{}^{\rho}{}_{|\sigma\rho} \cong 4\pi j_{\mu|\sigma} \quad . \tag{23}$$

The linearized energy tensor, as follows from (5.25), is given by

$$4\pi \mathcal{T}_{\mu\nu}=T_{\mu\nu}+r_o^2[\Gamma^{\rho}_{[\mu\sigma]}\Gamma^{\sigma}_{[\rho\nu]}-\frac{1}{2}g_{\mu\nu}g^{\alpha\beta}\Gamma^{\rho}_{[\alpha\sigma]}\Gamma^{\sigma}_{[\rho\beta]}$$
$$+ S^{\rho}_{\rho\mu|\nu}-\frac{3}{2}g_{\mu\nu}g^{\alpha\beta}S^{\rho}_{\rho\alpha|\beta}-S^{\rho}_{\mu\nu|\rho}] \ . \tag{24}$$

On substituting from the above relations in (24) we obtain the linearized energy tensor in the form

$$\mathcal{T}_{\mu\nu}=\frac{1}{4\pi}\ T_{\mu\nu}+4\pi r_o^2[\frac{1}{2}(s_\mu s_\nu+\frac{1}{2}g_{\mu\nu}s_\rho s^\rho)+j_\mu j_\nu+\frac{1}{2}g_{\mu\nu}j_\rho j^\rho] +$$
$$\frac{1}{2}\ r_o^2\ (f_\mu{}^\rho s_{\rho\nu}+f_\nu{}^\rho s_{\rho\mu}) + \frac{r_o^2}{4\pi}\ M^{\rho\sigma}_{\mu\nu|\rho\sigma} \tag{25}$$

where

$$T_{\mu\nu} = \frac{1}{2}\ \Omega g_{\mu\nu}-\Phi_{\mu\rho}\Phi_\nu{}^\rho$$

and where

$$M^{\rho\sigma}_{\mu\nu}=\frac{1}{2}[(\frac{1}{2}(\delta^\rho_\mu\delta^\sigma_\nu+\delta^\rho_\nu\delta^\sigma_\mu)-g_{\mu\nu}g^{\rho\sigma})\Omega+g_{\mu\nu}T^{\rho\sigma}+\Phi_\mu{}^\rho\Phi_\nu{}^\sigma+\Phi_\nu{}^\rho\Phi_\mu{}^\sigma], \tag{26}$$

is a symmetric tensor in both upper and lower indices. Now, by an appropriate choice of coordinates, we can bring the quantities $g_{\mu\nu}$, which describe gravitational field, into their Galilean form at any individual point of the curved space-time. In fact we can regard a small neighborhood of such a point as a flat space-time and replace the covariant derivatives in the last term of (25) by ordinary partial derivatives. The integration over the four-volume enclosed by this small hyper-surface of the last term in (25) is given by

$$\int M^{\mu\nu\rho\sigma}{}_{,\rho\sigma}\, d^4x = \int M^{\mu\nu\rho\sigma}{}_{,\sigma}\, dS_\rho = \frac{1}{2}\int M^{\mu\nu\rho\sigma}\, dS_{\rho\sigma} = 0 \ , \qquad (27)$$

where the infinitesimal surface elements $dS_{\rho\sigma}$ are given by

$$dS_{\rho\sigma} = \frac{1}{2}\,\varepsilon_{\rho\sigma\mu\nu}(dx^\mu dx'^\nu - dx^\nu dx'^\mu)$$

and where the hypersurface elements dS_ρ are defined in the usual way. In (27) we used Gauss' theorem and the relations $M^{\mu\nu\rho\sigma} = M^{\mu\nu\sigma\rho}$, $dS_{\rho\sigma} = - dS_{\sigma\rho}$. We may now go back to a curved space-time and extend the last integral to the entire space-time without reference to a Galilean point. Hence we see that the contribution of the last term in (25) to the total energy flow in space-time vanishes. Thus the last term in (25) may be interpreted as the energy density of the "new vacuum".

APPENDIX 2

Here we shall derive the fundamental identities of the nonsymmetric theory. One of the ways to obtain these identities can be based on the use of infinitesimal coordinate transformations. First we note that under an arbitrary transformation of the coordinates by

$$x'^\mu = f^\mu(x) \qquad (1)$$

we have the transformation rules

$$\hat{g}'_{\mu\nu} = \frac{\partial x^\rho}{\partial x'^\mu}\frac{\partial x^\sigma}{\partial x'^\nu}\,\hat{g}_{\rho\sigma} \ , \qquad (2)$$

and, as follows from the infinitesimal parallel

displacement law

$$\delta A^{\mu} = -\Gamma^{\mu}_{\rho\sigma} A^{\rho} \delta x^{\sigma} \qquad ,$$

the rules

$$\Gamma'^{\rho}_{\mu\nu} = \frac{\partial x^{\alpha}}{\partial x'^{\mu}} \frac{\partial x^{\beta}}{\partial x'^{\nu}} \frac{\partial x'^{\rho}}{\partial x^{\sigma}} \Gamma^{\sigma}_{\alpha\beta} - \frac{\partial^2 x'^{\rho}}{\partial x^{\alpha} \partial x^{\beta}} \frac{\partial x^{\alpha}}{\partial x'^{\mu}} \frac{\partial x^{\beta}}{\partial x'^{\nu}} \quad . \tag{3}$$

From (2) we obtain

$$\sqrt{(-\hat{g}')} = \left|\frac{\partial x}{\partial x'}\right| \sqrt{(-\hat{g})} \quad , \tag{4}$$

where

$$\left|\frac{\partial x}{\partial x'}\right| = \mathrm{Det}\left[\frac{\partial x^{\mu}}{\partial x'^{\nu}}\right] \quad .$$

We also have

$$\hat{g}'^{\mu\nu} = \left|\frac{\partial x}{\partial x'}\right| \frac{\partial x'^{\mu}}{\partial x^{\rho}} \frac{\partial x'^{\nu}}{\partial x^{\sigma}} \hat{g}^{\rho\sigma} \quad . \tag{5}$$

We may now apply an infinitesimal transformation of the coordinates

$$x'^{\mu} = x^{\mu} + \xi^{\mu}(x) \quad , \tag{6}$$

and obtain

$$\left|\frac{\partial x'}{\partial x}\right| \cong 1 + \xi^{\rho}_{,\rho} \quad , \quad \left|\frac{\partial x}{\partial x'}\right| \cong 1 - \xi^{\rho}_{,\rho} \quad , \tag{7}$$

where ξ^{μ} are small compared to 1. Hence

$$\delta\hat{g}^{\mu\nu} = \hat{g}'^{\mu\nu}(x) - \hat{g}^{\mu\nu}(x) = \hat{g}^{\mu\rho}\, \xi^{\nu}_{,\rho} + \hat{g}^{\rho\nu}\, \xi^{\mu}_{,\rho} - \hat{g}^{\mu\nu}\, \xi^{\rho}_{,\rho} - \hat{g}^{\mu\nu}_{,\rho}\, \xi^{\rho} \quad , \tag{8}$$

$$\delta\Gamma^{\rho}_{\mu\nu} = \Gamma^{\alpha}_{\mu\nu}\,\xi^{\rho}_{,\alpha} - \Gamma^{\rho}_{\mu\alpha}\,\xi^{\alpha}_{,\nu} - \Gamma^{\rho}_{\alpha\nu}\,\xi^{\alpha}_{,\mu} - \Gamma^{\rho}_{\mu\nu,\alpha}\,\xi^{\alpha} - \xi^{\rho}_{,\mu\nu} \quad . \tag{9}$$

From the definition of the nonsymmetric curvature tensor by

$$R_{\mu\nu} = -\Gamma^{\rho}_{\mu\nu,\rho} + \Gamma^{\rho}_{\mu\rho,\nu} + \Gamma^{\rho}_{\mu\sigma}\Gamma^{\sigma}_{\rho\nu} - \Gamma^{\rho}_{\mu\nu}\Gamma^{\sigma}_{\rho\sigma} \quad , \tag{10}$$

and from using (9) we obtain the change

$$\delta R_{\mu\nu} = -R_{\mu\nu,\rho}\,\xi^{\rho} - R_{\rho\nu}\,\xi^{\rho}_{\ ,\mu} - R_{\mu\rho}\,\xi^{\rho}_{\ ,\nu} \quad , \tag{11}$$

which follows also from

$$R'_{\mu\nu}(x+\xi) = \frac{\partial x^{\rho}}{\partial x'^{\mu}}\frac{\partial x^{\sigma}}{\partial x'^{\nu}}R_{\rho\sigma} = (\delta^{\rho}_{\mu}-\xi^{\rho}_{\ ,\mu})(\delta^{\sigma}_{\nu}-\xi^{\sigma}_{\ ,\nu})R_{\rho\sigma} \quad ,$$

as

$$R'_{\mu\nu}(x) + R'_{\mu\nu,\rho}\,\xi^{\rho} \cong R_{\mu\nu}(x) - R_{\mu\sigma}\,\xi^{\sigma}_{\ ,\nu} - R_{\rho\nu}\,\xi^{\rho}_{\ ,\mu} \quad .$$

Hence

$$\delta R_{\mu\nu} = R'_{\mu\nu}(x) - R_{\mu\nu}(x) \cong -R_{\mu\nu,\rho}\,\xi^{\rho} - R_{\mu\sigma}\,\xi^{\sigma}_{\ ,\nu} - R_{\rho\nu}\,\xi^{\rho}_{\ ,\mu} \quad .$$

The above results lead to

$$R_{\mu\nu}\,\delta\hat{g}^{\mu\nu} = \hat{g}^{\mu\nu}(R_{\underset{+-}{\mu\nu;\rho}} - R_{\underset{++}{\mu\rho;\nu}} - R_{\underset{--}{\rho\nu;\mu}})\xi^{\rho} \quad , \tag{12}$$

$$\hat{g}^{\mu\nu}\,\delta R_{\mu\nu} = \hat{g}^{\mu\nu}_{\underset{+-}{}\ ;\rho}\,\delta\Gamma^{\rho}_{\mu\nu} - \hat{g}^{\mu\nu}_{\underset{+-}{}\ ;\nu}\,\delta\Gamma^{\rho}_{\mu\rho} \quad , \tag{13}$$

where the divergence terms have been dropped and where we assumed that the variations $\delta\hat{g}^{\mu\nu}$, $\delta\Gamma^{\rho}_{\mu\nu}$ arise from the infinitesimal change of the coordinates defined by

(6). We also assumed that

$$\hat{g}^{\mu\nu}_{\underset{+-}{}\,;\rho} = 0 \quad . \tag{14}$$

The + and - signs under subscripts serve to rank the respective indices to be placed as first and second index, respectively, in the process of covariant differentiation with respect to the affine connection $\Gamma^{\rho}_{\mu\nu}$. Furthermore from the relations

$$\delta\surd(-\hat{g}) = \frac{1}{2}\,\hat{g}_{\mu\nu}\,\delta\hat{g}^{\mu\nu} \ , \ \delta\surd(-g) = \frac{1}{2}\,b_{\mu\nu}\,\delta\hat{g}^{\mu\nu}$$

we obtain

$$\delta\surd(-\hat{g}) = \frac{1}{2}\,\hat{g}_{\mu\nu}\,(\hat{g}^{\mu\rho}\,\xi^{\nu}_{\ ,\rho} + \hat{g}^{\rho\nu}\,\xi^{\mu}_{\ ,\rho} - \hat{g}^{\mu\nu}\,\xi^{\rho}_{\ ,\rho} - \hat{g}^{\mu\nu}_{\ \ ,\rho}\,\xi^{\rho})$$

$$= \frac{1}{2}\,\hat{g}^{\mu\nu}\,(\hat{g}_{\underset{+-}{\mu\nu};\rho} - \hat{g}_{\underset{++}{\mu\rho};\nu} - \hat{g}_{\underset{--}{\rho\nu};\mu})\xi^{\rho} \quad . \tag{15}$$

Hence the variational principle $\delta S=0$ lead to the differential identities

$$\hat{g}^{\mu\nu}(R_{\underset{+-}{\mu\nu};\rho} - R_{\underset{++}{\mu\rho};\nu} - R_{\underset{--}{\rho\nu};\mu}) = 0 \quad , \tag{16}$$

$$\hat{g}^{\mu\nu}(\hat{g}_{\underset{+-}{\mu\nu};\rho} - \hat{g}_{\underset{++}{\mu\rho};\nu} - \hat{g}_{\underset{--}{\rho\nu};\mu}) = 0 \quad . \tag{17}$$

Actually, the identities (16) and (17) which correspond to the Bianchi identities of the nonsymmetric field, were derived by Einstein without using variational principle but only by using various symmetries of the curvature tensor

$$R^{\sigma}{}_{\mu\nu\rho} = -\Gamma^{\sigma}_{\mu\nu,\rho}+\Gamma^{\sigma}_{\mu\rho,\nu}+\Gamma^{\sigma}_{\alpha\nu}\Gamma^{\alpha}_{\mu\rho}-\Gamma^{\alpha}_{\mu\nu}\Gamma^{\sigma}_{\alpha\rho} \quad . \tag{18}$$

We note that in (17) we have

$$\hat{g}_{\underset{+-}{\mu\nu;\rho}} = 0 \ , \quad \hat{g}_{\underset{++}{\mu\rho;\nu}} \neq 0 \ , \quad \hat{g}_{\underset{--}{\rho\nu;\mu}} \neq 0 \quad .$$

Now from (14) we have

$$\hat{g}^{\{\mu\nu\}}{}_{,\nu} = -\hat{g}^{\rho\sigma}\,\Gamma^{\mu}_{\rho\sigma} \quad . \tag{19}$$

Hence on carrying out the indicated covariant differentiations in (16), (17) and using (19) we may rewrite them in a more symmetrical form as

$$\left\{\sqrt{(-g)}[b^{\mu\nu}R_{\{\mu\rho\}}-\tfrac{1}{2}\delta^{\nu}_{\rho}b^{\mu\sigma}R_{\{\mu\sigma\}}]\right\}_{||\nu}=$$

$$\tfrac{1}{2}\hat{g}^{[\mu\nu]}[R_{[\mu\nu],\rho}+R_{[\nu\rho],\mu}+R_{[\rho\mu],\nu}] \quad , \tag{20}$$

$$\left\{\sqrt{(-g)}[b^{\mu\nu}g_{\mu\rho}-\tfrac{1}{2}\delta^{\nu}_{\rho}b^{\mu\sigma}g_{\mu\sigma}]\right\}_{||\nu} =$$

$$\tfrac{1}{2}\,\hat{g}^{[\mu\nu]}[\Phi_{\mu\nu,\rho}+\Phi_{\nu\rho,\mu}+\Phi_{\rho\mu,\nu}] \quad , \tag{21}$$

where the sign ($||$) indicates covariant differentiation in terms of the Christoffel symbols constructed out of the tensor $b_{\mu\nu}$. If we set $\Phi_{\mu\nu} = 0$ the identities (20) reduce to

$$\left\{\sqrt{(-g)}[g^{\mu\nu}G_{\mu\rho} - \tfrac{1}{2}\,\delta^{\nu}_{\rho}\,g^{\mu\sigma}G_{\mu\sigma}]\right\}_{|\nu} = 0 \quad , \tag{22}$$

which are the Bianchi identities of the symmetric theory, where $G_{\mu\nu}$ is the curvature tensor of general relativity. Hence the right hand side of (20), in analogy with general relativity, represents a force density. Einstein used the identities (16) alone in deriving his field equations and was, presumably, not aware of the fact that the same identities were also satisfied by the field tensor $\hat{g}_{\mu\nu}$, as in (17), as well as by the nonsymmetric tensor $b_{\mu\nu} + F_{\mu\nu}$. In general these identities are satisfied by the tensor $A_{\mu\nu} = \hat{g}_{\mu\nu} + \lambda(b_{\mu\nu}+F_{\mu\nu})$ where λ is an arbitrary constant. By direct substitution of $A_{\mu\nu}$ in (17) we obtain

$$\hat{g}^{\mu\nu}(b_{\mu\nu,\rho}-b_{\mu\rho,\nu}-b_{\rho\nu,\mu}+2b_{\rho\sigma}\Gamma^{\sigma}_{\mu\nu}+F_{\mu\nu,\rho}+F_{\nu\rho,\mu}+F_{\rho\mu,\nu}) =$$

$$\sqrt{(-g)}\,b^{\mu\nu}(b_{\mu\nu,\rho}-2b_{\mu\rho,\nu}) + 2b_{\rho\sigma}\,\hat{g}^{\mu\nu}\,\Gamma^{\sigma}_{\mu\nu} = 0 \quad ,$$

where we used the relations

$$\frac{1}{2}\,b^{\mu\nu}\,b_{\mu\nu,\rho} = \frac{[\sqrt{(-g)}]_{,\rho}}{\sqrt{(-g)}} \quad , \quad \hat{g}^{\mu\nu}\,\Gamma^{\rho}_{\mu\nu} = -\,[\sqrt{(-g)}\,b^{\rho\nu}]_{,\nu} \quad .$$

Einstein assumed that the field equations should stipulate the vanishing of either $R_{\mu\nu}$ or that the vanishing of $R_{\{\mu\nu\}}$ and the way $R_{[\mu\nu]}$ enter (15) viz.

$$R_{[\mu\nu],\rho} + R_{[\nu\rho],\mu} + R_{[\rho\mu],\nu} = 0 \quad .$$

On the other hand Schrödinger assumed the existence of a cosmological constant and proposed the field equations

$$R_{\mu\nu} = \lambda\,\hat{g}_{\mu\nu} \quad .$$

In fact the simultaneous existence of (16) and (17) or (20) and (21) implies that the role of these differential identities in the derivation of the field equations is more general than the use of $R_{\mu\nu}$ alone. The identities (16) or (20) are, because of the identities (17) or (21), invariant under the substitution

$$R_{\mu\nu} \to R_{\mu\nu} + \lambda \hat{g}_{\mu\nu} + \gamma(b_{\mu\nu}+F_{\mu\nu}) \quad . \tag{23}$$

Thus the most general possible form of the field equations is contained in the statement

$$R_{\mu\nu} + \lambda \hat{g}_{\mu\nu} + \gamma(b_{\mu\nu}+F_{\mu\nu}) = 0 \quad .$$

Hence we obtain

$$R_{\{\mu\nu\}} = - \lambda g_{\mu\nu} - \gamma b_{\mu\nu} \quad ,$$

$$R_{[\mu\nu\rho]} = - \lambda I_{\mu\nu\rho} \quad .$$

If we assume that for $\Phi_{\mu\nu}=0$ the field equations must reduce to the field equations of a pure gravitational field without a cosmological constant we obtain

$$\gamma = - \lambda \; (= - \tfrac{1}{2} \kappa^2)$$

or

$$R_{\{\mu\nu\}} = \tfrac{1}{2} \kappa^2 (b_{\mu\nu}-g_{\mu\nu})$$

$$R_{[\mu\nu\rho]} = - \tfrac{1}{2} \kappa^2 I_{\mu\nu\rho} \tag{24}$$

For the sake of completeness we shall use the above formalism to drive the conservation law (5.37). From (13) we have

$$\hat{g}^{\mu\nu} \delta R_{\mu\nu} = [(\hat{g}^{\mu\nu} R_{\mu\rho} + \hat{g}^{\nu\mu} R_{\rho\mu} - \delta^{\nu}_{\rho} \hat{g}^{\alpha\beta} R_{\alpha\beta})_{,\nu} + \hat{g}^{\alpha\beta}{}_{,\rho} R_{\alpha\beta}] \xi^{\rho} \quad , \tag{25}$$

where the divergence term has been dropped. In order to calculate the last term in (25) we shall calculate the variation of $\hat{g}^{\mu\nu}{}_{,\rho}$. From the definition

$$\hat{g}^{\mu\nu}{}_{,\rho} = - \hat{g}^{\alpha\nu}\Gamma^{\mu}_{\alpha\rho} - \hat{g}^{\mu\alpha}\Gamma^{\nu}_{\rho\alpha} + \hat{g}^{\mu\nu}\Gamma^{\alpha}_{\rho\alpha} ,$$

we obtain

$$\delta\hat{g}^{\mu\nu}{}_{,\rho}=\Gamma^{\sigma}_{\rho\sigma}\delta\hat{g}^{\mu\nu}-\Gamma^{\mu}_{\sigma\rho}\delta\hat{g}^{\sigma\nu}-\Gamma^{\nu}_{\rho\sigma}\delta\hat{g}^{\mu\sigma}+\hat{g}^{\mu\nu}\delta\Gamma^{\sigma}_{\rho\sigma}-\hat{g}^{\mu\sigma}\delta\Gamma^{\nu}_{\rho\sigma}-\hat{g}^{\sigma\nu}\delta\Gamma^{\mu}_{\sigma\rho} .$$

On multiplying through by

$$B^{\rho}_{\mu\nu} = \frac{1}{2} (\delta^{\rho}_{\mu} \Gamma^{\alpha}_{\nu\alpha} + \delta^{\rho}_{\nu} \Gamma^{\alpha}_{\mu\alpha}) - \Gamma^{\rho}_{\mu\nu} \tag{26}$$

we obtain

$$B^{\rho}_{\mu\nu} \delta\hat{g}^{\mu\nu}{}_{,\rho} = \hat{g}^{\mu\nu} \delta B_{\mu\nu} + 2B_{\mu\nu} \delta\hat{g}^{\mu\nu} , \tag{27}$$

where

$$B_{\mu\nu}=\Gamma^{\rho}_{\mu\sigma}\Gamma^{\sigma}_{\rho\nu}-\Gamma^{\rho}_{\mu\nu}\Gamma^{\sigma}_{\rho\sigma} , \quad B=\hat{g}^{\mu\nu}B_{\mu\nu} = \frac{1}{2} \hat{g}^{\mu\nu}{}_{,\rho} B^{\rho}_{\mu\nu} . \tag{28}$$

By using the variation of B we get the result

$$\delta B = B_{\mu\nu} \delta\hat{g}^{\mu\nu} + \hat{g}^{\mu\nu} \delta B_{\mu\nu} = - B_{\mu\nu} \delta\hat{g}^{\mu\nu} + B^{\rho}_{\mu\nu} \delta\hat{g}^{\mu\nu}{}_{,\rho} .$$

Hence the variational derivatives of B yields the result

$$\frac{\partial B}{\partial\hat{g}^{\mu\nu}} - \frac{\partial}{\partial x^{\rho}} \{\frac{\partial B}{\partial\hat{g}^{\mu\nu}{}_{,\rho}}\} = - R_{\mu\nu} . \tag{29}$$

Thus, using (29), we obtain

$$- g^{\mu\nu}{}_{,\rho} R_{\mu\nu} = \frac{\partial}{\partial x^{\sigma}} [\delta^{\sigma}_{\rho} \mathcal{B} - \hat{g}^{\mu\nu}{}_{,\rho} \mathcal{B}^{\sigma}_{\mu\nu}] \quad . \tag{30}$$

On combining (30) with (25) we obtain the conservation laws

$$\mathcal{F}^{\nu}_{\mu,\nu} = 0 \quad , \tag{31}$$

where the nonsymmetric tensor $\mathcal{F}^{\nu}_{\mu}$ is given by

$$-4\pi\kappa^2 q^{-2} \mathcal{F}^{\nu}_{\mu} = \hat{g}^{\nu\rho} R_{\mu\rho} + \hat{g}^{\rho\nu} R_{\rho\mu} - \delta^{\nu}_{\mu} \hat{g}^{\rho\sigma} R_{\rho\sigma} + \hat{g}^{\rho\sigma}{}_{,\mu} \mathcal{B}^{\nu}_{\rho\sigma} - \delta^{\nu}_{\mu} \mathcal{B} \quad . \tag{32}$$

Finally we shall include, for future reference, a different form of the identities (21). The right hand side of (21) can be written as

$$\frac{1}{2} \hat{g}^{[\mu\nu]} (\Phi_{\mu\nu|\rho} + \Phi_{\nu\rho|\mu} + \Phi_{\rho\mu|\nu}) = \frac{1}{2} \hat{g}^{[\mu\nu]} \Phi_{\mu\nu|\rho} + \hat{g}^{[\mu\nu]} \Phi_{\nu\rho|\mu}$$

$$= \frac{1}{2} \sqrt{(-g)} \, \frac{(1+\Omega-\Lambda^2)_{|\rho}}{(1+\Omega-\Lambda^2)} - \sqrt{(-g)} \left\{ \frac{\Phi^{\mu\nu}\Phi_{\rho\nu} - \Lambda^2 \delta^{\mu}_{\rho}}{\sqrt{(1+\Omega-\Lambda^2)}} \right\}_{|\mu}$$

$$= \sqrt{(-g)} \left\{ \frac{(1+\Omega)\delta^{\mu}_{\rho} - \Phi^{\mu\nu}\Phi_{\rho\nu}}{\sqrt{(1+\Omega-\Lambda^2)}} \right\}_{|\mu} = [\sqrt{(-g)} b^{\mu\sigma} g_{\rho\sigma}]_{|\mu} \quad . \tag{33}$$

Hence the covariant derivative in (21) with respect to $b_{\mu\nu}$ is replaced by the covariant derivative with respect to the metric tensor $g_{\mu\nu}$. From (33) we obtain

$$[(\tfrac{1}{2} b^{\rho}_{\rho} - 1)\delta^{\nu}_{\mu} - g^{\nu\rho} b_{\mu\rho}]_{|\nu} = 4\pi \, \Psi_{\mu\nu} \, s^{\nu} \quad , \tag{34}$$

where

$$\Psi_{\mu\nu} = - \tfrac{1}{2}\sqrt{(-g)} \varepsilon_{\mu\nu\rho\sigma} \Gamma^{\rho\sigma} \;, \quad \sqrt{(-g)} \Gamma^{\rho\sigma} = \hat{g}^{[\rho\sigma]} , \tag{35}$$

and

$$\frac{1}{4\pi}\frac{\partial}{\partial x^{\nu}}[\surd(-g)\Psi^{\mu\nu}] = \zeta^{\mu} \quad ,$$

or

$$\zeta_{\mu\nu\rho} = \Gamma_{\mu\nu,\rho} + \Gamma_{\nu\rho,\mu} + \Gamma_{\rho\mu,\nu} = -4\pi\varepsilon_{\mu\nu\rho\sigma}\,\zeta^{\sigma} \quad . \qquad (36)$$

REFERENCES

1. B. Kursunoglu, Phys. Rev. 9, No. 10, 2723 (1974).
2. A. Einstein, Can. J. Math. 2, 120 (1950),
B. Kaufman, Helv. Phys. Acta Supp. 4, 227 (1956);
A. Einstein and B. Kaufman, Ann. Math. 62, 128 (1955).
3. A. Schrödinger, Proc. R. Irish Acad. A LI, 213 (1948).
4. P.A.M. Dirac, Phys. Rev. 74, 817 (1948).
5. J. Schwinger, In Proceedings of the Third Coral Gables Conference on Symmetry Principles at High Energy, Univ. of Miami, 1966, edited by A. Perlmutter et al. (Freeman, San Francisco, 1966).
6. I.J. Aubert et al., Phys. Rev. Lett. 33, 1404 (1974);
J.-E. Augustin et al., Phys. Rev. Lett. 33, 1406, 1453 (1974);
C. Bacci et al., Phys. Rev. Lett. 33, 1408 (1974), 34, 43 (1975).

ERRATA IN THE PAPER (A)

Phys. Rev. 9, No. 10, May 15, 1974

Equation	should read
(2.52)	$\int s^{\mu} d\sigma_{\mu} = (-1)^{s} g_{o}$
(2.50')	$\int \zeta^{\mu} d\sigma_{\mu} = 0$
In matrix (3.17) the elements (23) and (32)	$\frac{\cos\Phi}{\upsilon \cosh\Gamma}$, $-\frac{\cos\Phi}{\upsilon \cosh\Gamma}$
(4.8)	$\frac{q}{\upsilon} \frac{\cos\Phi}{\cosh\Gamma}$
(8.3)	$Q_{o} = (-1)^{s} g_{o}$, $Q_{g} = 0$
(9.3)	$\kappa \ell_{o} = \sqrt{2}$
(9.6),(9.7),(9.8)	the value assigned to g is incorrect

The words "neutral" and "charged" magnetic currents and corresponding fields should refer to ζ^{μ}, s^{μ} and H, B, respectively, not as used in the paper A for s^{μ}, ζ^{μ} and B, H.

PARTICLES, FORCES AND THE NEW MESONS*

Jogesh C. Pati

Center for Theoretical Physics

Department of Physics and Astronomy

University of Maryland

College Park, Maryland 20742

I. INTRODUCTION

Conceptually it is appealing to postulate that symmetries of nature manifest themselves only in a hierarchial fashion, the highest form of the symmetry to be amenable to our experience only at super high energies. From this point of view, particles and interactions, which are quite diverse at present energies, might well be linked at a fundamental level. An example is the intriguing notion that the weak and electromagnetic interaction of vastly different strengths are intimately linked[1] and are governed by a single coupling constant e. Accepting this point of view, Salam and I noted a few years ago that an "ultimate" unification of <u>all matter and its interactions</u> would require that baryons and leptons be treated as members of a single family.[2-4]

*Supported in part by the National Science Foundation under Grant No. GP-43662X.

This led us to view the observed distinction between baryons and leptons in the realm of strong interactions as a low energy phenomenon to disappear at higher energies. Our main suggestion was thus to treat the fundamental baryons (the quarks) and the leptons as members of a single multiplet and to generate all interactions (the so-called weak, electromagnetic and strong) by utilizing the symmetry of this multiplet.

There are several appealing features, which emerge solely as a consequence of putting baryons and leptons together. First, because of the inclusion of the baryon $\leftrightarrow$ lepton-symmetry transformations, it becomes possible to generate electromagnetism within the gauge theory framework without introducing an abelian U(1)-group; this in turn provides a rationale for the quantisation of the electric charge. Second, it turns out that the particular manner of unification, which we chose, predicts uniquely the charges of the leptons to be (0, -1, -1, 0); this matches precisely the charges of the known leptons (ν_e, e^-, μ^-, ν_μ). Since the charges of the leptons vis-a-vis baryons get fixed, one also obtains a reason for the empirical fact that the low energy weak interactions have picked V-A for baryons and leptons (ν_e, e^-, μ^-, ν_μ) rather than for baryons and antileptons ($\bar{\nu}_e$, e^+, μ^+, $\bar{\nu}_\mu$). None of these features could have been realized without the inclusion of the baryon-lepton-local symmetry transformations.

The notion that all fundamental fermions have their origin within one multiplet and that all basic interactions are generated universally by utilizing the symmetry of this multiplet has two striking experimental consequences:

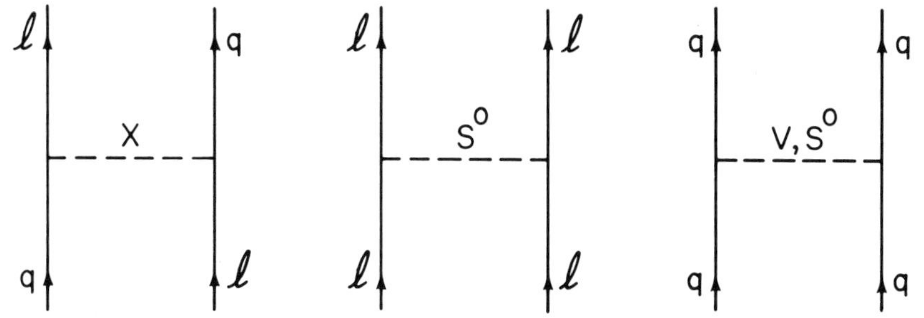

Fig. 1

(1) First, there must exist <u>a new class of interactions</u> between leptons and baryons and leptons and leptons depicted in Fig. 1, different from the familiar weak and electromagnetic interactions. The same universal effective "strong" coupling f governs the quark-quark, quark-lepton and lepton-lepton forces. The fact that quark-lepton and lepton-lepton forces are still weak at present energies is attributed to the fact that the X's and S^o-particles are heavy compared to available energies (typically their masses lie in the range of 100 to 10,000 GeV in our model depending upon the details of the unification scheme). The quark-quark force on the other hand is strong even at low energies because the gauge particles V's are relatively light. The mass splitting between the gauge particles in the same family (i.e. V's, X's and S^o) in turn is assumed to arise not via the basic laws but due to asymmetric boundary conditions (or equivalently properties of the vacuum-state). At energies exceeding the masses of the X and S^o-particles, lepton-hadron and lepton-lepton interactions should become effectively as "strong" as hadron-hadron interactions. In other words, at these energies all interactions (weak, electromagnetic as well

as strong) would be universal with respect to baryons and leptons. The energy in question thus defines a new scale in particle physics.

One does not, of course, have to attain energies comparable to the new scale to be able to feel the existence of the new interactions. For example even with $m_X \approx 300$ GeV, we estimate that the new X-like interactions should lead to significant departures of the energy-dependence of $\sigma(e^- e^+ \rightarrow \text{hadrons})$ froms its expected behaviour (on the basis of one photon-contribution) at electron-positron centre of mass energies as low as 10 GeV. Such departures should also be seen in lepton-pair production in hadronic collisions ($p + p \rightarrow \mu^- \mu^+ +$ hadrons). Analogously one might begin to see at presently available energies anomalous interactions of neutrinos with hadrons (with the possibility that electron-neutrinos may interact differently with hadrons in neutral-current process compared to muon neutrinos). I will return to a list of such consequences at the end of my talk. (2) Secondly, once baryons and leptons are put in the same multiplet, (even though the fundamental interactions, generated by the symmetry of this multiplet, necessarily conserve baryon number (B), lepton number (L), and therefore fermion number F = B + L) there arises the logical and likely possibility that baryonic quarks can transform into leptons (if they possess integer charges like the leptons) in a manner depicted in Fig. 2.

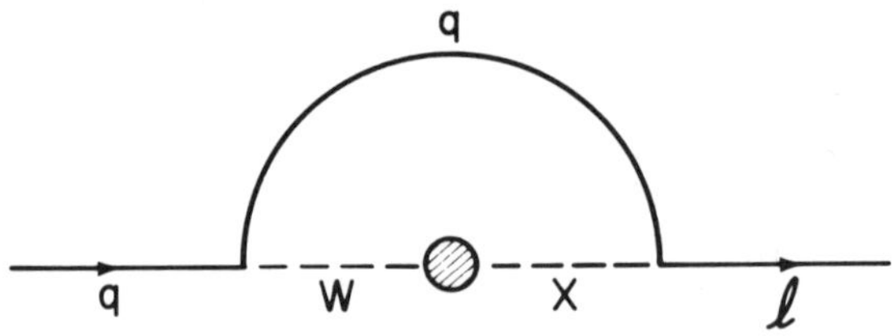

Fig. 2

The transformation of $q \to \ell$ and vice versa (exhibited in Fig. 2), violates the age-old conservation laws of baryon and lepton numbers, while still conserving fermion number $F = B + L$. Theoretically, the violation of these quantum numbers arises in our scheme due to the mixing between X's and W's, represented by the shaded blob in Fig. 2, which in turn is induced, in general, as we attempt to assign masses to these particles.

The nonconservation of baryon and lepton-numbers, we thus find, is a natural and likely consequence of the notion that baryons and leptons have a linked origin. In turn, this leads to the following intriguing consequences:

(i) Unstable Integer-Charge-Quarks:

The fundamental constituents of nucleonic matter- the quarks- if they are integer charged, would be unstable, when produced as free particles in collisions of nucleons. We estimate that they would decay into (lepton + pions), i.e.

$$p^{+}_{b,c} \to \pi^{+}\nu_{e}$$

$$n^{o}_{b,c} \to \pi^{+}e^{-},\ \pi^{o}\nu_{e}$$

$$p^{o}_{b,c} \to \pi^{o}\nu_{e}$$

$$q_{a,b,c} \to \text{(Several Pions)} + \text{lepton}$$

$$q_{a,b,c} \to \text{(color gluon)} + \text{lepton} + \text{pion, etc.}$$

with lifetimes in the range of 10^{-14} to 10^{-6} sec., if their masses are of order 2 to 3 GeV. In above, the indices a,b,c correspond to various quark-colors, which we define later. This can provide the resolution of a major puzzle as to why quarks, so basic to our understanding of the nucleonic particles, have not yet been observed. The point is that even though they might have been produced quite "abundantly" in the laboratory at present energies, they could not have been seen (especially if their lifetimes are shorter than 10^{-9} sec.), since the quark-searches[5] have so far been designed to look only for relatively stable quarks ($\tau \gtrsim 10^{-8}$ sec.). This strongly suggests the need for a search for unstable integer-charge quarks decaying into (lepton + pions). A study of (lepton + pion) and (lepton + eta)-type mass-correlations in high energy hadronic collisions should thus be of major interest. (Optimistically,[6] one might expect $q\bar{q}$-production cross section to be as high as 10^{-31} cm^2 for $m_q \sim 3$ GeV at Fermilab and ISR-energies). In addition to mass correlations, the emission of highly energetic leptons may also provide suggestive evidence for the production of integer-charged quarks, especially if the "production"-cross section for such leptons is higher than nanobarns, so that they cannot be associated with decays of heavy leptons.

(ii) Long-Lived But Unstable Proton:

In spite of the short lived quarks, the proton (a composite of three quarks with B = F = 3) is extraordinarily stable against decay into (leptons + pions) assuming that quarks and diquarks are heavier than the proton. This follows by noting that each of the quarks inside the proton must disintegrate in order to undergo a real decay (a possible decay mode of the proton is shown in Fig. 3):

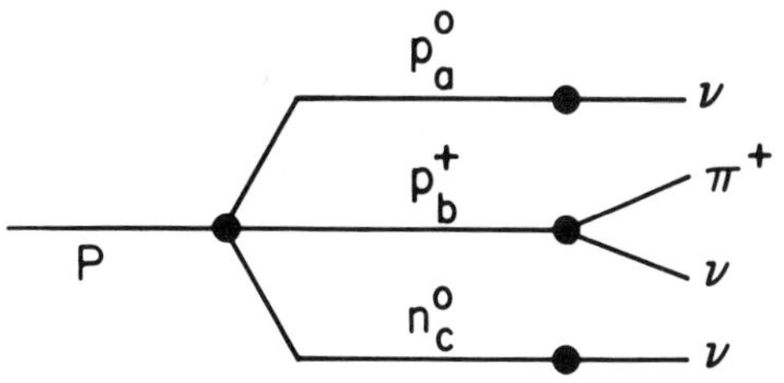

Fig. 3

Thus the probability for the decay is reduced enormously (analogous to triple-beta-decay of a nucleus). Based on this, we estimate (within our basic model) that the proton is unstable with a lifetime in the range

$$\tau_{proton} \sim 10^{28} \text{ to } 10^{35} \text{ years}$$

The extraordinary stability of the proton may thus merely be a reflection of the fact that it is a three quark-composite. It does not by any means prove that the basic strength of baryon-number violating effective interaction is vanishingly small. Experimentally there are monumental efforts on the measurement of proton life-time; the best limit so far is set by Reines and Crouch,[7] which is about 2×10^{30} years (the authors, however, note that there are five μ-events, which they choose to attribute to background). A number of experiments on the search for proton decay have been designed to look for two-body decays of the proton (like $p \to \pi^o + e^+$). It is an important feature of our scheme that as long as fermion number is conserved, proton may decay only into those states which carry net fermion number and therefore (in this case) lepton number = 3. The allowed decay modes of the proton thus are:

$$p \to 3\nu + \pi^+, \; (\nu\nu + e^-) + \pi^+ + \pi^+$$
$$\to 4\nu + e^+, \text{ or } 4\nu + \mu^+ \text{ etc.}$$

Note that no two or three body decays of the proton are allowed with $\Delta F = 0$. Even though we allow the possibility that eventually fermion number is also violated (see Sec. III. 7) in a manner similar to the violations of B and L mentioned above (i.e. via gauge meson mixing), it is quite possible that the strength of such violation is much weaker than that of $\Delta F = 0$, $\Delta B = -\Delta L$-transitions, in which case the two and three body decays of the proton might be suppressed compared to the multiparticle decays. Thus a test of our hypothesis would require a search for multiparticle decays[8] in addition to two or three body decays.

I now discuss the following features of our hypothesis in more detail:

(II) A choice of the Fundamental Fermions

(III) Minimal and Maximal Symmetries:

- (i) The Basic Model, Left ↔ Right Symmetry, CP-violation
- (ii) Unification of Coupling Constants
- (iii) Fermion Number As part of the Non-abelian symmetry

(IV) Masses of Gauge Particles:

- (i) Color as a Classification Symmetry
- (ii) Confinement versus Emission of Color
- (iii) Asymptotic Freedom

(V) Experimental Consequences

- (i) Neutral Currents
- (ii) Search for Color, Dimuon Events
- (iii) Color and Charm and the ψ-Particles

II. THE FAMILY OF FUNDAMENTAL FERMIONS

For over a decade, it has been known following the suggestions of Han and Nambu and Tavkhelidze[9] that baryonic quarks (p, n, λ) must exist in three sets, which may be labelled by three different colors. This corresponds to assuming that there are nine basic quarks. The idea is that low lying baryons and mesons, though made out of nine quarks and antiquarks, are singlets under SU(3)'-color symmetry. The necessity[10] of postulating this tri-color degree of freedom arises from considerations of low energy baryon-spectroscopy.[11] Subsequently it has been realized following the observation of Glashow, Iliopoulos and Maiani[12] that to obtain a satisfactory theory of the weak interactions, there must exist four valency-quark-indices (p, n, λ and χ) instead of three; the fourth quark χ is popularly called as charm.

The combination of four valency indices with three colors did not appear to be elegant. It also left no room to combine baryons and leptons. Thus, seeking for a unified description of all matter, it appeared but natural to us to postulate that the fundamental fermionic matter possesses four valency indices (p, n, λ and χ) as well as four color-indices (a, b, c and d). Three of these colors (a,b, c) correspond to baryonic quarks, while the fourth color d is the lepton number L. The basic set of fermions is thus a sixteen fold, of four-component fields transforming as $(4, \bar{4})$ of SU(4) × SU(4)'.

$$F_{L,R} = \begin{bmatrix} p_a & p_b & p_c & p_d = \nu_e \\ n_a & n_b & n_c & n_d = e^- \\ \lambda_a & \lambda_b & \lambda_c & \lambda_d = \mu^- \\ \chi_a & \chi_b & \chi_c & \chi_d = \nu_\mu \end{bmatrix}_{L,R} \qquad (1)$$

The muon-electron-distinction in this picture is

identical to lambda-neutron-distinction. It is also necessary that the electron-neutrino ν_e be distinct from the muon-neutrino ν_μ. All matter, baryons and leptons, are now in one multiplet F.

The Electric Charge:

It is a remarkable property of the $SU(4) \times SU(4)'$-group-structure that the requirement[13] that the known baryons are neutral with respect to color (i.e. their $F'_3 = F'_8 = 0$) leaves us with just the following choice for the charge operator Q:

$$Q = [F_3 + F_8/\sqrt{3} - \sqrt{2/3}\, F_{15}] + [\alpha F'_3 + \beta F'_8 - \sqrt{2/3}\, F'_{15}] \quad (2)$$

where F_i and F'_i ($i = 1, \ldots 15$) are the generators of $SU(4)$ and $SU(4)'$ respectively [In terms of the diagonal generators I_{3L} and I_{3R} of the gauge groups $SU(2)_L^{I+II}$ $SU(2)_R^{I+II}$ (introduced later); $(F_3 + F_8/\sqrt{3} - \sqrt{2/3}\, F_{15}) = I_{3l} + I_{3R}$]. The coefficients α and β are arbitrary; all other coefficients are, however, fixed.

Since F'_3 and F'_8 cannot contribute to the fourth color, this has the important consequence that the charges of the leptons (i.e. fermions of the fourth color) are uniquely fixed to be (0, -1, -1, 0). In other words, even if we wanted to, we could not put $(\bar{\nu}_e, e^+, \mu^+, \bar{\nu}_\mu)$ together with baryonic quarks. This in turn provides the reason why the positively charged proton and the negatively charged e^- carry the same helicity in low-energy weak interactions. It also suggests that the hypothesis of $SU(4) \times SU(4)'$ as a classification symmetry with four valencies and four colors might very possibly be an ingredient of the true theory.

Returning to formula (2), since α and β are arbitrary, one may in general have a wide variety of charges for the quarks. However there are two choices worthy of special considerations:

(i) $\alpha=\beta=1$; in this case both valency and color contribute symmetrically to electric charge leading to integer charges for quarks and leptons.

(ii) $\alpha=\beta=0$, in this case the tri-color symmetry generators (F'_3 and F'_8) make no contribution to electric charge; as a result the photon does not "see" any difference between the colors (a,b,c). It makes a real distinction however between the baryonic colors (a,b,c) and the leptonic color "d" leading to fractionally charged quarks and integer charge leptons. The charges for the fermionic multiplet in the two cases are given by:

$\alpha=\beta=1$

Symmetrical Integer-Charge-Quark Model

$$Q_F = \begin{bmatrix} 0 & +1 & +1 & 0 \\ -1 & 0 & 0 & -1 \\ -1 & 0 & 0 & -1 \\ 0 & +1 & +1 & 0 \end{bmatrix}$$

$\alpha=\beta=0$

Baryon-lepton asymmetric
Fractionally charged quark Model

$$Q_F = \begin{bmatrix} 2/3 & 2/3 & 2/3 & 0 \\ -1/3 & -1/3 & -1/3 & -1 \\ -1/3 & -1/3 & -1/3 & -1 \\ 2/3 & 2/3 & 2/3 & 0 \end{bmatrix}$$

Both the charge assignments are logically allowed[4]

within our scheme. The two assignments agree on a number of experimental consequences such as those based on the anomalous lepton-hadron-interactions mediated by the X and S^o particles (See Fig. 1), these being the consequences solely of the existence of the fourth color. On the other hand, they possess profound differences with respect to others: Most notably integer-charge-quarks are unstable, while fractionally charged quarks are necessarily stable by charge conservation, even if we eventually violate baryon number together with fermion-number conservation in our scheme (so that proton would be unstable, but not the fractionally charged quarks, see later). Other important differences between the two assignments concern the emission of color in photon-induced processes and the whole subject of color-emission versus color-confinement, which I discuss later.

III. MINIMAL AND MAXIMAL SYMMETRIES: A SINGLE COUPLING CONSTANT

Consistent with our goal, we have demanded since our early attempts at unification that a desirable local symmetry $\mathcal{G}$ should at the very least incorporate the following features: (i) it should treat baryons and leptons universally; (ii) it should introduce the left and right-handed local symmetry transformations in a symmetrical manner (this is necessary to satisfy our requirement that eventually parity violation and for that matter all asymmetries in nature, i.e. CP non-conservation, strangeness violation, etc. may be attributed to assymetric boundary conditions rather than to intrinsic asymmetries in the basic laws); (iii) subject to appropriate spontaneous symmetry breaking, it should reproduce the known phenomena of low-energy weak, electromagnetic and strong interactions; (iv) it must generate electromagnetism such that electric charge is made up only of non-abelian charges; (v) it should predict the charges of the leptons while accounting for the fact that the proton and the electron (e^-) acquire the same helicity in low-energy weak interactions and (vi) the symmetry $\mathcal{G}$, if it is not maximal (corresponding to the choice of the basic fermions) should be imbeddable within a suitable higher symmetry G (permissible by the fermion-content) such that all basic interactions (leaving out gravity for the moment), may be associated with a single[14] fundamental coupling constant e.

The minimal local symmetry satisfying all the six requirements mentioned above, is uniquely given within our model (consisting of thirty two two-component fundamental fermions) by the group:

$$\mathcal{G} = SU(2)_L^{I+II} \times SU(2)_R^{I+II} \times SU(4)'_{L+R} \qquad (3)$$

for which the chiral multiplets F_L and F_R transform as $(2 + 2, 1, \bar{4})$ and $(1, 2 + 2, \bar{4})$ respectively with

$$F_L = \frac{1 + i\gamma_5}{2} F \text{ and } F_R = \frac{1 - i\gamma_5}{2} \qquad (4)$$

The groups $SU(2)^{I}_{L,R}$ and $SU(2)^{II}_{L,R}$ act on the indices $(p,n)_{L,R}$ and $(\lambda,\chi)_{L,R}$ respectively, while $SU(2)^{I+II}_{L,R}$ are their diagonal sums. The group $SU(4)'_{L+R}$ acts on the color-indices (a,b,c,d) and generates vector gauge interactions. Thus, the minimal symmetry $\mathcal{G}$ introduces 21 gauge particles listed below:

Gauge Particles	Effective-low-energy coupling
$$W_{L,R} = \frac{1}{2}\begin{bmatrix} \vec{\tau}.\vec{W} & 0 \\ 0 & \tau_1(\vec{\tau}.\vec{W})\tau_1 \end{bmatrix}$$	$\frac{g_{L,R}^2}{4\pi} \simeq 2\alpha$
$$V(15) = \frac{1}{\sqrt{2}}\begin{bmatrix} V_{11} & V_\rho^- & V_{K*}^- & \bar{X}^\circ \\ V_\rho^+ & V_{22} & \bar{V}_K^{\circ *} & X^+ \\ V_{K*}^+ & V_{K*}^\circ & V_{33} & X'^+ \\ X^\circ & X^- & X'^- & \sqrt{3/4}\, S^\circ \end{bmatrix}$$	$f^2/4\pi \approx (1 \sim 10)$

where $V_{11} = 1/\sqrt{2}\ (V_3 + V_8/\sqrt{3} - S^\circ/\sqrt{6}$; $V_{22} = \frac{1}{\sqrt{2}}\ (-V_3 + V_8/\sqrt{3} - S^\circ/\sqrt{6})$; $V_{33} = 1/\sqrt{2}\ \ (-2V_8/\sqrt{6} - S^\circ/\sqrt{6})$ and $S^\circ \equiv V_{15}$. The color-octet of gauge mesons V(8) given by $V(\rho)$, $V_K{}^*$, V_3 and V_8 are generated by the SU(3)' - sub-group of SU(4)', which acts on the (a,b,c)-indices only. They couple only to the baryonic quarks and correspond to the V-particles of Fig. 1. The charges of V(15) shown above correspond to the integer charge model. For the fractionally charged quark-model the V(8)-octet are elctrically neutral, while the X's carry charges $\pm\ 2/3|e|$.

Defining the covariant derivative of the model by

$$\nabla_\mu F = \partial_\mu F + igW_\mu F - if\ FV_\mu \tag{6}$$

the Fermi-lagrangian of the model is given by

$$-Tr[\bar{F}_L(\gamma_\mu \nabla_\mu)_L F_L + L \to R] \tag{7}$$

With the requirement that the bare coupling constants

$g_L^{(o)}$ and $g_R^{(o)}$ are equal, the gauge-interactions of the basic lagrangian are left-right symmetric and, therefore, parity conserving. This <u>left ↔ right-discrete symmetry</u>, can in fact be maintained[15] as a "natural symmetry" by imposing that it is broken in the lagrangian in no other way except via Higgs meson mass terms. In this case the renormalized coupling constants are equal up to finite (in principle calculable) radiative corrections; i.e.

$$g_L = g_R + O(\alpha) \tag{8}$$

The observed left-right-asymmetry (i.e. parity violation) together with predominance of left-handed V-A-interactions at low and medium-energies are to be attributed to heavier masses for the "right-handed"-gauge mesons W_R's compared to the "left-handed"-gauge mesons W_L's:

$$m_{W_R^\pm} \text{ and } m_{W_L^\pm} \tag{9}$$

which, in turn, is attributed to an allowed scheme of spontaneous symmetry breaking. With this hypothesis, we would expect parity violation as well as predominance of V-A over V+A to disappear at high energies ($E >> m_{W_R}$).

A second distinct advantage of a left-right symmetric gauge theory is that it allows one to generate a desirable milliweak theory of CP violation[16,17] via spontaneous symmetry breaking. Arranging a suitable fermion mass matrix such that the physical $(n, \lambda)_{L,R}$ field are related to the "bare" $(n^\circ, \lambda^\circ)_{L,R}$-fields by complex-Cabibbo rotations; i.e.

$$\begin{pmatrix} n \\ \\ \lambda \end{pmatrix}_{L,R} = \begin{pmatrix} \cos\theta_{L,R} & -\sin_{L,R}\, e^{i\delta_{L,R}} \\ \\ \sin\theta_{L,R}\, e^{-i\delta_{L,R}} & \cos\theta_{L,R} \end{pmatrix} \begin{pmatrix} n^{o} \\ \\ \lambda^{o} \end{pmatrix}_{L,R} \tag{10}$$

the CP violation introduced into the gauge-interactions (<u>regardless</u> of the parameters of the mass matrix) yields[16]:

$$n_{+} = \eta_{oo}$$

$$\phi_{+-} \simeq \tan^{-1}(2\Delta m/\Gamma_s)$$

$$|\eta_{+-}| \simeq \left| 2\left(\frac{m_{W_L}}{m_{W_R}}\right)^2 \left(\frac{\sin 2\theta_R}{\sin 2\theta_L}\right) \sin(\delta_R - \delta_L)\right|$$

e.d.m. of neutron $\tilde{\sim}\ 10^{-24}$ to 10^{-29} ecm

CP violation in $\Lambda \to N\pi$-decays $\sim 10^{-3}$.

Thus the scheme (despite its milliweak character) coincides with the predictions of the superweak theory[18] for the relations $\eta_{+-} = \eta_{oo}$ and $\phi_{+} = \tan^{-1}(2\Delta m/\Gamma_s)$, both of which are consistent with experiments. Even allowing for intrinsic CP violation to be maximal (i.e. $\delta_R - \delta_L \tilde{\sim} \pi/2$), the smallness of CP violation can be naturally related in this scheme to the known suppression of right handed interactions compared to the left-handed ones (see the expression for $|\eta_{+-}|$). It should be stressed that the left $\leftrightarrow$ right-discrete symmetry of the gauge interactions is essential for realising such a scheme of CP violation.

2. Unification of Coupling Constants, Extended Local Symmetries:

It is appealing to postulate that the observed interactions (weak, electromagnetic and strong) are manifestations of a single basic set of interactions governed by a single coupling constant. The empirical difference between the effective strengths of these interactions at low energies may be attributed[2] in such a scheme to differing gauge meson-masses on the one hand and differing finite charge renormalisations on the other; both of which arise in turn through spontaneous symmetry breaking.

To realise this possibility, it is necessary that the gauge group must either be a simple group or direct product of such groups with appropriate discrete symmetries linking them. This would require imbedding of the minimal symmetry $\mathcal{G}$ into higher symmetries. Perhaps the most natural extension of $\mathcal{G}$ is provided by the local symmetry;[19]

$$G = SU(16)_L \times SU(16)_R \tag{11}$$

with respect to which F_L and F_R transform as (16,1) and (1, 16) respectively. Assuming that fermiom number is not part of the non-abelian local symmetry, the group $SU(16)_L \times SU(16)_R$ is the <u>maximal symmetry</u> permissible by our fermion content (with fermion number included, the symmetry in question is SU(32) - see later). Such a symmetry would involve a single coupling constant, once we impose the requirement[15] that the lagrangian possess a left ↔ right discrete symmetry except possibly in scalar mass terms. The symmetry G may be broken in stages via spontaneous symmetry breaking so as to reduce the level

$$\mathcal{G}_o = SU(2)_L^{I+II} \times U(1) \times SU(3)'_{L+R} \tag{12}$$

which appears to be the appropriate local symmetry[20] to describe low-energy weak, electromagnetic and strong interactions (after further spontaneous symmetry breaking).

A priori, there exist several alternative paths for the maximal symmetry G to reduce the level of $\mathcal{G}_o$ including the possibility that the reduction takes place via the left ↔ right symmetric[21] minimal symmetry $\mathcal{G} = SU(2)_L^{I+II} \times SU(2)_R^{I+II} \times SU(4)'_{L+R}$. These various paths are associated with different intermediate symmetries, which are lower than G, but higher than $\mathcal{G}_o$. Accordingly, they are characterized by different unification-energy-scales corresponding to the masses of the heaviest gauge mesons. This is discussed for two specific cases in the next section. It is good to emphasize, however, that <u>none of these possibilities need the heaviest masses in the theory to be any higher than about 10^5 GeV</u>.

This might be contrasted from alternative schemes of unification (in particular the SU(5)-theory[22] and the extension of our minimal symmetry $\mathcal{G}$ to the SO(10)-symmetry),[23] in which ultraheavy masses ($\gtrsim 10^{15}$ GeV) are <u>needed</u> to obtain a consistent scheme. The main reason for this difference is that in the SU(5) and SO(10)-theories, the gauge mesons are coupled to currents carrying <u>mixed</u> fermion number, baryon-number as well as lepton-number; as a result these quantum numbers are violated directly in the lagrangian (even without sponteneous symmetry breaking) leading to proton-decay in the second order of gauge interactions; hence the need for ultraheavy masses to account for the proton-stability.

Within our approach, on the other hand, we have insisted that the basic lagrangian should conserve all quantum numbers (obtainable within the maximal symmetry) including fermion number F, lepton number L and therefore baryon number B = F-L. As a result the gauge mesons of the basic lagrangian are coupled to currents carrying pure quantum numbers F, B and L. Violation of such quantum numbers occur, in general, only because spontaneous symmetry breaking mixes gauge mesons, whose quantum numbers do not match. For our maximal symmetry $G = SU(16)_L \times SU(16)_R$, or the minimal symmetry $\mathcal{G} = SU(2)_L \times SU(2)_R \times SU(4)'$, fermion number is outside the gauge group, so that all gauge mesons carry zero fermion number. The mixing of gauge mesons, therefore, still conserves fermion number F, while leading, in general, to violations of B and L. This leads to decay of proton (B=F-3) only in the sixth order of gauge coupling (as discussed earlier) and thus obviates the need for ultraheavy masses to suppress proton-decay.

3. A More Economical Scheme:

It is not necessary to gauge the full symmetry $SU(16)_L \times SU(16)_R$ to realize unification of coupling constants. By imposing that the lagrangian respects left ↔ right as well as color ↔ valency discrete symmetries (except possibly in scalar mass terms) the local chiral-version of our SU(4) × SU(4)'-symmetry, i.e.

$$\bar{\mathcal{G}} = SU(4)_L \times SU(4)_R \times SU(4)'_L \times SU(4)'_R$$

provides a theory with a single fundamental coupling constant. The multiplets F_L and F_R transform as $(4, 1, \bar{4}, 1)$ and $(1, 4, 1, \bar{4})$ respectively with respect to $\bar{\mathcal{G}}$. The symmetry $\bar{\mathcal{G}}$ is considerably more economical (in $\bar{\mathcal{G}}$

introducing fewer gauge particles) than the symmetry $G = SU(16)_L \times SU(16)_R$, one must arrange the scheme of spontaneous symmetry breaking such that $SU(2)_L^{I+II} \times SU(2)_R^{I+II} \times SU(3)'_{L+R} \times U(1)_L \times U(1)_R$ is realized as a symmetry much better than $\bar{\mathcal{G}}$ itself. This is necessary to avoid $|\Delta S| = 1$-neutral-current processes (such as $K_L \to \mu\bar{\mu}$) and also to ensure that low-energy strong interactions be described by $SU(3)'_{color}$. Such a pattern of spontaneous symmetry breaking[24] appears possible to arrange.

The consequences of the $\bar{\mathcal{G}}$ symmetry are very similar to those of the minimal symmetry $\mathcal{G}$. The unification-scales for both symmetries are in the range ~ 10^5 GeV. (see later). They differ from each other in one major respect. The interactions of the X and S^o-like particles are vector in the minimal scheme, while with the $\bar{\mathcal{G}}$-symmetry they may be either chiral (if X_L's and X_R's are the eigenstates) or vector and axial vectors if $(X_L \pm X_R)/\sqrt{2}$ are the eigenstates.

4. The Minimal Versus Maximal Symmetries:

Neither the minimal symmetry $\mathcal{G}$ nor the unified symmetry $\bar{\mathcal{G}}$ possess, as rich a variety of experimental consequences[19] as the maximal symmetry $G = SU(16)_L \times SU(16)_R$. Most notably; (i) the latter introduces gauge mesons (Y's) coupled to currents, which simultaneously change valency and color (i.e. $\bar{p}_a n_b$, $\bar{p}_a \bar{e}$ etc.), which are absent in either $\mathcal{G}$ or $\bar{\mathcal{G}}$- symmetries, (ii) secondly, (if we start with the maximal symmetry $SU(16)_L \times SU(16)_R$, spontaneous symmetry breaking may allow four sets of X-particles carrying different valencies (p, n, λ and χ) to remain unmixed and chiral with their couplings given by:

$$f\ [X^{o}_{pL}(\bar{\nu}_e p_a)_L + X^{o}_{nL}\ (\bar{e} n_a)_L + X^{o}_{\lambda L}(\bar{\mu}\lambda_a)_L + X^{o}_{\chi L}(\bar{\nu}_\mu \chi_a)_L$$

$$+ X^{-}_{pL}(\bar{\nu}_e p_b)_L + X^{-}_{nL}\ (\bar{e} n_b)_L + X^{-}_{\lambda L}\ (\bar{\mu}\lambda_b)_L + X^{-}_{\chi L}(\bar{\nu}_\mu \chi_b)_L$$

$$+ X'^{-}_{pL}(\bar{\nu}_e p_c)_L + X'^{-}_{nL}\ (\bar{e} n_c)_L + X'^{-}_{\lambda L}\ (\bar{\mu}\lambda_c)_L + X'^{-}_{\chi L}(\bar{\nu}_\mu \chi_c)_L$$

$$+ (L \to R) + h.c.]$$

where,

$$X_p \neq X_n \neq X_\lambda \neq X_\chi \quad (\text{For } SU(16) \times SU(16))$$

whereas,

$$X_p = X_n = X_\lambda = X_\chi \quad (\text{For } \mathcal{G} \text{ and } \bar{\mathcal{G}}) \qquad (14)$$

This, in turn has the important consequence that whereas for the minimal symmetry $\mathcal{G}$ and its extension $\bar{\mathcal{G}}$, the X-interactions induce $K_L \to \bar{\mu}e$-decays in second order (Fig. 4).

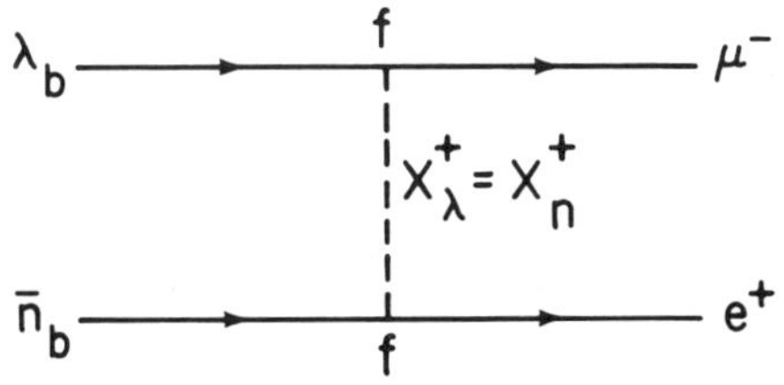

Fig. 4

the decay in question can not proceed for the maximal symmetry (assuming $X_n \neq X_\lambda$). In turn, from the known upper limit on the rate of $K_L \to \bar{\mu}e$-decays, we deduce the limit

$$m_x^{\ 2} \gtrsim f^2 \times 10^9\ (\text{GeV})^2$$

(For the minimal model and for $\bar{\mathcal{G}}$-model)

No such stringent limit on m_x is necessary within the maximal symmetry SU(16) × SU(16). A second important difference is that the X-interactions contribute to <u>charged as well as neutral current</u> semileptonic processes in the minimal model and $\bar{\mathcal{G}}$-model:

$$n \xrightarrow{X_p = X_n} p + e^- + \bar{\nu}_e \quad \text{(minimal and } \bar{\mathcal{G}}\text{-models)}$$

$$\left.\begin{array}{l} \nu_e + p \xrightarrow{X_p} \nu_e + p \\ e^- + n \xrightarrow{X_n} e^- + n \text{ etc.} \end{array}\right\} \quad \text{(minimal \underline{and} maximal models)}$$

While, they contribute <u>only</u> to <u>neutral-current semi-leptonic processes</u> for the maximal-symmetry model. (Subject to (14)).

The net effect of this distinction between maximal and minimal symmetries is that the anamalous lepton-hadron interactions ($e^- + e^+ \to$ hadrons, $\nu + N \to \nu + N$ etc.) mediated by the X-particles can be felt at rather low energies ($E_{CM} \gtrsim 10$ GeV) for the maximal symmetry-model corresponding to the mass of X-mesons being of order 100 to 300 GeV; whereas in the minimal model the presence of such interactions would not be felt significantly until we attain considerably higher energies ($E_{CM} \gtrsim 10^4$ GeV) corresponding to the mass of X-particles being of order 10^4 to 10^5 GeV. The rich variety of experimental consequences involving ν_e and ν_μ-induced reactions and e^-e^+-annihilation, which could arise within the maximal symmetry model, are spelled out in more detail in Ref. 19.

5. Triangle Anomalies, Mirror Image - Fermions

The minimal symmetry $SU(2)_L \times SU(2)_R \times SU(4)'_{L+R}$ is an anomaly free group. On the other hand, both the simple extension $\bar{\mathcal{G}} = SU(4)_L \times SU(4)_R \times SU(4)'_L \times SU(4)'_R$ and the maximal extension $G = SU(16)_L \times SU(16)_R$ suggested by our unification hypothesis possess triangle anomalies, which are unacceptable insofar as we wish to realize a renormalizable theory. Resolution of this problem requires that we must introduce two sets of 32 two-component fermions, i.e. F and its mirror image set F', which couple with opposite chiralities to the same set of gauge bosons. Admittedly such a doubling of fermions is unattractive unless one finds a "reason" for such a doubling deeper than the mere cancellation of anomalies. At present the "only" reason appears to be the realization of a renormalizable unified theory. Perhaps there is a still deeper reason. The set F' must be associated with new heavier quarks and leptons, which are (presumably) dynamically unrelated to the observed baryons and leptons. Is there then a new heavier world?

6. Anomaly-Free Extensions:

It is possible to realize anomaly-free extensions of $\mathcal{G}_0 = SU(2)_L \times U(1) \times SU(3)'$ so as to obtain a unified theory. Two such examples, as mentioned before, are SU(5) and SO(10). The former is anomaly free by choice of fermion representation $(10 + 10 + \bar{5} + \bar{5})$. Such a scheme does not, however, satisfy several of our criteria mentioned before. Most notably it does not respect the left $\leftrightarrow$ right discrete symmetry in the gauge interactions and introduces gauge mesons, coupled to currents carrying mixed quantum numbers B, L and F.

The SO(10)-theory is an extension of our minimal symmetry $\mathcal{G} = SU(2) \times SU(2)_R \times SU(4)'$ with 32 two-component fermions. As a group, it is anomaly-free. It respects the left $\leftrightarrow$ right discrete symmetry and as such is preferable over the SU(5) theory. However, like the SU(5)-scheme, it also introduces gauge mesons carrying mixed baryon-number, lepton-number and fermion-number, a feature, which we regard as "unnatural". The SO(10)-model would of course preserve several features of the minimal model, in particular the consequences of left $\leftrightarrow$ right symmetry and the special class of milliweak CP-violation[16] mentioned before.

7. Fermion Number As Part of the Non-Abelian Symmetry:

If we include the 16 two-component fermions F_L and the antifermions F_L^c in the same multiplet,[25] the maximal symmetry of this multiplet is SU(32). Such a local symmetry includes fermion-number as one of its diagonal generators and involves one basic coupling parameter. It introduces gauge bosons coupled to currents with fermion number,

$$F = 0 \text{ and } F = \pm 2 \tag{15}$$

which define the fermion number for the corresponding gauge bosons. The F = 2-gauge bosons carry:

either,	B=0, L=2	(~ di-lepton → M)
or,	B=2, L=0	(~ di-quark → E)
or,	B=1, L=1	(~ quark-lepton → N) (16)

The F = 0 gauge bosons on the other hand carry either B=L=0 (these are the W, V(8), S^o-type of gauge particles introduced before) or B = -L = ± 1 (these are the X-like gauge particles).

Note that as per our requirement, all gauge particles are coupled to currents with pure quantum numbers within this maximal symmetry. Thus, once again, F, B and L are conserved by the basic lagrangian. Spontaneous symmetry breaking, while giving masses to the gauge particles, could induce a mixing between gauge bosons carrying different quantum numbers and, therefore, to a violation of these quantum numbers. If all possible mixings are induced, a rich variety of selection rules and transitions would follow. Some of these mixings and the associated violation of F, B and L are shown below:

Mixing	Selection Rules	Process
$W \to X$	$\Delta F = 0,\ \Delta B = -\Delta L = -1$	$q \to \ell$
$W \to M$	$\Delta F = 2,\ \Delta B = 0,\ \Delta L = 2$	$q + \bar{q} \to \ell\ell$
$W \to E$	$\Delta F = 2,\ \Delta B = 2,\ \Delta L = 0$	$q + \bar{q} \to qq$
$W \to N$	$\Delta F = 2,\ \Delta B = \Delta L = 1$	$q + \bar{q} \to q\ell$
$\bar{M} \to E$	$\Delta F = 4,\ \Delta B = \Delta L = 2$	$\bar{q} + \bar{q} \to \ell\ell$
$\bar{M} \to N$	$\Delta F = 3,\ \Delta B = 1,\ \Delta L = 3$	$\bar{q} + \bar{\ell} \to \ell\ell$
$\bar{E} \to N$	$\Delta F = 4,\ \Delta B = 3,\ \Delta L = 1$	$\bar{q} + \bar{q} \to q\ell$
$X \to M$	$\Delta F = 2,\ \Delta B = -1,\ \Delta L = 3$	$q \to \ell\ell\ell$

Note that in addition to the familiar $q \to \ell$ transition (which is induced only in the integer-charge quark-model and which leads to proton decay in the sixth order),[3,4] there are now new varieties of baryon-lepton number violating transitions allowed for the integer as well as fractionally charged quark models. In particular, the E-$\bar{N}$-mixing leads to proton decay (Fig. 5)

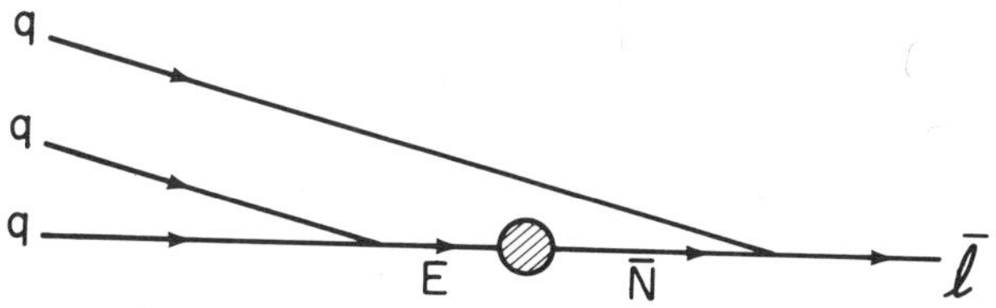

Fig. 5

in the second order of gauge-coupling via the mixing mass. This can thus induce a two-body decay of the proton like ($e^+ + \pi^o$) as in the SU(5) or SO(10)-models. The origin of such a decay is, however, very different in the two cases. It is a property of spontaneous symmetry breaking and fermion number being part of the non-abelian symmetry in the SU(32)-model;[25] where as in the SU(5) and SO(10)-models,[22,23] it is a consequence of mixed gauging. This can lead to an important difference for the masses of the exotic gauge bosons.

The amplitude for proton-decay arising as above in the SU(32)-model is given by[26] $(g^2\Delta^3/m_E^2 m_N^2)$ where Δ^2 is the E-$\bar{N}$-mixing mass. If $\Delta^2 \approx 1(\text{GeV})^2$, proton-life time being $\gtrsim 10^{30}$ years would require $M_E \approx M_N \gtrsim 10^7$ GeV (on the other hand, if the gauge interactions had directly induced $q + q \rightarrow \bar{q} + \bar{\ell}$ in second order, the amplitude would have been of order g^2/m_E^2, and, therefore m_E would have to be in excess of 10^{14} -10^{15} GeV to ensure proton stability).

Thus the unifying scale for SU(32) may lie in the range 10^7 -10^9 GeV (this depends on the mixing mass Δ^2, and should reduce to the unification scale of the fermion number conserving $SU(16)_L \times SU(16)_R$-symmetry or its subsymmetries as $\Delta^2 \rightarrow 0$). It should be stressed that within this maximal symmetry SU(32), quarks would be unstable or stable depending upon whether they carry integer or fractional charges, but in <u>either</u> case proton is unstable with $\Delta^2 \neq 0$.

IV. MASSES OF GAUGE PARTICLES IN THE MINIMAL MODEL: COLOR AS A CLASSIFICATION SYMMETRY

I list below the masses of the 21 gauge particles for the minimal model; the true complexion of these particles would involve mixing (especially among the neutral particles), which I note later. [As explained in the previous section, some of the mass restrictions (most notably the restriction on the masses of the

X-like particles) alter drastically if we extend the minimal to the maximal local symmetry (SU(16) × SU(16))].

Particle	Relevant Process	Mass
V(8)-color gluons	strong q-q force	3 ~ 5 GeV (or, zero)
$\vec{W}_L$	V-A Weak Interactions	50 ~ 100 GeV
$\vec{W}_R$	V+A Weak Interactions	$\gtrsim$ 300 GeV
S^o	$\nu + N \to \nu + N$	$\gtrsim$ 1000 GeV
	$\nu_\mu + e \to \nu_\mu + e$	$(f^2/m_s^2 \lesssim G_{Fermi})$
X	$K_L \to \bar{\mu}e$	$\gtrsim 10^5$ GeV

[In writing the above mass restrictions, we have used $f^2/4\pi \simeq 10$. The mass of the color-octet of gluons, which generate strong quark-quark force, is taken to be 3 to 5 GeV for the integer-charge quark-model and zero for the fractionally charged quark model. See later for reasons for such a choice. For the massless-gluon theory, it is, of course, necessary to solve the associated infrared problem. It should be stressed that unlike the minimal model, the mass of the X-like particles could be as low as 100 to 300 GeV in the maximal symmetry model, since in this case the X-particles need not induce $K_L \to \bar{\mu}e$-decays (as explained earlier). Such "light" X would generate observable effects of anomalous lepton-hadron-interactions even at presently attained energies].

The masses shown above can be obtained in the integer-charge-quark-model with simple representations of Higgs-Kibble multiplets and an allowed pattern of spontaneous symmetry breaking.[4] (For example, the multiplets A = (2 + 2, 2 + 2, 1), B = (1, 2 + 2, $\bar{4}$), C = (2 + 2, 1, $\bar{4}$), D = (1, 1, 15) and E = (1, 3, 1) are adequate to generate the desired mass-pattern). For the fractionally charged quark-model,[4] on the other hand, simple representations of scalar multiplets (such as B, C and D) cannot be utilized to give masses to the V(8)-octet of color-gluons, though they can furnish masses to the W's, X's and S°. If one wishes to give masses to the V(8)-octet, one must introduce in this case higher reducible scalar multiplets such as (1, 1, 4 × 4 × 4). I discuss later motivations for leaving the V(8)-octet massive for the integer charge quark model and massless for the fractionally charged mode,.

2. Mass-Eigenstates:

Spontaneous symmetry breaking, while giving masses to the gauge bosons, induces mixing between several of them so that the physical gauge-particles are, in general, mixtures of the canonical gauge particles. The nature of such mixing is determined to a large extent by the composition of the photon and the values of the effective coupling constants in the W and V-sectors. I list below the five neutral and six charged eigenstates for the integer charge-model for the simplest case of spontaneous symmetry breaking (the W-X mixing effect is ignored for this purpose, since X's are superheavy).

$$A = \frac{e}{fg}\,[f(W - \sqrt{2/3}\,(g/f)S^{\circ}) + \frac{2}{\sqrt{3}}\,gU^{\circ}],\quad m_A = 0$$

$$\tilde{U} \simeq \frac{[\sqrt{3}\,fU^{\circ} - g(W - \sqrt{2/3}\,(g/f)\,S^{\circ})]}{(3f^2 + 2g^2)^{1/2}},\quad m_U \approx 3 \text{ to } 5 \text{ GeV}$$

$$V = \frac{1}{2}\,(\sqrt{3}\,V_8 - V_3) \qquad ,\quad m_{V^{\circ}} \approx 3 \text{ to } 5 \text{ GeV}$$

$$Z^{\circ} \simeq \frac{(W_R^3 - W_L^3) - \sqrt{2/3}\,(g/f)S^{\circ}}{\sqrt{2}},\quad m_{Z^{\circ}} \approx 100 \text{ GeV}$$

$$\tilde{S} \simeq [S^\circ + \sqrt{2/3}\ gW_R^3] \qquad , \ m_S \gtrsim 1{,}000 \text{ GeV} \tag{17}$$

where

$$U^\circ \equiv (1/2)\ (\sqrt{3}\ V_3 + V_8)$$

$$W \equiv W_L^3 + W_R^3$$

$$2e^2 = g^2 f^2/(g^2 + f^2) \tag{18}$$

In above, correction terms of order (g^2/f^2) or smaller (in magnitude) are dropped.

The charged-particle eigenstates (neglecting $O(\varepsilon^2)$ terms; $\varepsilon \tilde{\sim} 10^{-4}$) are given by:

$$\begin{aligned} \tilde{V}_\rho^{\pm} &\approx \cos\beta\ V_\rho^{\pm} + \sin\beta\ W_L^{\pm} \\ \tilde{V}_K^{*\pm} &\approx \cos\alpha\ V_{K*}^{\pm} + \sin\alpha W_L^{\pm} \\ W_L^{\pm} &\approx W_L^{\pm} - V_\rho^{\pm}\ \sin\beta - V_{K*}^{\pm}\ \sin\alpha \end{aligned} \tag{19}$$

where,

$$\sin\alpha \approx -\sin\theta_L \sqrt{2}\ (m_V/m_{W_L})^2\ (g/f)$$

$$\sin\beta \approx -\cos\theta_L \sqrt{2}\ (m_V/m_{W_L})^2\ (g/f) \tag{20}$$

θ_L is the Cabbibo-rotation in the left-handed fermion-space. Thus, note that the mixing gets fully determined within our framework. It is given by,

$$\sin\beta \tilde{\sim} (6 \sim 20) \times 10^{-5} \tag{21}$$

with $(m_V/m_{W_L}) \approx (1/25)$ and $(g/f) \approx (3 \text{ to } 10) \times 10^{-2}$. Such mixings of the charged $W_L^{\pm}$ with $V_\rho^{\pm}$ and $V_{K*}^{\pm}$ leads to weak violation of color quantum numbers $(F_3'$ and $F_8')$. Despite the smallness of such mixings, they are crucial to the search for color-particles (in the integer-charge-quark-scheme), since in the absence of such mixings, color quantum numbers would have been exactly conserved and the lowest mass color-carrying particles would be absolutely stable, even though SU(3)'-color as a symmetry is violated by photon.

A priori, we expect that $V_\rho^\pm$ and $V_{K^*}^\pm$ may mix with the right-handed gauge mesons $W_R^\pm$ in addition to or as an alternative to their mixing with $W_L^\pm$. This would involve an even smaller mixing angle, since $W_R^\pm$ are heavier than $W_L^\pm$. It however presents the interesting possibility (if the V's mix with only W_R's and not W_L's) that once the $\tilde{V}_\rho^\pm$ and $\tilde{V}_{K^*}^\pm$ are produced (see Sec. V) they would decay via W_R-components and could thus be a major source or right-handed neutrinos $(\nu_e$ and $\nu_\mu)_R$.

The mixings and eigenstates for the fractionally charged quark-model are very different from those shown above. Most notably, the composition of photon would be the same as shown in Eq. (17) except that it would not contain U^0. Furthermore, $W^\pm$ cannot mix with the V(8)-octet of gluons, since the latter would be electrically neutral.

3. Tri-Color As A Classification Symmetry:

Even though we generate masses for the color octet of gauge mesons thereby breaking SU(3)'-color as a local symmetry, it is possible to preserve in the integer-charge quark case a global $\tilde{SU}(3)'$-symmetry[27] (different from but related to the local SU(3)'-symmetry) as an approximate classification symmetry; the symmetry becoming exact as $\alpha \to 0$. Briefly speaking, this comes about by introducing a new global SU(3)"-symmetry[28] of the lagrangian in the space of the scalar multiplets;

fermions and gauge-bosons are treated as singlets under SU(3)". Spontaneous symmetry breaking breaks SU(3)' as well as SU(3)", but leaves their diagonal sum $\tilde{SU}(3)'$ preserved (in the limit $\alpha \to 0$). In the space of quarks and gluons $\tilde{SU}(3)'$ acts as a tri-color classification symmetry and thus justifies the use of color in hadron spectroscopy with massive color-gluons. For subsequent discussions, we do not distinguish between $\tilde{SU}(3)'$ and SU(3)'.

In contrast to the integer charge model, however, if quarks carry fractional charges and if electric charge receives no contribution from an abelian U(1)-symmetry, it turns out that the introduction of the new SU(3)"-symmetry is possible only with such scalar-multiplets, which cannot provide masses to the V(8)-octet of gluons. On the other hand, the multiplets (such as (1, 1, 4 × 4 × 4) for the minimal model), which can provide mass to the V(8)-octet do not permit any effective color symmetry to be preserved.[27] Thus it appears that the only way to maintain SU(3)'-color as a classification symmetry in the fractionally charged quark-model is to leave it exact as a local symmetry and therefore the octet of gluons massless.

This is our motivation, therefore, to leave the color-gluons massless[29] in the fractionally charged model. For the integer charge model, one cannot in any case maintain color as an exact symmetry either locally or globally arising due to the fact that after spontaneous symmetry breaking photon must break color like it breaks SU(3) and isospin. Hence, it is natural to assign masses to the octet of gluons in the integer-charge model.

In summary, there are only two possibilities

consistent with the requirement that the tri-color symmetry must emerge either as an exact or as an approximate classification symmetry within the framework of an unified theory. These are (i) integer charge quarks with massive color gluons and (ii) fractionally charged quarks with massless gluons.

4. Confinement Versus Emission of Color:

If quarks carry fractional charges, there must exist some stable quarks or diquarks by charge conservation alone. By now, there exist, however, fairly exhaustive searches[30] for stable fractionally charged objects (the limits are: $m_q \gtrsim 10$ GeV if $\sigma(q) \gtrsim 10^{-36}$ to 10^{-40} cm^2 and $m_q \gtrsim 25$ GeV if $\sigma(q) \gtrsim 10^{-32}$ cm^2). Assuming that quarks are not unnaturally heavy, this strongly suggests that if quarks are fractionally charged, there should be some field theoretic mechanism to prevent their emission from normal hadrons.

A related problem is that the color gluons ought to be left massless for the case of fractionally charged quarks for reasons as mentioned above. This poses the problem of infra-red divergence associated with S-matrix elements. It has been suggested[29] that the infrared property may indeed be a virtue in providing a "shielding" against emission of quarks, color-gluons and all color non-singlets from normal hadrons. The realization of this noval hypothesis remains yet to be demonstrated by actual calculations. Pending such theoretical developments, however, there appear to be two internally consistent sets of hypotheses:

(i) Quarks are fractionally charged. The color gluons are massless. The three colors (a, b, c) are permanently hidden inside normal hadrons. In this case it is natural

to assume further that quarks are extremely light (especially the (p, n, λ)-quarks) like the leptons.
(ii) Quarks are integer-charged like the leptons. The color gluons are massive ($m \stackrel{\sim}{\sim} 3 \sim 5$ GeV). Quarks color-gluons and the whole panorama of color-composites can be emitted at appropriate collision energies. There is no real color hiding. Quarks are relatively light ($m_q \approx 2 \sim 3$ GeV) and decay into (lepton + pions) with lifetime $\approx 10^{-14}$ to 10^{-6} sec.

Both these possibilities arise within our unification scheme of the minimal or the maximal symmetries. With either charge assignment, as emphasized before, proton would be unstable if we utilize the full SU(32) symmetry and allow for fermion number non-conservation.[25]

A choice between these two sets of hypotheses may be made by searching for color (in particular in photon induced processes, see later) and for unstable integer-charge quarks.

5. Asymptotic Freedom:

Our theory being non-abelian satisfies the first necessary criterion[31] to be asymptotically free. The "apparent" only obstacle is that Higgs scalars utilized to provide masses to the gauge bosons spoil asymptotic freedom. There are two possible solutions to this problem:
(i) First, the most attractive possibility is that spontaneous breaking might be dynamical[32] arising through non-perturbative solutions to the field equations. The Higgs-scalars might then arise effectively as $(\bar{\psi}\psi)$-type-composites held together by low-energy attractive strong forces of the asymptotically free theory. Such a theory is aesthetically more appealing since the only

fundamental fields in the lagrangian would then be the fermions and the gauge bosons. The Higgs scalars have all along been a somewhat unpleasant feature of unified theories, since the choice of representations for scalar multiplets is rather arbitrary[33] and one typically needs large number of such scalars to assign desired masses to the gauge bosons.

(ii) Alternatively, to realize asymptotic freedom for the strong interaction sector only, one might leave the color-octet of gluons massless. This possibility can be entertained (for reasons mentioned before) only in the fractionally charged quark-model and has been advanced by a number of authors.[29]

The second alternative does not however guarantee asymptotic freedom for the full theory; since the gauge bosons of the W and X-variety must necessarily be massive and if they are to receive their mass through elementary Higgs scalars developing non zero vacuum expectation values, the virtue of asymptotic freedom within the color-gluon sector would be spoiled at sufficiently high momenta by the W and X-interactions. We, therefore, conclude that one must depend upon dynamical symmetry breaking in any case (regardless of whether one wishes to keep the color gluons massless or massive) to realize a true asymptotically free theory.

In summary, one does not yet have any fully developed theory satisfying asymptotic freedom. The most important problem, yet to be properly solved, is that of dynamical symmetry breaking. If one wishes to appeal to the massless color-gluon theory, the associated infra-red problem must be resolved and even then the full theory would not be asymptotically free without relying on dynamical symmetry breaking.

Insofar as one may hope that dynamical symmetry breaking is to replace the presently available Higgs-Kibble-mechanism, exploration of <u>all</u> the consequences of asymptotic freedom should apply to the massless as well as massive color-gluon theories. Examples are the calculations of (i) octet-enhancement in nonleptonic weak decays,[34] (ii) asymptotic behaviour[35] of $\sigma(e^-e^+ \to$ hadrons) etc.

V. EXPERIMENTAL CONSEQUENCES

I confine myself to discussing those experimental consequences of our minimal symmetry, which are pertinent to the talks of other speakers at this conference.

1. Neutral Currents:

The leptonic and semileptonic neutral current-processes

$$\nu_\mu + e \to \nu_\mu + e$$
$$\nu_e + e \to \nu_e + e. \qquad \text{(leptons)}$$

$$\nu + p \to \nu + \text{hadrons etc. (semi-leptonic)}$$

receive contributions from three main exchanges in our scheme: (See Fig. 6)

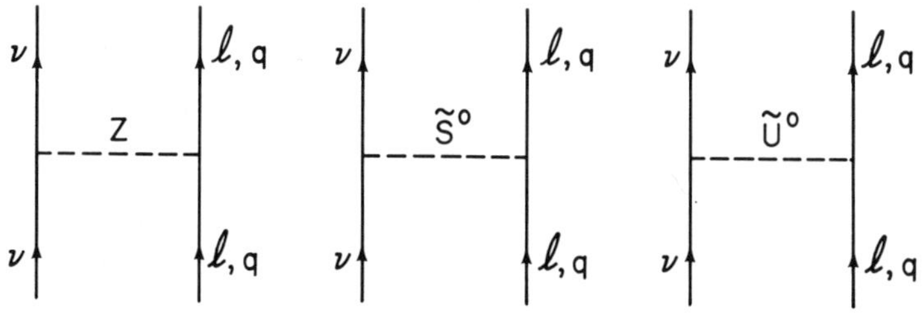

Fig. 6

The Z° (see Eq. (17)) of our scheme is almost <u>identical</u> to the Z° of the simple $SU(2)_L \times U(1)$-theory[1] insofar as leptonic currents are concerned. The correspondence is $g_L \to g$ and $g_R \to g'$; thus the weak-gauge angle is given in our scheme (with $g_L = g_R + O(\alpha)$) by,

$$\sin^2\xi = g_R^2/(g_L^2 + g_R^2) \approx 0.5 \tag{22}$$

The $\tilde{S}^o$-exchange contributes to both leptonic and semileptonic neutral-current processes. Its contributions can compete and even dominate over that of Z^o (with $f^2/m_S^2 \sim G_{Fermi}$). In the minimal symmetry model its coupling is pure <u>vector</u> and <u>isoscalar</u> and is given by:

$$\frac{f}{\sqrt{24}}\Big[\sum_{\alpha=a,b,c}(\bar{p}_\alpha\gamma_\mu p_\alpha + \bar{n}_\alpha\gamma_\mu n_\alpha + \bar{\lambda}_\alpha\gamma_\mu\lambda_\alpha + \chi_\alpha\gamma_\mu\chi_\alpha)$$

$$-3(\bar{\nu}_e\gamma_\mu\nu_e + \bar{e}\gamma_\mu e + \bar{\mu}\gamma_\mu\mu + \bar{\nu}_\mu\gamma_\mu\nu_\mu)\Big]S^o_\mu \tag{23}$$

There is thus a distinct possibility in our scheme of a new variety of contributions, which does not exist in the simple $SU(2)_L \times U(1)$-theory. It is a consequence of the full SU(4)'-gauging. Note that the hadronic part of the S^o-current is a singlet under both SU(3) and SU(3)'. Its contribution to semileptonic processes is thus not suppressed by SU(3)' selection rules. The reported absence of N*(1238) in neutral-current processes (which suggests dominant I=0-contributions) may thus be attributed[36] to the S^o-interaction (the Z^o-contribution would contain both I=0 and I=1, however, its contribution would depend upon Z^o-mass, which is, in general, flexible).

The $\tilde{U}$-meson couples to neutrinos only through correction terms of order $(m_V/m_W)^2$ (which are not shown in Eq. (17)). It thus contributes[4] to leptonic and semileptonic neutral current processes with strength of order (1/10) G_{Fermi}.

So-called neutral-current processes also receive contributions from X-interactions as mentioned before.

Such contributions are, however, negligible in the minimal symmetry model (since $m_x \gtrsim 10^5$ GeV). On the other hand, within the maximal symmetry $SU(16)_L \times SU(16)_R$, the X's can be light (if $X_p \neq X_n \neq X_\lambda \neq X_\chi$) and can make significant contributions to neutral current processes. If the vector and axial-vector combinations (i.e. $(X_L + X_R)/\sqrt{2}$) are the eigenstates, then one significant feature of such X-like interactions is that they can induce[37] after Fierz-reshuffling scalar and pseudoscalar neutral current interactions:

$$(f^2/m_x^2)\ (\bar{p}\gamma_\mu\nu)\ (\bar{\nu}\gamma_\alpha p) = \frac{f^2}{m_x^2} \sum_{S,P,V,A} (\bar{p}\Gamma_i p)\ (\bar{\nu}\Gamma_i\nu) \qquad (24)$$

Thus, if the need[38] for S and P neutral-current interactions is established, it must be attributed within a gauge theory framework to X-like interactions with "light" X ($m_X \simeq 10^3$ GeV).

2. Color-Excitations:

A. Among the fifteen gauge particles of the four-color-symmetry, the ones which may be produced at presently available energies are the fundamental octet of color-gluons V(8) which provide the basic "glue" for quark binding. As discussed before, the emission of such color-particles is a natural possibility only with the integer-charge quark model; I therefore confine myself to the integer-charge assignment only for discussions in this section.

The V(8)-octet are predicted to occur in the mass range 3 to 5 GeV. They contain four charged members ($\tilde{V}_\rho^\pm$, $\tilde{V}_{K*}^\pm$) and four neutral ones (V_3, V_8, V_{K*}^o). The V_3 and V_8 particles may occur in the combinations $\tilde{U}$ and $\tilde{V}^o$ or linear combinations of them as discussed in Sec. IV.2.

In addition to the fundamental color-octet of gauge particles V(8), introduced into our basic lagrangian, we expect the entire set of S-wave ($J^P = 0^-$ and 1^-) quark-anti-quark composites and their radial excitations to materialize as physical particles. The color non-singlet composites[9] should typically lie about 2 GeV higher than the color-singlet hadrons. The $q\bar{q}$-composites transform as:

$$(q\bar{q}) = (4, 3^*) \times (\bar{4}, 3) = (1, 1) + (15, 1) + (1, 8) + (15, 8) \qquad (25)$$

under[39] SU(4) × SU(3)'. The (1,1) + (15,1) are the familiar color-singlet composites ($\pi, \eta, K, \eta', \eta_c, \ldots$) with $J^P = 0^-$ and ($\rho, \omega, K^*, \phi, \phi_c, \ldots$) with $J^P = 1^-$; while (1,8) and (15, 8) are the analogous color non-singlet composites. We call them π(1, 8) and π(15, 8) respectively for $J^P = 0^-$ and C(1, 8) and C(15, 8) respectively for $J^P = 1^-$. Note that the quantum numbers of the C(1, 8) composites are identical to those of the V(8)-elementary gluons (this is analogous to $^3S_1$-positronium being "identical" to the photon execpt for its mass). I discuss below the production and decay modes of the color-octet of gluons only. Similar remarks apply to the C(1,8)-composites. [The characteristic decay modes apply to the lightest color-octet].

The V(8)-octet would be produced, in general, in pairs (or in an associated manner together with other color-octet baryons or mesons) in collisions of energetic hadrons [Pair Production is necessary to conserve the tri-color symmetry]. The charged members (and V^o_{K*} and $\bar{V}^{o*}_K$) would be produced in pairs also in e^-e^+ annihilation at appropriate energies. Thus,

$$p + p \rightarrow V_\rho^+ + V_\rho^- + \text{Hadrons}$$

$$p + p \rightarrow U + U + \text{Hadrons}$$

$$P + P \rightarrow U + (\text{Color Baryon}) + \text{Hadrons}$$

$$e^- + e^+ \rightarrow V_\rho^+ + V_\rho^- \qquad \text{etc.} \qquad (26)$$

Apart from pair production, there is the exciting possibility (if quarks carry integer charges) that the two neutral members V_3 and V_8 (or their linear combination $U^\circ = 1/\sqrt{4}\ (\sqrt{3}\ V_3 + V_8)$) can be produced singly[4] in the collision of electron-positron pairs and in general in all photon induced reactions:

$$e^-e^+ \rightarrow U$$
$$\gamma + p \rightarrow U + p \qquad \text{etc.} \qquad (27)$$

This is because the photon so to say is made up partly of U° (and partly of W and S°, see Eq. (17)). Note that the physical particle is really $\tilde{U}$ (and not U°), which is directly coupled to e^-e^+ by its W-component. For ease of writing, we write U for $\tilde{U}$.

B. Decays of U and U like Particles:

The allowed decay modes of U and the expected order of magnitudes for the corresponding amplitudes are shown below:

$$U \rightarrow \text{Hadrons} + \gamma \quad (O(e))$$
$$\rightarrow \text{Hadrons} \quad (O(\alpha),\ O(H_8'))$$
$$\rightarrow e^-e^+,\ \mu^-\mu^+ \quad (O(\alpha)) \qquad (28)$$

H_8' denotes the effective non-electromagnetic color-symmetry breaking term in the lagrangian, which arises[27] from the quartic terms in the scalar potential. We assume that H_8' generated amplitudes are small of order

(1 to Few) α and H'_8 has a dominant piece transforming as $(1,8)_{I'_3=Y'=0}$ under SU(3) × SU(3)'.

The order e amplitudes involving the emission of a real color-photon are expected to be further suppressed[40] owing to the fact that the intermediate states linked to the photon in this case must be color-octet states (see Fig. 7) and thus necessarily heavy ($m^2 \gtrsim 10\ (GeV)^2$).

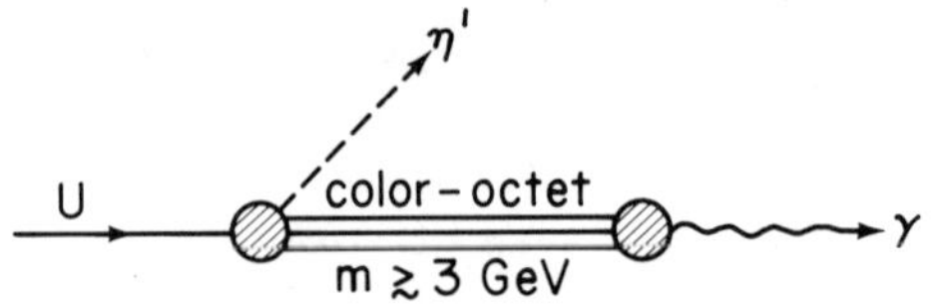

Fig. 7

These provide (on the basis of a dispersion theoretic treatment) a damping by about an order of magnitude in the amplitude for U → (hadrons + γ) compared to normal radiative transitions such as $\rho \to \pi^0 + \gamma$. Taking this into account we find that the U-particle is expected not only to be narrow, but extremely narrow:

$$\Gamma(U) \sim 100 \text{ keV} \tag{29}$$

C. Do The ψ-Particles Represent Color?

A search for narrow width U-like particles in the mass range 3 to 5 GeV through e^-e^+-annihilation experiments was suggested by us over a year ago. It is intriguing that two extremely narrow width particles ψ and ψ' have been discovered[41] recently in the same reactions as mentioned above with masses 3.1 and 3.7 GeV respectively. The presently known characteristics of ψ and ψ' are consistent with the hypothesis[40] that one of them is the color-gluon U and the other is the U-like

$q\bar{q}$-composite C_U belonging to the multiplet C(1,8). Most notably, the extreme narrow widths of ψ and ψ' can be understood qualitatively by attributing them to color for reasons as mentioned above.

There are alternative assignments for the ψ-particles. Their narrow widths suggest in the first place that new quantum numbers provide selection rules for their decays to known hadrons. From the point of view of our scheme, such quantum numbers may be either color or charm, both of which were found essential for our unification hypothesis. Several authors[42] have considered the possibility that the ψ and ψ' represent charm-anti-charm composites ϕ_c and ϕ_c' with $J^{PC} = 1^{--}$. I first outline some of the distinguishing features of the color-hypothesis for the ψ-particles. Next I discuss three alternative assignments for ψ, ψ' and the broad width ψ'' (at 4.1 GeV) assuming that these particles represent color as well as charm (in the sense of ϕ_c) and how one should be able to make an unambiguous choice between these assignments experimentally.

D. Characteristic Features of the Color-Assignment for ψ:

Since the color-octet part of the electromagnetic current (responsible for the decay of U-like particles) is SU(3)-singlet, there are various selection rules associated with the decays of U to (hadrons + photon). First, this forbids the decays:

$$\begin{aligned} &U \not\to \pi + \gamma \\ &U \not\to (\text{odd Number of pions}) + \gamma \\ &U \not\to \eta + \gamma \end{aligned} \tag{30}$$

The $(\eta + \gamma)$-mode can proceed through SU(3)-breaking. The allowed radiative decay modes of U are:

$$U \to \eta' + \gamma \qquad U \to \text{Even number of pions} + \gamma \tag{31}$$

The $(\eta' + \gamma)$-mode should be replaced by $(E^o + \gamma)$-mode if E^o is the 0^- SU(3)-singlet.

The decays of U → hadrons can occur (a) via photon loop, (b) via the small components of U (see Eq. (17)) and (c) via non-electromagnetic color-symmetry breaking term H_8'. Noting that H_8' is a SU(3) singlet operator, it would lead to only isospin conserving decays. Thus H_8' cannot induce decays of U into even number of pions. The latter may occur only through photon loop and the small components of U. The expected orders of magnitudes for the amplitudes of some typical hadronic decay modes of U are thus given by:

$$\begin{aligned} U &\to 3\pi,\ 5\pi,\ \omega\pi\pi,\ K^*\bar{K},\ B\bar{B}\ \ (O(H_8'),\ O(\alpha)) \\ &\to \pi^+\pi^-,\ 4\pi,\ K\bar{K},\ \eta\pi\pi,\ \rho\rho\ \ (O(\alpha)) \end{aligned} \tag{32}$$

If H_8' is few times α, one may expect H_8' contributions to dominate over photon loop-contributions and thus U-decays to be essentially isospin conserving.

Allowing for the damping of the order e amplitudes for radiative decay modes, we estimate that the sum of (hadrons + one photon)-mode-partial widths is comparable to the sum of hadronic partial widths of U. The (hadrons + one photon)-modes must constitute, therefore, a significant fraction (≈ 20 to 50%) of all decay modes. This is the most distinct characteristic, which ought to be satisfied if ψ is the color gluon U. Among these, the two body mode $(\eta' + \gamma)$ (or $(E^o + \gamma)$) should be an appreciable mode ($\Gamma(U \to \eta' + \gamma) \sim 5$ to 10 keV), which should show in a search for <u>monoenergetic γ-rays</u> in the U-mass region.

If $\psi(3.1)$ represents color, $\psi'(3.7)$ must also be associated with color owing to the fact that ψ' decays "rapidly" to $(\psi+\pi+\pi)$. One likely assignment in this case is that ψ is the color-gluon U and ψ' is a $q\bar{q}$-composite with color-quantum numbers overlapping with (or identical to) U:

$$\psi(3.1) = U; \; \psi'(3.7) = C_U \tag{33}$$

The reasons for assigning ψ and ψ' to two different color-octets rather than to the third and eighth members (for example) of the same color-octet multiplet are two fold: (i) First if ψ and ψ' were members of the same multiplet, the 600 MeV mass difference between them would reflect a rather large color symmetry breaking and this would be inconsistent with the observed narrow partial widths for ψ and $\psi' \to$ hadrons. (ii) Secondly, the observed partial width $\Gamma(\psi' \to \psi\, \pi^+ \pi^-) \gtrsim$ (100-300) keV implies that the effective decay constant $(h^2/4\pi)$ is $\gtrsim$ (10 to 30), which in turn suggests[43] that $\psi' \to \psi+\pi+\pi$ is an allowed strong decay and this could not have been the case if ψ and ψ' were members of the same color-octet.

E. Color and Charm for the ψ-Particles:

From the point of view of our scheme if quarks carry integer charges, we would expect charm as well as color to manifest themselves at appropriate energies. Assuming the validity of the "asymptotic" formula $R \equiv \sigma(e^-e^+ \to \text{hadrons})/\,\sigma(e^-e^+ \to \mu^-\mu^+) = \sum_i Q_i^2$, we expect, $R = 10/3$ if only charm is excited but not color (this is equivalent to the fractionally charged quark-scheme); R = 4 if only color is excited, but not charm; and R=6 if both charm and color are excited (for the integer-charge-quark scheme). The recently reported value[44] of R seems to be steady at about 2.5 from $E_{CM} \approx 3$ to 3.8 GeV, but rises dramatically to 5 or higher as $E_{CM} \rightarrow$ 4.8 GeV. Based on this, we are inclined to the view that thresholds for new quantum numbers are being crossed as E_{CM} passes from 3.8 to 4.8 GeV and that perhaps both color and charm are being excited at SPEAR energies yielding $R \gtrsim 5$. We therefore consider[45] below the possibility that the ψ-particles (ψ(3.1), ψ'(3.7) and the broadwidth ψ"(4.1)) reflect both these quantum numbers with quarks being integer-charged like the leptons.

The following remark is worth noting before considering the possible assignment of quantum numbers to the ψ-particles. SU(4)-breaking may in general induce mixings between (1,8)'s and (15,8)'s, however, we expect that such mixings might take place only between the composites C(1,8) and C(15,8); but the gauge multiplet V(8) being coupled to the generators of the SU(3)'-color-group remains unmixed. The C(1,8) ↔ C(15,8)-mixing will follow the (ω-φ)-mixing pattern[46] if SU(6) × SU(3)'-spin containing-symmetry holds for these high mass $(q\bar{q})$-composites. But, there is also the alternative possibility that the gauge particles V(1,8) (being themselves "pure"), may influence the composites C(1,8) with identical quantum numbers also to remain essentially unmixed, especially if the composites and the gauge particles are not too far apart in mass. We thus allow in our assignments both these possibilities.

With these prepatory remarks and the known informations on ψ,ψ' and ψ", we are led to suggest mainly three alternative assignments for these new particles:

Model I: $\psi(3.1)$ = Color-gluon U

$\psi'(3.7)$ = Color-composite C_U

$\psi''(4.1) = \chi\bar{\chi}$-Composite ϕ_c (34)

The consistence of ψ and ψ' being associated with color as above and its experimental consequences are discussed before. The broadness of ψ'' ($\Gamma(\psi'') \approx 250$ MeV) with the identification $\psi'' = \phi_c$ may be accounted for as follows: (i) First, such a large width can be associated with the decays $\phi_c \to \rho\pi$, 5π, $K\bar{K}$, $N\bar{N}$, etc., if we assume that the Zweig-rule-suppression for $\phi_c \to$ known hadrons works nearly to the same extent (about 1:100 in the amplitude) as it does for $\phi \to \rho\pi$ decay. The standard dilemma of assigning the narrow width particles ψ and ψ' to ϕ_c's has been that the Zweig-rule must be assumed to be good to about 1:3000 in the amplitude for ϕ_c-decay, where as it is good to only about 1:30 in the amplitude for ϕ-decay. The assignment $\psi'' = \phi_c$ avoids this dilemma. (ii) Secondly, ψ'' could also decay with a large partial width into a pair of charmed pseudoscalars $D + \bar{D}$, if the D's are lighter than about 1.9 GeV. If this is a significant decay mode, one should expect to see an enhancement in the (K/π)-ratio as the energy approaches the ψ''-peak region from below. [Ordinarily, however, one would expect the D's to lie at about 3 to 3.2 GeV if $\psi''(4.1)$ = lowest ϕ_c].

Model II: If we allow the C(1,8) and C(15,8) to mix with each other in the ω-ϕ pattern, still maintaining that the V(8)-octet does not mix with C(15,8), there are three color particles which may be formed in e^-e^+-annihilation (U^o, $C(\omega,\gamma_c)$ and $C(\phi, \gamma_c)$). We are thus led to the identifications:

$$\begin{aligned} \psi(3.1) &= \text{Color-guon } U \\ \psi'(3.7) &= C(\omega,\gamma_c) = \sqrt{2/3}\, C(\omega_1,\gamma_c) + \sqrt{1/3}\, C(\phi,\gamma_c) \\ \psi''(4.1) &= C(\phi,\gamma_c) = -\sqrt{1/3}\, C(\omega_1,\gamma_c) + \sqrt{2/3}\, C(\omega_8,\gamma_c) \end{aligned} \tag{35}$$

with[47] ϕ_c lying either below 3 GeV or under the ψ'' peak. In either case ϕ_c may be reasonably broad ($\Gamma(\phi_c) \approx$ 20 to 200 MeV, say) for reasons as explained under model I. The broadness of $C(\phi,\gamma_c)$ may be attributed to the allowed strong decay

$$\psi'' = C(\phi,\gamma_c) \to \psi + \eta \tag{36}$$

With the present hypothesis $\psi' \to \psi + \eta$ is also allowed under SU(4) × SU(3)' selection rule; we estimate $\Gamma(\psi' \to \psi + \eta) \approx$ (100 to 300) KeV. (Note that in model I, $\psi' \to \psi + \eta$ should be suppressed by SU(3)-selection rule). Thus a search for <u>monoenergetic η-particles</u> in the decays of ψ'' and ψ' can distinguish between models I and II.

<u>Model III</u>: If the validity of the Zweig rule to about 1:3000 in the amplitude for $\phi_c \to$ known hadrons and the exceptions to the rule for $\phi_c' \to \phi_c + \pi + \pi$-decays can be understood theoretically,[48] or else if one accepts it as an empirical rule, there would be a third possible assignment for the ψ-particles. The two lower ones, in this case, may be assigned to ϕ_c-like objects, as suggested by several authors,[42] while the upper one $\psi''(4150)$ may be the color-gluon U.

$$\begin{aligned} \psi(3.1) &= \phi_c \\ \psi'(3.7) &= \phi_c' \\ \psi''(4.1) &= U \end{aligned} \tag{37}$$

In this case, the broadness of ψ'' can be explained by assuming that it is decaying strongly to color pseudoscalars $\pi(1,8)$ (which may have a mass of about 3 GeV) plus known mesons, i.e. $\psi''(4.1) = U \to \pi(1,8)$ + pions. The color pseudoscalars in turn will decay out rapidly into lepton pairs (i.e. $\bar{\mu}\nu$, $e\bar{e}$, etc., see later).

In summary, the above three alternatives (together with possible minor variations) represent our view that these new particles are associated with both color and charm. Experimental information on: (a) Whether ψ possesses significant radiative decay modes; (b) whether ψ'' cascades into ψ and/or ψ', and (c) whether monoenergetic η-particles are emitted in the decays of ψ'' and ψ' might be helpful in distinguishing between these possibilities. At present, given our lack of understanding of the Zweig-rule and its exceptions, they all appear to be consistent with the known data.

In particular, it is worth remarking that the recently reported[49] photoproduction data ($\gamma + p \to \psi(3.1)$ + hadrons) does not help choose between these alternatives, because the reported cross-section is roughly consistent with the ϕ_c-hypothesis for ψ (taking into account the expected reduced coupling[50] of ϕ_c to the pomeron) as well as[51] with the color-gluon-hypothesis for ψ (taking into account the heavy mass damping[40,46] involved in the emission or absorption of a real "color" photon).

F. Search for Partners of ψ-Particles; Dimuon Events:

We should now like to emphasize that a clear distinction between the models I, II and III and an answer to the question whether ψ, ψ' and ψ'' represent color or charm, or neither can be obtained by searching for the remaining members of the multiplets to which ψ, ψ' and ψ'' belong.

First, if ψ and ψ' are associated with color-octets (as in models I and II), there should exist a nearly degenerate octet[52] of gluons $\vec{V}_\rho$, $V_K{}^*$, and V_8) with mass around 3.1 GeV and a nearly degenerate octet of composites ($\vec{C}_\rho$, C_{K*} and C_8) with mass around 3.7 GeV. The members ($V^\pm_\rho$, $V^\pm_{K*}$, V^o_{K*}, and $\bar{V}^o_{K*}$) and likewise the composites, which carry nonzero I'_3 and Y, can be produced in pairs in hadronic collisions and in e^-e^+-annihilation (Eq. (26)).

The charged members and the U-particles may also be produced singly in neutrino-interactions via the V-W mising terms. (Note that such mixings get fully determined within the gauge theory framework (Se Eqs. (19) and (20)). For ease of writing, we drop the tilde on the physical particles.):

$$\nu_\mu + N \to \mu^- + V^+_\rho + \text{"X"}$$
$$\nu_\mu + N \to \nu_\mu + U + \text{"X"} \qquad (38)$$

once produced, if there are no lowerlying color-octet states, the gluons $\tilde{V}^\pm_\rho$ and $V^\pm_{K*}$ with non-zero I'_3 and Y' will decay only via the induced V-W mixings. Thus they would decay to lepton-pairs and to hadrons:

$$V^+_\rho,\ V^{+*}_K \to \mu^+ + \nu,\ e^+ + \nu,\ \pi^+\pi^o,\ 3\pi,\ K\bar{K},\ \text{etc.} \qquad (39)$$

with lifetime $\lesssim 10^{-14}$ sec. This is based on the V^+-W^+-mixing angle $\sin\beta \simeq 6 \times 10^{-5}$. Consistent with the old estimates of $W^\pm$-decay branching ratios (with $m_{W_\pm} \sim 3$ GeV), we expect[53] the leptonic branching ratios for $V^\pm_\rho$ and $V^\pm_{K*}$ to be significant ($\gtrsim 20\%$ for each of the e and μ-modes); the hadronic modes, while numerous in number, are expected to be individually suppressed by form-factors.

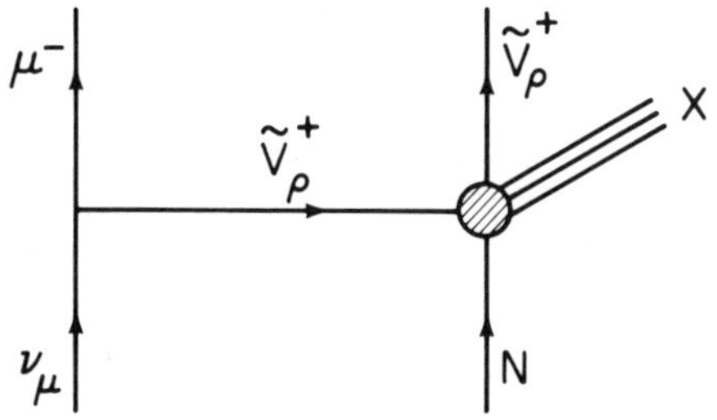

Fig. 8

The large leptonic-decay-branching ratio of (V_ρ^+, V_{K*}^+) together with the mixing angle ~6 × 10^{-5} implies that the neutrino-productions of V_ρ^+ and V_ρ^+ (see Fig. 8) followed by their decays to (μ^+ ν_μ) should lead to observable dimuon event rates (ν_μ + N → μ^- + μ^+ + "X") of order 1 few percent compared to the single muon events. This is one likely explanation of the recently observed[54] dimuon events.

Turning now to the charm-hypothesis, if the ψ-particles are $\bar{\chi}\chi$-composites ϕ_c's, there should exist their charmed partners[55] (D^o = $\bar{p}\chi$, D^+ = $\bar{n}\chi$, F^+ = $\bar{\lambda}\chi$) with J^P = 1^- and similar composites with J^P = 0^-. These charm carrying mesons are expected to lie <u>lower in mass</u> (the D's by about 1 GeV and F by about .7 GeV, say) than their respective ϕ_c-partners (with 0^--composites lying somewhat lower than the 1^--composites). <u>Thus they may lie in the range 3 to 3.4 GeV (approximately) for models I and II and in the range 2 to 2.4 GeV for model III.</u> These mesons (like the color-carrying gluons) can also be produced in <u>pairs</u> in e^-e^+-annihilation and in hadronic collisions and <u>singly</u> (especially the F-particles) in neutrino interactions.

With simple arguments, one expects[55] the lightest members of such particles (especially the D^o and F^+) to decay dominantly to nonleptonic systems ($D^o \to K^- \pi^+$, $F^+ \to K^+ K^{-o}$ etc.) with only a few percent branching ratio ($\lesssim 5\%$) to the sum of leptonic and semileptonic modes ($D^o \to K^- \mu^+ \nu_\mu$, $F^+ \to \mu^+ \nu_\mu$, $\eta\mu^+\nu$ etc.).

Despite the similarity of charges, the particles (D^o, D^+ and F^+) can be clearly distinguished from (V^o_{K*}, V^+_{K*} and V^+_ρ) as follows. First, in contrast to the charmed particles (especially D^o and F^+), color-particles are expected to possess significant leptonic branching ratios ($\gtrsim 20\%$ for each e and μ-modes). However, even the D and F-particles might decay to leptons with appreciable branching ratios,[56] their semileptonic decay-modes should compete favourably with their pure leptonic-modes. <u>For the gluons V^+_ρ and V^+_{K*}, on the other hand, the semileptonic modes are non-existent</u> (ignoring order α corrections). This is the clearest distinction between the charmed-particles and the color-gluons (V^+_ρ, V^+_{K*}). Other suggestive distinctions may, of course, arise from mass consideration (as mentioned above) and the preferential decays of the charmed particles (D and F) to systems involving K-mesons.

The search for these (narrow width) charged particles <u>carrying color and/or charm</u> with masses around or within 1 GeV of 3.1, 3.7 and 4.1 GeV together with a determination of their leptonic versus semileptonic and nonleptonic decay branching ratios is thus of paramount importance in deciding whether color and/or charm exist and are emitted. In turn, this should provide an unambiguous answer to whether the ψ-particles are associated with charm and/or color. If the association of color with any of the ψ-particles is indeed established, that would determine an important parameter of the theory - the charges of the quarks.[57]

G. A Summary:

A brief summary of new experimental possibilities arising within our unification scheme is given below:

Features	Main Characteristics
(1) S°-Effect	Isoscalar, vector Neutral current Interactions
(2) X-Effects (In maximal symmetry model with "light" X)	(1) Anamalous energy dependence of $e^-e^+ \to$ hadrons $E_{CM} \gtrsim 10$ GeV; (2) Anomalous $p+p \to \ell^+ + \ell^-$ hadrons (3) Possible large S and P neutral-current Interactions (4) possibility[58] of (ν_e+p) neutral current Interactions >> $(\nu_\mu+p)$ neutral current Interactions.
(3) Color Emission with Integer charge quarks; massive color gluons ($m \simeq 3$ to 5 GeV)	(1) short-lived quarks $(q \to \ell + \pi)$ (2) unstable proton $(p \to \ell\ell\ell\pi)$ (3) possible significant cosmoligical effects[59] of B-L-violation at early stages of the universe. (4) $e^-e^+ \to U$; $p + p \to$ color + color + "X" (5) $\nu_\mu + N \to \mu^-$ + color + "X" (6) $e + p \to e + U$ + Hadrons (small violation of scaling)[60]
(4) Color Hiding[29] with Fractionally charged quarks (massless gluons)	(1) stable quark, but unstable proton with [25] $\Delta F \neq 0$ $(p \to e^+\pi^0)$ (2) observable particle spectrum to be devoid of color
(5) W_R Effects	V + A Interactions with emission of right handed ν_e and ν_μ.

VI. CONCLUSION

The model presented so far provides the basic framework for unification and answers to some of the questions raised in the introduction. It leaves, however, several important questions unanswered: Most notably: (1) What precisely sets the scales of masses for sponteneous symmetry breaking? Is there a self-consistent pattern, which may determine all parameters in terms of perhaps one or few? (2) how, precisely the effective low energy coupling in the color-gluon sector is enhanced relative to the W-sector within a unified theory? and (3) how does gravity fit together with the other interactions (the graviton-coupling having a dimension appears to pose a problem)?

Not withstanding such theoretical problems, if our basic suggestion that the fundamental family of fermions is a sixteen fold carrying four valency and four color-quantum numbers with baryons and leptons in the same family is correct, we should expect to see a rich variety of new phenomena and new particles at higher and higher energies as summarized above. The energies at which the new class of interactions between leptons and baryons arising in our scheme should manifest themselves lie in the range of 100 to 100,000 GeV. Such a range can certainly be covered by Cosmic ray experiments and may even be available in the laboratory in the near future. We might hope that even at energies already available at SPEAR II, the Fermi lab and ISR, the effects of such interactions may begin to show. An important test of our hypothesis would, of course, be the discovery of unstable proton with our without unstable integer charge quarks.

I thank L. Clavelli, O. W. Greenberg, G. A. Snow, J. Sucher and C. H. Woo for several inspirational and helpful discussions.

REFERENCES AND FOOTNOTES

1. J. Schwinger, Ann. Phys. (N.Y.) 2, 407 (1957); Abdus Salam and J. C. Ward, Nuovo Cim. 11, 568 (1959); Physics Lett. 13, 168 (1964); S. L. Glashow, Nucl. Phys. 22, 579, (1961); S. Weinberg; Phys. Rev. Lett. 19, 1264 (1967); Abdus Salam, in Elementary Particle Theory, Nobel Symposium, Edited by N. Svartholm (Almqvist, Stockholm, 1968), p. 367.

2. J. C. Pati and Abdus Salam, Phys. Rev. D 8, 1240 (1973).

3. J. C. Pati and Abdus Salam, Phys. Rev. Lett. 31, 661 (1973).

4. J. C. Pati and Abdus Salam, Phys. Rev. D10, 275, (1974). Erratum (ibid, Feb. 1, 1975).

5. For a review of ten year quark-search results, see L. G. Landsberg and A. M. Zaytsev, Serpukhov preprint; Brief Version of report presented at the seminar, "Quarks and Partons" (Moscow, June, 1974).

6. For some estimates on pair production of heavy particles, see T. K. Gaisser and F. Halzen (Preprint, Jan., 1975).

7. F. Reines and M. Crouch, Phys. Rev. Lett. 32, 493 (1974). Other references may be found here.

8. In addition to searches by more familiar methods, geochemical search similar to the ones used for double β-decay might be helpful, as recently pointed out by S. P. Rosen (Purdue Univ., Preprint, 1975).

9. The notion of color symmetry with nine quarks was first explicitly introduced by M. Y. Han and Y. Nambu, Phys. Rev. 139, B 1006 (1965) and A. N. Tavkhelidze et. al., High Energy Physics and Elementary Particles IIAEA, ICTP Trieste, 1965), p. 763. These authors stressed the integer charge possibility for quarks. However, once there are nine quarks classified under two commuting SU(3)'s (i.e. $SU(3) \times SU(3)'_{color}$), the quark-charges can be either integral or fractional depending upon whether SU(3)' contributes to electric charge or not. The strong interaction quantum numbers are

the same for either charge-assignment. This latter evident fact has been noted in the literature subsequently by several authors: [O. W. Greenberg and D. Zwanziger, Phys. Rev. 150, 1177 (1966), J. C. Pati and C. H. Woo, Phys. Rev. 3, 1173, 1971].

10. Implicitly, the necessity for color was introduced first by O. W. Greenberg, Phys. Rev. Lett. 13, 598 (1964) via a single triplet of paraquarks of order 3.

11. Apart from the need for color based on the considerations of Pauli principle for the 56-plet of baryons, other suggestive motivations for color are based on (i) the rate of $\pi^0 \to 2\gamma$-decay, (ii) the validity of the $\Delta I = 1/2$-rule for nonleptonic decays and (iii) a satisfactory gauge theory for strong interactions and (iv) asymptotic freedom (see later). Relevant references may be found in Ref. 2 and 4.

12. S. L. Glashow, J. Iliopoulos and L. Maiani, Phys. Rev. D2, 1285 (1970).

13. This requirement suffices from the point of view $SU(2)_L^{I+II} \times SU(2)_R^{I+II} \times SU(4)'_{L+R}$- gauge symmetry (introduced later). With $SU(4) \times SU(4)'$-symmetry, one needs to impose in addition that p and χ- have same charge. Note we insist in any case no abelian U(1)-contribution to electric charge.

14. Such a viewpoint has been advocated by J. C. Pati and A. Salam (Ref. 2); H. Georgi and S. L. Glashow, Phys. Rev. Lett. 32, 438 (1974) and H. Fritzsch and P. Minkowski, Cal. Tech. Preprint (1974). More theoretical work is needed to sustain this viewpoint dynamically.

15. R. N. Mohapatra and J. C. Pati; City-College Preprint, Oct. 1974 (Phys. Rev., to be published).

16. R. N. Mohapatra and J. C. Pati, Maryland Univ. Tech. Rep. 74-085 (March, 1974) (Phys. Rev. Feb. 1, 1975).

17. J. Frenkel and M. Ebel, Nuclear Physics (to be published). The model of this paper differs from that of Ref. 16 in that it is not left-right symmetric in the lepton-sector and would need

additional fermions to avoid anomalies.

18. L. Wolfenstein, Phys. Rev. Lett. 13, 562 (1964).

19. J. C. Pati and Abdus Salam, Proceedings of the Williamsburgh Conference of the American Physical Society (Division of Particles and Fields), No. 23, p. 604 (1974); Phys. Rev. D. Feb. 1, 1975. Appropriate spontaneous symmetry breaking of this extended symmetry and other unifying symmetries such as $\bar{\mathcal{G}} = SU(4)_L \times SU(4)_R \times SU(4)'_L \times SU(4)'_R$ (see later) are being considered in collaboration with R. N. Mohapatra. The extension of our minimal symmetry $\mathcal{G}$ to $SU(16)_L \times SU(16)_R$ and $\bar{\mathcal{G}}$ has been considered independently by H. Fritizsch and P. Minkowski, Cal. Tech. Preprint 68-467 (1974).

20. Such a combined local symmetry (suggested in Ref. 2) has several desirable features: (i) calculability of parity and strangeness violations and the strength of such violations being of order (e^2/m_W^2). (R. N. Mohapatra, J. C. Pati, and P. Vinciarelli, Phys. Rev. D 8, 3652 (1973); S. Weinberg, Phys. Rev. Lett. 31, 494 (1973)), (ii) classification symmetry of hadrons being limited to SU(3) × SU(3)' and no higher (J. C. Pati and A. Salam, ICTP preprint Trieste, No. IC/73/81 (unpublished) and (iii) Asymptotic freedom of strong interactions (D. Gross and F. Wilczek, Phys. Rev. Lett. 30, 1343 (1973); and D. Politzer, ibid, 30, 1346 (1973)). (The loss of asymptotic freedom with massive color gluons is not serious if Higgs-scalars are composites, see discussions later). It should be noted that the local symmetry $\mathcal{G}_o$ is the same for either charge assignment for quarks (integer or fractional).

21. If the reduction takes place via a left-right asymmetric intermediate symmetry, it would be natural to generate a superweak scheme of CP violation rather than a milliweak scheme [R. N. Mohapatra, J. C. Pati and L. Wolfenstein, Carnegie-Mellon Univ. Preprint (COO-3060-48), 1975].

22. H. Georgi and S. L. Glashow, Phys. Rev. Lett. 32, 438 (1974).

23. H. Georgi and S. L. Glashow, Proceedings of the Williamsburg Conference of the American Physical Society (Division of Particles and Fields), No. 23, p. 582 (1974) and H. Fritzsch and P. Minkowski (CALT 68-467). The symmetry $SU(2)_L \times SU(2)_R \times SU(4)'_{L+R}$, being isomorphic to $SO(4) \times SO(6)$ permits a natural extension to SO(10). The SU(5)-model with 30 two-component fermions (Ref. 22) has a built in left-right asymmetry. Its extension to SO(10) requires the introduction of two additional two-component fermions making a total of 32 two-component fermions, which is the fermion content of our minimal symmetry-model (Ref. 2-4).

24. Some considerations of $SU(4)_L \times SU(4)_R$- breaking has been considered by S. Eliezer and D. A. Ross (Nucl. Phys. 1974) and D. A. Ross (Imperial College Preprint, 1973, unpublished). We would, however, require a breaking which preserves L ↔ R and color ↔ valency discrete symmetries in the lagrangian (except in scalar mass terms).

25. J. C. Pati, Abdus Salam and J. Strathdee, Trieste Preprint IC/74/121 (October, 1974); To appear in Nuovo Cim.

26. Note that one cannot utilize a loop-diagram, in this case, if we want proton to decay in second order of gauge coupling. The tree diagram is suppressed by both m_E^2 and m_N^2.

27. R. N. Mohapatra, J. C. Pati and Abdus Salam (forthcoming preprint).

28. Such a symmetry can be preserved by all terms in the lagrangian except the quartic terms in the scalar potential (Ref. 27). The basic technique of introducing auxilliary global symmetries in the space of scalar multiplets was suggested by B. DeWitt Nucl. Phys. B51, 237 (1973); and I. Bars, M. B. Halpern and M. Yoshimura, Phys. Rev. D7, 1233 (1973).

29. Motivation for massless gluons based on the infrared shielding hypothesis has been forcefully suggested by H. Frotzsch, M. Gell-Mann and H. Leutwyler, Phys. Lett. B47, 365 (1973), S. Weinberg,

Phys. Rev. Lett. 31, 494 (1973) and D. J. Gross and F. Wilczek, Phys. Rev. D8, 3633 (1973).

30. The known limits are summarized in Ref. 5.

31. D. Gross and F. Wilczek, Phys. Rev. Lett. 30, 1343 (1973); D. Politzer ibid 30, 1346 (1973). S. Coleman and D. Gross, Phys. Rev. Lett. 31, 8511 (1973).

32. R. Jackiw and K. Johnson, Phys. Rev. D8, 2386, (1973), J. M. Cornwall and R. E. Norton, Phys. Rev. D8, 3338 (1973); D. J. Gross and A. Neveu (to be published in Phys. Rev.), E. Eichten and F. L. Feinberg (UCLA Preprint, 1974), See other references in R. Jackiw (Report at this conference). For excellent discussions, see S. Coleman, Erice lectures (1973).

33. This viewpoint does, of course, alter within a super-symmetry theory, which can provide solutions to the problem of asymptotic freedom with elementary scalars. See Adbus Salam (report at this conference).

34. M. Gaillard and B. W. Lee, Phys. Lett. 33, 108 (1974). G. Alterelli and L. Maiani; Rome Preprint (1974).

35. A. Zee, Phys. Rev. D8, 4043 (1973); T. Applequist and H. Georgi, Phys. Rev. D8, 4000 (1973).

36. The consistency of this possibility with the semileptonic and leptonic data taking into account finite renormalization differences between hadronic and leptonic vertices is presently under study.

37. This is noted in the first two papers of Ref. 19.

38. Possible need for S and P on the basis of threshold pion-production data in neutral-current processes has been stressed by S. Adler, Phys. Rev. Lett. 33, 1511 (1974). General possibilities of such interactions have been considered by B. Kayser, G. T. Garvey, E. Fishbach and S. P. Rosen, Phys. Lett. 52B, 385 (1974). R. L. Kingsley, F. Wilczek, R. Shrock, and S. Treiman (to be published).

39. The approximate symmetry for low-energy strong interactions in our model is SU(4) × SU(3)^{1}. There is the intriguing question of whether combined with spin, this should lead to SU(8) × SU(3)' or the mutually exclusive possibility SU(4) × SU(6)'. Theoretically, there is a fundamental distinction in our scheme between the SU(4) and SU(3)'-sides, since we gauge SU(3)' strongly, but not SU(4). The color-octet of gauge mesons, thus introduced, cannot be assigned to a 35 of SU(6)'. It may not thus be surprising if SU(4) × SU(6)' is not a good classification symmetry. On the other hand the (ρ,ω,ϕ, ...) together with (π,η,η, ...) interpreted as ($q\bar{q}$)-composites, can be assigned to multiplets of SU(6) × SU(3)'.

40. J. C. Pati and Abdus Salam, Phys. Rev. Lett. 34, 613 (1975).

41. J. J. Aubert et al., Phys. Rev. Lett. 33, 1404 (1974); J. E. Augustin et al., ibid 33, 1406 (1974); G. S. Abrams et al., ibid 33, 1408 (1974).

42. See relevant references in F. Gilman, Review at this conference (SLAC-PUB-1537).

43. We have examined whether the large enhancement of a somewhat similar decay $\rho' \to \rho+\pi\pi$ ($h'^2_{\rho}/4\pi \gtrsim 400$) may be relevant to enhance $\psi' \to \psi+\pi+\pi$ to the extent needed (if it were a forbidden decay) and find that this is unlikely.

44. R. Lynch, Report of SPEAR data (at this conference).

45. J. C. Pati and Abdus Salam, Univ. of Maryland Tech. Rep. 75-056 (Feb., 75); submitted to Phys. Rev. Letters.

46. Such a mixing has been suggested by I. Bars and R. D. Peccei (SLAC-preprint), W. Alles (Bologna Univ.) and M. A. B. Beg and H. Pagels (private communications). They have assumed, however, that only one (1,8) multiplet is involved, which mixing with (15,8) in the ω-ϕ-manner gives rise to $\psi = (\omega,\gamma_c)$ and $\psi' = (\phi,\gamma_c)$. Beg and Pagels and Clavelli and Yang (private communications) have pointed out to us a possible difficulty with this assignment, which is this. Following the SU(6) ×

SU(3)'-hypothesis, one should expect the (ρ,γ_c)-member to lie around 3.1 GeV nearly degenerate with (ω,γ_c). This should permit the decay $\psi' = (\phi,\gamma_c) \to (\rho,\gamma_c) + \pi$ (analogous to $\phi \to \rho\pi$) with a relatively large partial width $\gtrsim$ 500 KeV. No such difficulty appears to arise with our assignment even if we allow C(1,8) ↔ C(15,8)-mixing (see model II), because of our choice ψ = U = color-gluon and the presence of two color-octets in our scheme.

47. We use the information that no fourth narrow particle ($\Gamma \lesssim$ 20 MeV) was seen at SPEAR between 3.2 to 5.9 GeV (A. M. Boyarski et al., SLAC-PUB-1523).

48. The fact that there is at least some suppression in the conversion of a $\lambda\bar{\lambda}$ or $\chi\bar{\chi}$-quark pair to a $(N\bar{N})$-quark pair might have its origin in the basic force being due to color-gluon exchange. The color-gluons are coupled to currents, which change color, but not valency. The t-channel exchanges of color-gluons thus cannot change the valency of quarks. The s-channel exchanges can change valency, but they require a minimum of three color-gluons in the intermediate state (thus $m^2_{\text{intermediate}} \gtrsim (80)\ \text{GeV}^2$), if the initial $(q\bar{q})$-pair is a color-singlet with $J^{PC} = 1^{--}$. This might lead to a suppression of order 1:100 in the amplitude.

49. B. Knapp et al., Fermi Lab Results (Preprint, 1975).

50. L. Clavelli (Maryland Tech. Rep. 75-058). We should note that the conventional assumption that the $\phi_c \to \gamma$-transition is a constant for virtual photon $(\text{mass})^2$ varrying from 9 $(\text{GeV})^2$ to zero must be taken with caution.

51. With the damping, the photoproduction data (Ref. 49) yields $\sigma(\psi N \to \psi + X) \approx 12$ mb for ψ = color gluon U, which is comparable to ρ,ω and ϕ cross sections.

52. This is consistent with our requirement (Ref. 2, 27) that non-electromagnetic color symmetry breaking

term H_8' is at most of order (1 to few)α. Thus members within the same color-octet should be degenerate to within (1/2 to 50) MeV (say).

53. The analog of the formula $R = \sigma(e^-e^+ \to \text{hadrons})/\sigma(e^-e^+ \to \mu^-\mu^+) = \Sigma Q^2$ suggests $\Gamma(\tilde{V}_\rho^+ \to \mu^+\nu)$; $\Gamma(\tilde{V}_\rho^+ \to e^+\nu)$: $\Gamma(\tilde{V}_\rho^+ \to \text{hadrons}) \approx 1{:}1{:}3$, (ignoring charmed particle modes) for $m_{\tilde{V}} \approx 3$ GeV. The mixing of $V^\pm_{K*}$ and $V^\pm_\rho$ with $W^\pm$ leads to a mixing of V^o_{K*} with U^o. This induces decays of V^o_{K*} and $\bar{V}^o_{K*} \to$ hadrons + γ, hadrons and lepton pairs with lifetimes $\lesssim 10^{-12}$ sec.

54. A Benvenuti et al., Phys. Rev. Lett. 34, 419 (1975).

55. For excellent discussions on phenomenology and weak decays of charmed hadrons, see M. K. Gaillard, B. W. Lee and J. L. Rosner, Rev. Mod. Phys. (to be published); G. Altarelli, N. Cabibbo and L. Maiani (Preprint, 1974); R. L. Kingsley, S. B. Treiman, F. Wilczek and A. Zee (Preprint, 1974).

56. Short distance expansion arguments suggest (Ref. 55) that SU(4)-20 plet is enhanced, so that charmed particle decays ($D^o \to K^-\pi^+$, $F^+ \to K^+\bar{K}^o$, ...) should be enhanced nearly to the same extent as strange-particle decays ($K_S \to \pi^+\pi^-$). On the other hand, SU(4)-breaking may alter this picture. On the hypothesis of "tadpole"-dominance (or dispersion theoretic arguments) or the simple loop diagram enhancement (S. Oneda, J. C. Pati and B. Sakita, Phys. Rev. 119, 482 (1960)) (which is available for strange particle decays but not for the $\cos^2\theta$ dependent charm particle decays), it is possible that charm particle nonleptonic decays are not quite as enhanced; this may increase their leptonic or semileptonic decay branching ratios.

57. Once color association with any of the ψ-particles is established, it would imply α and/or $\beta \neq 0$ (see Eq. (2)). This would eliminate the familiar fractional charge hypothesis for quarks. Within the class α and/or $\beta \neq 0$, integer-charge quarks (with $\alpha=\beta=1$) are most natural, since that allows

us to resolve the quark-puzzle.

58. This comes about by noting that ν_e couples to proton-quark via X_p, but ν_μ couples to charmed-quark via X_χ. Due to the absence of charmed quarks in normal hadrons, this interaction cannot enhance $\nu_\mu + p \rightarrow \nu_\mu + p$, but it can enhance $\nu_e + p \rightarrow \nu_e + p$ (See discussions in the first two papers of Ref. 19).

59. Quark-lepton transitions can be rapid at sufficiently high energies, which are available at the early stages of the universe. Its effects on cosmological models are being studied by P. Yasskin and R. Gowdy.

60. Due to propagators of the form $(q^2-m_U^2)^{-1}$ with space like $q^2 < 0$, the production of color objects in ep-reactions above threshold would be more prominent at low q^2 and high energy. To test scaling, one needs at least moderately large native q^2, at which color-production is damped (since $m_U^2 \gtrsim 9\ (\mathrm{GeV})^2$).

61. It is tempting to ask: can gravity be generated entirely spontaneously?

THEORETICAL INTERPRETATION OF RECENT NEUTRAL CURRENT RESULTS*

Stephen L. Adler

The Institute for Advanced Study

Princeton, New Jersey 08540

I. INTRODUCTION

I wish to describe work on the structure of the weak neutral current stimulated by data from the Argonne bubble chamber which were presented in preliminary form at the London Conference last summer[1] and in revised form at the Annaheim meeting.[2] The Argonne (ANL) results for the $p\pi^-$ invariant mass distribution in $\nu n \to \nu p\pi^-$ raise two intriguing possibilities:

(i) That the threshold (in invariant mass) cross section for neutral current $p\pi^-$ production may be appreciable. The Argonne measurements correspond[2] to a cross section of $(18.9 + 9.4) \times 10^{-41}$ cm^2 for producing $p\pi^-$ in the first two 20 MeV bins above threshold, as obtained from 5 events with an estimated background of 0.42 ± 0.24 events. That is,

*Research sponsored in part by the Atomic Energy Commission, Grant No. AT(11-1) 2220.

$$\sigma_{2\ \mathrm{bin}}^{\mathrm{ANL}} = \sigma\left(\begin{matrix}\nu n\to\nu p\pi^- \\ \mathrm{ANL\ flux\ averaged}\end{matrix}\ 1080 \leq W \leq 1120\right) \sim \qquad (1)$$

$$(18.9 \pm 9.4) \times 10^{-41}\mathrm{cm}^2 \quad .$$

(ii) That the (3,3) resonance may not be excited by the weak neutral current. This possibility will be crucially tested by a high statistics Brookhaven (BNL) experiment which should have preliminary results in a few months.

I will assume, as the basis for the subsequent discussion, that the indications (i) and (ii) from the ANL experiment are in fact correct, and will explore their consequences for the structure of the weak neutral current.

II. V, A CASE

2A. Analysis of the Threshold Region - ANL Experiment

The basic idea which I exploit in analyzing[3] the ANL experiment is that soft pion methods, based on current algebra and PCAC, can be used to relate threshold or low energy pion production to the same form factors which determine elastic neutrino scattering, once the basic spatial and internal symmetry structure of the weak neutral current is specified. Hence known bounds on $\sigma(\nu p)$ and on the deep inelastic neutral current ratios $R_{\nu,\bar{\nu}} = \sigma(\nu,\bar{\nu} + N \to \nu,\bar{\nu} + X)/\sigma(\nu,\bar{\nu} + N \to \mu^-,\mu^+ + X')$, imply definite upper bounds on the low energy pion production cross section, for a given assumed structure of the weak neutral current. The specific restrictions imposed in analyzing the ANL experiment are the 95% confidence level limits

(a) $\sigma^{ANL}(\nu p) \leq 0.32\ \sigma^{ANL}(\nu n \to \mu^- p) \sim 0.26 \times 10^{-38} cm^2$,

(b) $3R_\nu + R_{\bar{\nu}} \leq 1.5$. (2)

I calculate the pion production cross section $\sigma^{ANL}_{2\ bin}$ taking into account the Born (external line insertion and pion pole) diagrams and equal time commutator contributions, which give the standard soft pion prediction. In the V,A case (but not in the S, P, T case discussed below) I also take into account the effects of the tail of the (3,3) resonance and of a well-defined class of pion recoil $[O(q_\pi)]$ corrections. The numerical precedure is to maximize $\sigma^{ANL}_{2\ bin}$ subject to the constraints of Eq. (2), giving the following results for various assumptions about the structure of the weak neutral current:

(1) Pure isoscalar V,A. We assume dipole vector and axial-vector form factors with, for definiteness, a characteristic dipole mass $M_N = 0.94$ GeV,

$$\begin{aligned} F_1^S &= \lambda_1(1-k^2/M_N^2)^{-2} \quad , \\ 2M_N F_2^S &= \lambda_2(1-k^2/M_N^2)^{-2} \quad , \\ g_A^S &= \lambda_3(1-k^2/M_N^2)^{-2} \quad . \end{aligned} \tag{3}$$

Searching over $\lambda_{1,2,3}$ subject to constraint (a) in Eq. (2) gives the bound

$$\sigma^{ANL}_{2\ bin} \leq 1 \times 10^{-41} cm^2 \quad . \tag{4}$$

(2) Weinberg-Salam model, one parameter form. The neutral current here has the form

$$J_N^\lambda = F_3^\lambda - F_3^{5\lambda} - 2\sin^2\theta_W(F_3^\lambda + \frac{1}{\sqrt{3}} F_8^\lambda) + \Delta J^\lambda \ , \tag{5}$$

with ΔJ^λ an isoscalar addition which is generally assumed to couple weakly to the low-energy pion-nucleon system. Neglecting ΔJ^{λ} for the moment, and giving $\sin^2\theta_W$ the favored value $\sin^2\theta_W \sim 0.35$, I get

$$\sigma_{2\ \mathrm{bin}}^{\mathrm{ANL}} = 0.75 \times 10^{-41}\mathrm{cm}^2 \quad . \tag{6}$$

(3) Weinberg-Salam model, two parameter form. Let us continue to neglect ΔJ_{λ}, but we put an adjustable strength parameter κ into the current of Eq. (5), giving

$$J_N^{\lambda} = \kappa[F_3^{\lambda} - F_3^{5\lambda} - 2x(F_3^{\lambda} + \frac{1}{\sqrt{3}} F_8^{\lambda})], \; x = \sin^2\theta_W \; . \tag{7}$$

Imposing constraint (b) in the form

$$\kappa^2 \; [1 + (1-2x)^2] < 3R_{\nu} + R_{\bar{\nu}} \leq 1.5 \; , \tag{8}$$

and constraint (a), and searching over all values of κ and x gives the bound

$$\sigma_{2\ \mathrm{bin}}^{\mathrm{ANL}} \leq 1.5 \times 10^{-41}\mathrm{cm}^2 \quad . \tag{9}$$

(4) Weinberg-Salam two parameter model plus general isoscalar current. Adding isoscalar V,A currents parameterized as in Eq. (3) to the current of Eq. (7) gives the most general neutral current structure which can be formed from the usual V,A nonets. Again imposing constraints (a) and (b) and searching over the 5-parameter space $\kappa, x, \lambda_1, \lambda_2, \lambda_3$, I find

$$\sigma_{2\ \mathrm{bin}}^{\mathrm{ANL}} \leq 4.4 \times 10^{-41}\mathrm{cm}^2 \quad . \tag{10}$$

This bound is substantially reduced if one uses simple quark model information to incorporate the isoscalar current couplings into the deep inelastic constraint of Eq. (8). Specifically, I make the following three assumptions:

(i) The isoscalar axial renormalization $\sim\frac{3}{5}$ (isovector axial renormalization = 1.24) $\sim$ 0.74.

(ii) The isoscalar vector current magnetic moment is not large

$$|2M_N F_2^S/F_1^S| \leq 1.5.$$

(iii) The strange parton and antiparton content of the nucleon can be neglected, an approximation which should be valid to the 20% level.[4] For targets with equal numbers of protons and neutrons, the parton longitudinal momentum distributions then simply give a single overall x-dependent factor in the deep inelastic scattering cross sections $d^2\sigma/dx\,dy$, which can be eliminated by always considering ratios relative to charged-current-induced reactions.

Using (i) - (iii) and again searching over the parameter space I find the bound

$$\sigma_{2\ \mathrm{bin}}^{\mathrm{ANL}} \leq 1.5 \times 10^{-41}\mathrm{cm}^2 \quad . \qquad (11)$$

Evidently, all of the bounds given above are substantially below the 2 bin cross section observed in the Argonne experiment.

Finally, as a check on both the current algebra procedure and the Argonne flux estimates, I have repeated the above analysis for the charged current reaction $\nu p \to \mu^- p \pi^+$. Here the predicted cross section for $\pi^+ p$ invariant mass in the first two bins is $6.9 \times 10^{-41}\mathrm{cm}^2$, in satisfactory agreement with the observed value of $(9.3 \pm 4.7) \times 10^{-41}\mathrm{cm}^2$.

2B. Analysis of the Region W ≤ 1.4 in the BNL Experiment

So far only one result is available from the Brookhaven experiment. For the ratio

$$R_0' = \frac{\sigma(\nu A\ell \to \nu\pi^0 + \ldots)}{\sigma(\nu A\ell \to \mu^-\pi^0 + \ldots)} \quad , \tag{12}$$

the BNL experiment finds the preliminary result

$$0.15 < R_0' < 0.21 \quad . \tag{13}$$

This range for R_0' is in good agreement with the value expected in the Weinberg-Salam model for $\sin^2\theta_W \sim 0.35$. Hence *if* (3,3) excitation, which is expected in the Weinberg-Salam model, is observed in the Brookhaven experiment, the presumption would be strongly in favor of the standard gauge theory interpretation of neutral currents, and one would be forced to conclude that the Argonne results are spurious. On the other hand, what are the implications for neutral current structure if the BNL experiment does not see (3,3) excitation? Absence of the (3,3) would suggest an isoscalar neutral current, since isovector V,A currents strongly excite the (3,3). The R_0' range of Eq. (13), together with the assumption of an isoscalar neutral current, implies that the Brookhaven-flux-averaged cross section for $\nu n \to \nu p\pi^-$ with $W \leq 1.4$ GeV is

$$\sigma^{BNL}\begin{pmatrix}\nu n \to \nu p\pi^- \\ W \leq 1.4\end{pmatrix} \sim (63 - 89) \times 10^{-41}\text{cm}^2 . \tag{14}$$

In the absence of resonance excitation, the current algebra pole plus commutator expression for weak pion production should be valid over the larger W interval extending up to 1.4 GeV, so using the current algebra matrix element, together with the form factors of Eq. (3), we can set a bound on the cross section in Eq. (14). I impose the constraints

$$\text{(a)}\ \sigma^{BNL}(\nu p) \leq 0.24\sigma^{BNL}(\nu p \to \mu^- n), \tag{15a}$$

(This is the old Cundy et al.[5] 95% confidence level limit from CERN, which has a similar neutrino flux to the AGS);

$$\text{(b)} \quad 3R_\nu + R_{\bar{\nu}} \leq 1.5 \quad . \tag{15b}$$

Again, I assume the quark model result $g_A^{\text{isoscalar}} \sim 0.74$ and neglect strange partons and antipartons in incorporating isoscalar currents into the deep inelastic constraint.

The resulting bounds are plotted in Fig. 1 versus the isoscalar vector current g-factor $g \equiv 2M_N F_2^S / F_1^S$.

Evidently, to agree with the observed cross section magnitude it is essential to have an isoscalar vector current with $|g|$ larger than about 6 in magnitude. This rather peculiar vector current produces a characteristic change in the W-spectrum predicted for the BNL flux, as plotted in the dashed curve in Fig. 2. [The plotted curve is calculated for the case of a vector current

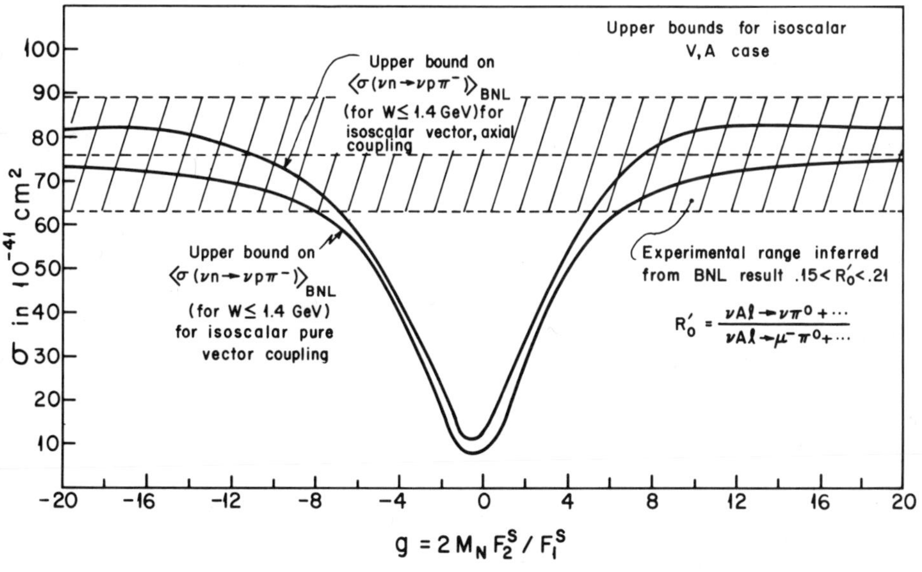

Figure 1

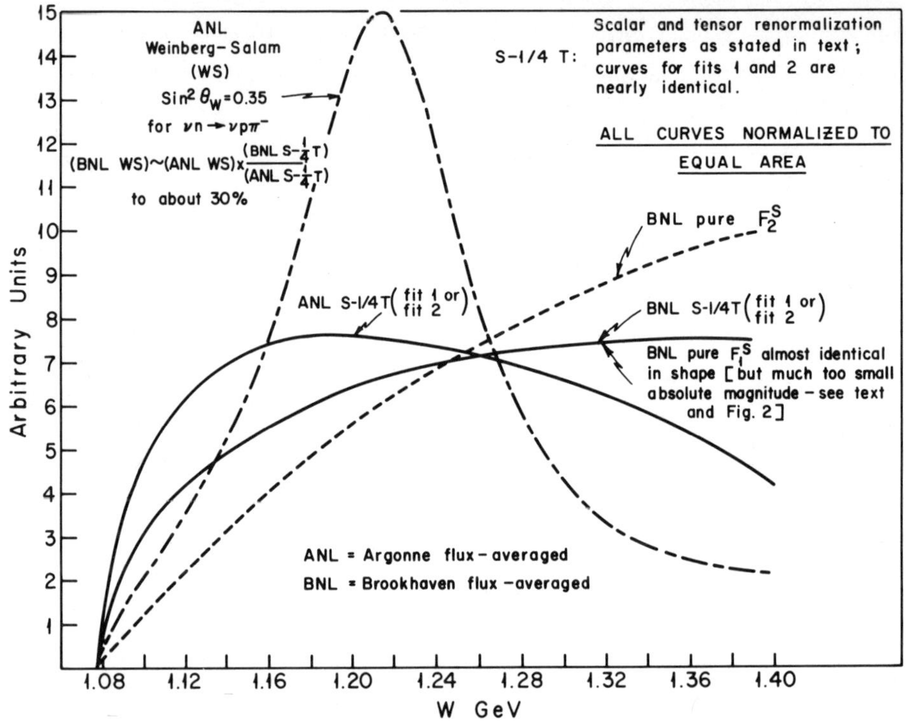

Figure 2

containing only an F_2^S form factor; for the F_1^S, F_2^S admixture corresponding to $|g| = 6$, the curve is barely changed.] As shown in Fig. 2, a vector current with very large nucleon magnetic moment produces a depression in the W distribution for small W (relative to the pure F_1^S case), with an almost linear rise from threshold, and a corresponding enhancement at the large W end of of the range. An experiment with good statistics should be able to see this effect.

III. S, P, T CASE

If the Argonne results described above are confirmed in subsequent experiments, then as I have argued above, the neutral current cannot have a purely V, A structure. The logical next step is to consider the possible presences of S, P, T type couplings.[6] Since V, A coupling leave neutrino helicity unchanged, while S, P, T flip neutrino helicity, the two groups of couplings do not interfere. Hence it suffices to consider S, P, T couplings alone. If both V, A and S, P, T turn out to be present, one merely adds the corresponding cross section formulas to get the total cross section in any neutral current reaction. Even for S, T, P in isolation, the labor involved in analyzing weak pion production is very substantial. The work which I will now describe was done in collaboration with Bill Colglazier, Bruce Healy, Inga Karliner, Judy Lieberman, Yee-Jack Ng and Hung-Sheng Tsao, all postdoctoral members at the Institute for Advanced Study.

For the neutral current induced reaction $\nu+A\to\nu+B$, with A, B hadronic states, we assume the following matrix element structure when left-handed neutrinos are incident:

$$M_{A\to B} = \frac{G}{\sqrt{2}} [\bar{\nu}(1-\gamma_5)\nu \langle B|F + F^5|A\rangle + \bar{\nu}\sigma_{\lambda\eta}(1-\gamma_5)\nu \langle B|F^{\lambda\eta}|A\rangle] \quad . \tag{16}$$

The scalar, pseudoscalar and tensor neutral currents F, F^5 and $F^{\lambda\eta}$ are built out of quark model S, P, T nonets,

$$\begin{aligned} F &= g_{S0}F_0 + g_{S3}F_3 + g_{S8}F_8 \quad , \\ F^5 &= g_{P0}F_0^5 + g_{P3}F_3^5 + g_{P8}F_8^5 \quad , \\ F^{\lambda\eta} &= g_{T0}F_0^{\lambda\eta} + g_{T3}F_3^{\lambda\eta} + g_{T8}F_8^{\lambda\eta} \quad , \end{aligned} \tag{17}$$

with

$$\begin{aligned} F_j &= \bar{\psi}\tfrac{1}{2}\lambda_j \psi , \\ F_j^5 &= \bar{\psi}\tfrac{1}{2}\lambda_j \gamma_5\psi , \\ F_j^{\lambda\eta} &= \bar{\psi}\sigma^{\lambda\eta} \tfrac{1}{2}\lambda_j\psi \quad . \end{aligned}$$

The one nucleon matrix elements of F_j, F_j^5 and $F_j^{\lambda\eta}$ involve the following vertex structures (k = momentum transfer)

$$\text{S:} \quad F_S^{(j)}(k^2) \qquad , \; j=0,3,8,$$

$$\text{P:} \quad F_P^{(j)}(k^2)\,\gamma_5 \qquad , \; j=0,3,8$$

$$\text{T:} \quad T_1^{(j)}(k^2)\sigma^{\lambda\eta} + i\,\frac{\hat{T}_2^{(j)}(k^2)}{M_N}(\gamma^\lambda k^\eta - \gamma^\eta k^\lambda) + \frac{T_3^{(j)}(k^2)}{M_N}(\sigma^{\lambda\nu} k_\nu k^\eta - \sigma^{\eta\nu} k_\nu k^\lambda) \quad , \; j=0,3,8 \tag{19}$$

The calculation divides naturally into 3 phases.

(1) First it is necessary to get a table of the renormalization constants describing the S, P, T current couplings to nucleons. That is, one must know the zero momentum transfer values $F_S^{(j)}(0)$, $F_P^{(j)}(0)$, $T_1^{(j)}(0)$,... of the form factors appearing in the vertex structure of Eq. (19). For the scalar and pseudoscalar couplings, we obtained expressions relative to the constant $F_S^{(8)}(0)$ by using SU_3 and chiral $SU_3 \times SU_3$ within the framework of the Gell-Mann-Oakes-Renner model. For $F_S^{(8)}(0)$ and the tensor renormalization parameters, we used the quark model with spherically symmetric quark wave functions to relate the wanted parameters to known parameters (g_A, $dg_A/dk^2|_0$, μ_p and r_p^2) of the vector and axial-vector currents. We additionally evaluated $F_S^{(8)}(0)$ and the tensor parameters using the explicit wave functions of the MIT "bag" model. A detailed description of the calculational methods used, and a table of re-results, is contained in a paper describing this aspect of the work.[7]

(2) Next it is necessary to evaluate the various cross sections needed to repeat the analysis described above in the case when S, P, T couplings are present. As a warm-up, we began by calculating the elastic neutrino proton scattering cross section implied by the matrix element structure of Eqs. (16)-(19). The result may be written as

$$\frac{d\sigma}{dt} = \frac{G^2}{8\pi M_N^2 E^2} \Sigma , \tag{20}$$

$$\begin{aligned}\Sigma = \tfrac{1}{2}t \{\tfrac{1}{2}(t+eM_N^2)|F_S'|^2 + \tfrac{1}{2}t|F_P|^2 \\ + 4\mathrm{Re}(F_S' T_2^*)(4M_NE-t) + 2\frac{|T_2|^2}{M_N^2}[(4M_NE-t)^2 - t^2]\} \\ - \mathrm{Re}[(F_S' - F_P) T_1^*]\, t(4M_NE-t) - 4\,\mathrm{Re}(T_2T_1^*)t^2 \\ + 2\,|T_1|^2 [(4M_NE-t)^2 - 2M_N^2 t] ,\end{aligned}$$

with

$$\begin{aligned} t &= -k^2 , \\ F_S' &= F_S + \frac{2T_3}{M_N^2}(4M_NE-t) , \\ T_2 &= \hat{T}_2 - 2T_3 . \end{aligned} \tag{21}$$

For future use, let me record the principal scalar-tensor and pseudo-scalar-tensor interference terms:

scalar tensor

$$t(4M_NE - t)\, F_S(2\hat{T}_2 - T_1) , \tag{22a}$$

pseudoscalar-tensor

$$t(4M_NE - t)F_PT_1 . \tag{22b}$$

The deep inelastic cross section can be obtained from the papers of Kayser et al.[6] or Kingsley et al.[6] [As a check, it also can be obtained as a special limiting case of Eq. (20).] In terms of the coupling constants introduced in Eq. (17), we find

$$3R_\nu + R_{\bar{\nu}} = \frac{1}{8}\left[\left(g_{S0}\sqrt{\frac{2}{3}} + g_{S8}\frac{1}{\sqrt{3}}\right)^2 + g_{S3}^{\ 2} + \left(g_{P0}\sqrt{\frac{2}{3}} + g_{P8}\frac{1}{\sqrt{3}}\right)^2 + g_{P3}^2\right] + 7\left[\left(g_{T0}\sqrt{\frac{2}{3}} + g_{T8}\frac{1}{\sqrt{3}}\right)^2 + g_{T3}^{\ 2}\right], \tag{23}$$

with related expressions for R_ν and $R_{\bar{\nu}}$ individually and for the y-distributions $(\sigma^\nu)^{-1}\, d\sigma^\nu/dy$ and $(\sigma^{\bar{\nu}})^{-1} d\sigma^{\bar{\nu}}/dy$.

To evaluate the pion production matrix element in the S, P, T case we use soft pion methods, which gives the matrix element as the sum of Born approximation pole terms and equal time commutator contributions. We neglect $O(q_\pi)$ corrections except where they occur in pion pole diagrams, which are treated exactly. The commutator structure in the S, P, T case is very different from that when only V, A currents are present. In the V, A case the commutator term is of SU_3 F-type, and vanishes identically for isoscalar currents. By contrast, in the S, P, T case the commutator has SU_3 D-type structure, and is non-vanishing even when the currents are isoscalar SU_3 singlets. Specifically, the commutator term in the S, P, T SU_3-singlet case involves the form factors defined in Eq. (19) according to the following pattern:

$$F_S^{(0)} \rightarrow F_P^{(3)} ,$$
$$F_P^{(0)} \rightarrow F_S^{(3)} , \qquad (24)$$
$$T^{(0)} \rightarrow -T^{(3)}$$

{Same pattern for all three tensor structures.}

Terms in elastic scattering and pion production pole diagrams.

Corresponding terms in pion production equal-time commutator term

Our calculational procedure was to express the Born diagrams and the commutator terms in terms of a convenient set of 11 basic covariants, from which the cross section was calculated by squaring and using standard trace techniques. The result is very complicated, covering two pages when written out in full. (The algebraic aspects of the cross section calculation were checked by independently calculating the amplitude acting on nucleon Pauli spinors and assembling it using the complex arithmetic feature of Fortran 4, and then checking this program against the program for the covariant cross section evaluation. The computational advantage of the covariant expression was that it allowed explicit averaging over the pion azimuthal angle, reducing by one the number of numerical integrations needed to get the pion production cross section.)

In order to permit study of the case when isovector S, P, T contributions are present as well as isoscalar, we evaluated (3,3) excitation in the static model using a straightforward extension of the method used by Bell and Berman[8] in the V, A case. We find that F_3^{5} and $F_3^{\lambda\eta}$ excite the (3,3) resonance in leading order in the static approximation; the excitation of the (3,3) by F_3 is non-static but turns out only to be reduced by a factor $|q_\pi|/(W-M_N)$ (rather than $|q_\pi|/M_N$), relative to the pseudo-scalar and tensor contributions, and so is not small. Hence if the couplings g_{S3}, g_{P3}, g_{T3} are appreciable, a visible (3,3) bump should be seen, but so far we have made no quantitative studies of the effects of isovector admixtures.

(3) The third and final phase of the calculation is to do numerical searching. For the moment, we have concentrated on the case in which the S, P, T currents are pure SU_3-singlets [and hence do not excite the (3,3) resonance], and even here we have only very preliminary results to present. Bearing this in mind, let me nonetheless describe some of the qualitative features which have emerged from our numerical studies so far. In all of the numerical work, we assume the nucleon form factors to have the dipole form

$$ff(k^2) = ff(0)\,[1 - k^2/(0.9\ \mathrm{GeV})^2]^{-2} \quad , \qquad (25)$$

with 0.9 GeV the typical dipole mass suggested by the quark model calculations described above. The only exception to Eq. (25) occurs in the pion pole terms where, in addition to the explicit pion propagator, we assume a single pole pion form factor

$$[1 - k^2/(0.9\ \mathrm{GeV})^2]^{-1} \quad . \qquad (26)$$

Our results in various cases are as follows:

(3.1) Pure scalar. For an SU_3-singlet pure scalar weak neutral current we find [with a pion-nucleon scattering "sigma term" of 28 MeV, which corresponds to the quark model prediction of equal $F_S^{(0)}(0)$ and $F_S^{(8)}(0)$, but independently of the actual value of $F_S^{(0)}(0)$] that the maximum Argonne 2 bin cross section, subject to the elastic scattering and deep inelastic scattering constraints (a) and (b) of Eq. (2), is

$$\sigma_{2\ \mathrm{bin}}^{\mathrm{ANL}} \leq 2.1 \times 10^{-41}\mathrm{cm}^2 \quad . \tag{27}$$

That is, there is a gain of a factor of 2 relative to the isoscalar V, A case. The predicted W-distribution shapes are essentially identical to the S - ¼T case plotted in Fig. 2. For values of the "sigma term" smaller than 28 MeV (such values are possible but not experimentally favored) the renormalization constant $F_S^{(0)}(0)$ can become small relative to $F_S^{(8)}(0)$, permitting a substantially larger $\sigma_{2\ \mathrm{bin}}^{\mathrm{ANL}}$ without violating the elastic scattering constraint. Values of $\sigma_{2\ \mathrm{bin}}^{\mathrm{ANL}}$ up to a maximum of order $(8\text{-}14) \times 10^{-41}\mathrm{cm}^2$ can be obtained in this way. In the fits presented below we keep the "sigma term" at its quark model value of 28 MeV, although a systematic study of the effects of relaxing this condition will be made later on. <u>(3.2) Tensor-scalar mixtures</u>. We consider next SU_3-singlet tensor-scalar mixtures. If we give all scalar and tensor renormalization constants their quark model values, then subject to constraints (a) and (b) we find that $\sigma_{2\ \mathrm{bin}}^{\mathrm{ANL}}$ is still bounded by $\sim 2 \times 10^{-41}\mathrm{cm}^2$. (A similar statement holds for pseudoscalar-tensor mixtures.) However, if we permit reasonable variations of the renormalization constants from the quark model predictions, then values of $\sigma_{2\ \mathrm{bin}}^{\mathrm{ANL}}$ of order $(7\text{-}10) \times 10^{-41}\mathrm{cm}^2$ can be obtained for scalar-tensor mixtures. This range is roughly an order of magnitude larger than the maximum obtained in the V,A isoscalar case, and although smaller than the ANL cross section is not in serious disagreement with experiment, given the limited statistics of the Argonne experiment. A common qualitative feature of parameter sets which give large values of $\sigma_{2\ \mathrm{bin}}^{\mathrm{ANL}}$ is that $\hat{T}_2^{(0)}$ is of opposite sign from its quark model value, leading to destructive S-T interference in νp scattering while, at the same time, there is constructive S-T interference in the commutator term contributing to the pion production reaction. To examine this in more detail, we note that the commutator term in weak pion production makes a contribution to the pion production cross section identical in form to the elastic cross section Eq. (20), except that where the elastic cross section has contributions (in the S, T, SU_3-singlet case) from $F_S^{(0)}$ and $T_1^{(0)}$, $\hat{T}_2^{(0)}$, $T_3^{(0)}$, the pion production commutator contribution will have contributions from $F_P^{(3)}$, $-T_1^{(3)}$, $-\hat{T}_2^{(3)}$, $-T_3^{(3)}$, according to the correspondence rule of Eq. (24). So the relevant S-T interference terms in the two cases are:

	Interference term-see Eq. (22)	Quark model value
elastic νp scattering	$[2(\hat{T}_2^{(0)})-T_1^{(0)}]F_S^{(0)}$	$[2\times(-3.75)-0.87]F_S^{(0)} = -8.4F_S^{(0)}$

Sample fit #1	Sample fit #2
$[2\times(7.5)-0.62]F_S^{(0)} = 14.4F_S^{(0)}$	$[2\times(1.9)-6.62]F_S^{(0)} = 3.2F_S^{(0)}$

	Interference term-see Eq. (22)	Quark model value
pion production commutator term	$-T_1^{(3)}\ F_P^{(3)}$	$-1.45F_P^{(3)}$

Sample fit #1	Sample fit #2
$-2.1F_P^{(3)}$	$-2.1F_P^{(3)}$

(all multiplied by $g_{S0}g_{T0}$, which is <0 for both fits) (28)

The quark model value for $\hat{T}_2^{(0)}$ gives the interference terms in both cases the same sign, so that strong constructive interference in neutrino proton scattering, leading to too large a cross section for $\sigma^{ANL}(\nu p)$ when the parameters are adjusted to try to make $\sigma_{2\ bin}^{ANL}$ large. (This is just the mechanism operative in the V,A case which leads to the small upper bounds on $\sigma_{2\ bin}^{ANL}$ derived above.) When the sign of $\hat{T}_2^{(0)}$ is reversed, a large pion production cross section relative to the neutrino proton scattering cross section becomes possible. The parameter values in fit #1 are rather extreme [we will see below that they suppress $\sigma^{ANL}(\nu p)$ much more than necessary], but those for fit #2 may not be unreasonable. Although it is perhaps worrysome that one has to change the sign of $\hat{T}_2^{(0)}$ from the quark model prediction, there is one important respect in which tensor currents differ from vector and axial-vector currents, where all of the quark model predictions of static quantities are quite good. In the tensor case, order k vector meson couplings of the form $gF^{\lambda\eta} = g(\partial^\lambda A^\eta - \partial^\eta A^\lambda)$ are possible, with A the vector meson field, and would contribute to the renormalization constant $\hat{T}_2$. By contrast, in the vector current case, vector mesons make no contribution to order k as a result of gauge invariance, and so do not make an analogous contribution to the nucleon magnetic moment.) Thus, if SU_3-singlet, color-singlet "gluons" are present, they could make an important contribution to $\hat{T}_2^{(0)}$ through couplings of the form of Eq. (29), resulting in possible large deviations from the quark model predictions, where "glue" contributions are neglected.

One interesting, experimentally testable qualitative feature of our satisfactory fits so far is that since, as just discussed, the S-T interference in νp scattering is destructive, the S-T interference in $\bar{\nu}p$ scattering is constructive, and so one finds $\sigma(\bar{\nu}p) > \sigma(\nu p)$. This prediction is just the opposite of what is expected in the Weinberg-Salam model, where $\sigma(\bar{\nu}p) < \sigma(\nu p)$. However, I should caution that further searching may give satisfactory S, T fits with $\sigma(\bar{\nu}p)$ and $\sigma(\nu p)$ comparable, or even with $\sigma(\nu p) > \sigma(\bar{\nu}p)$, particularly if the "sigma term" is allowed to be smaller than 28 MeV. Further study of this is planned.

Let me now review in more detail the properties of the two sample fits alluded to in Eq. (28). Table 1 summarizes the parameters of the fits. (The value of $F_P^{(3)}(0)/F_S^{(8)}(0)$ is uniquely fixed by pion pole dominance, and so was not varied.)

In both fits, the values of $T_1^{(0,3)}$ were kept reasonably close to the quark model predictions, since these renormalization constants should, in principal, be well determined by the quark model. As discussed in Ref. 7, $\hat{T}_2^{(3)}$ and $T_3^{(0,3)}$ are not expected to be accurately determined within the quark model, and so the values given these constants in the fits are probably reasonable. As I have already discussed, the change in sign of $\hat{T}_2^{(0)}$ from its quark model value is less easy to justify, unless important "glue" contributions are present.

In Figs. 2-6 various quantities of physical interest are plotted for the two fits. In Fig. 2 I have drawn the W-distributions appropriate to the ANL and BNL neutrino fluxes; the two fits give essentially identical curves here. The ANL curve is shifted to the low-W end compared with the BNL curve, as expected for a much softer neutrino beam, but there is no dramatic

Table I

Coupling:	g_{SO}	g_{TO}	
fit #1	1.67	$-\frac{1}{4} \times 1.67 = -.042$	Both S - ¼ T
fit #2	2	$-\frac{1}{4} \times 2 = 0.5$	

Renormalization constant:	$F_S^{(0)}(0)=F_S^{(8)}(0)$ [b]	$T_1^{(0)}(0)$	$T_1^{(3)}(0)$	$\hat{T}_2^{(0)}(0)$	$\hat{T}_2^{(3)}(0)$	$T_3^{(0)}(0)$	$T_3^{(3)}(0)$
Quark model value	1.86 or 2.95[a]	0.87	1.45	-3.75	-0.66	-1.32	0.60
fit #1	3.72	0.62	2.1	7.5	-3.7	2.6	-1.2
fit #2	3.72	0.62	2.1	1.9	-1.9	0.66	-0.3

[a] Obtained by applying SU_3 to the quark model prediction for $F_S^{(3)}(0)$

[b] Equality of $F_S^{(0)}(0)$ and $F_S^{(8)}(0)$ is a quark model prediction, and corresponds to a "sigma term" of 28 MeV.

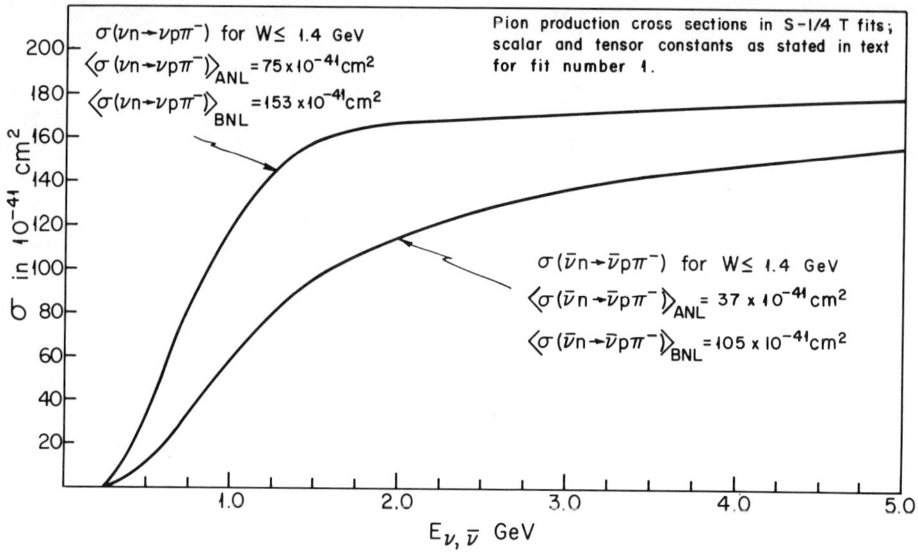

Figure 3

peaking near threshold. Fig. 3 gives the pion production cross section in fit #1 for incident neutrinos and antineutrinos. The curves are quite normal looking in appearance. For neutrinos, the Argonne 2 bin cross section is $\sigma^{ANL}_{2\ bin}$ (fit #1) = $6.6 \times 10^{-41} cm^2 \sim 1.5$ events, about a factor of 3 below what is seen (with very limited statistics); the total ANL pion production cross section for $W \leq 1.4$ GeV of $75 \times 10^{-41} cm^2$ is in reasonable accord with observation. The total Brookhaven cross section for $W \leq 1.4$ GeV is $153 \times 10^{-41} cm^2$, somewhat on the high side as compared with the preliminary range of Eq. (15). Fig. 4 gives the cross sections $\sigma(\nu p)$ and $\sigma(\overline{\nu} p)$ for fit #1, showing that $\sigma(\overline{\nu} p) >> \sigma(\nu p)$. The Argonne flux averaged cross section is $\sigma^{ANL}(\nu p) = 0.07 \times 10^{-38} cm^2$, showing that the parameters of fit #1 suppress νp scattering in the ANL neutrino energy range much more drastically than is needed to satisfy the bound of Eq. (2). In Figures 5 and 6, pion production and neutrino proton scattering

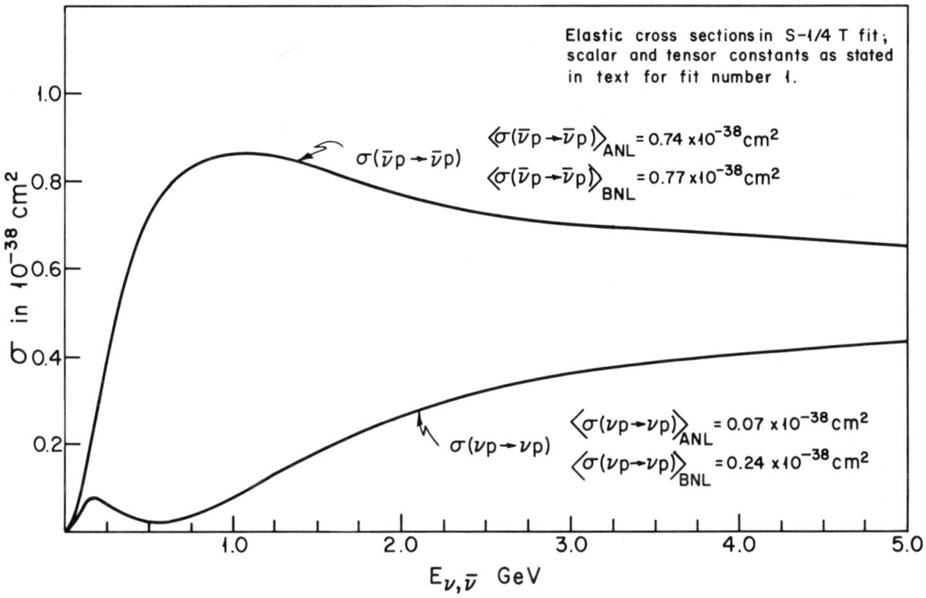

Figure 4

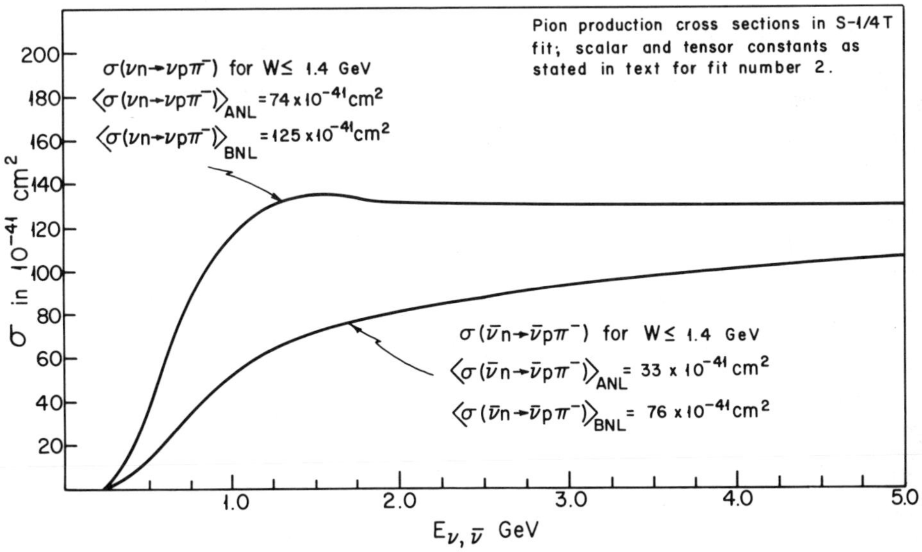

Figure 5

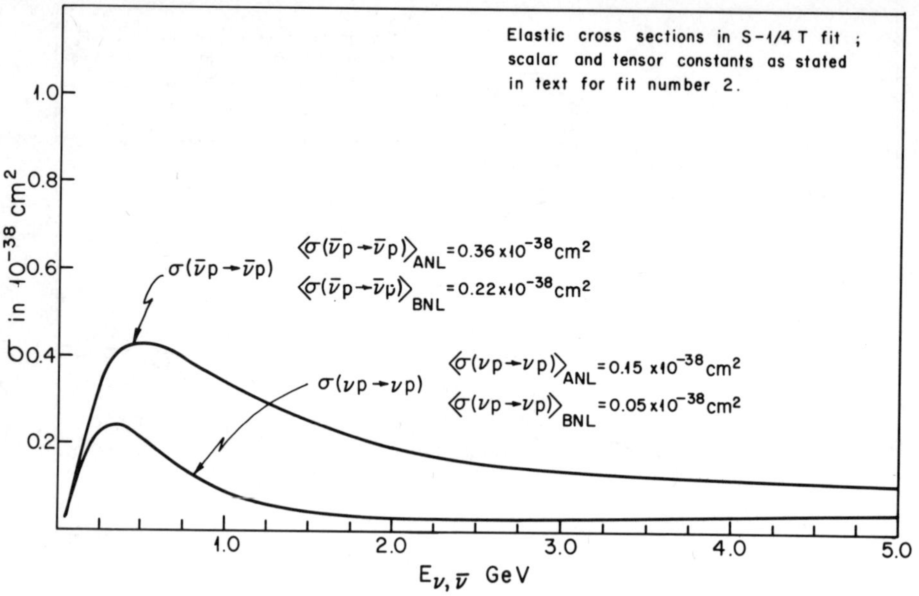

Figure 6

cross sections are shown for the parameters of fit #2. Again, the pion production cross sections have a very normal looking appearance. For neutrinos, the Argonne 2 bin cross section in this case is $\sigma^{ANL}_{2\ bin}$(fit #2) = $6.7 \times 10^{-41}\mathrm{cm}^2$ and the total ANL pion production cross section for $W \leq 1.4$ GeV is $74 \times 10^{-41}\mathrm{cm}^2$, essentially just as in fit #1. The total Brookhaven cross section for $W \leq 1.4$ GeV is $125 \times 10^{-41}\mathrm{cm}^2$, again somewhat high but an improvement over fit #1. The elastic cross section $\sigma(\bar{\nu}p)$ is again larger than $\sigma(\nu p)$, but the disparity is not as extreme as in fit #1; the Argonne flux averaged cross section is $\sigma^{ANL}(\nu p) = 0.15 \times 10^{-38}\mathrm{cm}^2$, about 60% of the maximum allowed by the bound of Eq. (2)

Let me continue now to give some further parameters of interest in the two fits.

	$\frac{\sigma^{ANL}(\nu p)}{0.26\times10^{-38}\,cm^2}$	$\frac{3R_\nu + R_{\bar\nu}}{1.5}$	R_ν	$R_{\bar\nu}$	a_0^2	
fit #1	0.3	0.7	0.25	0.29	13	(30)
fit #2	0.6	1.0	0.36	0.42	19	

The numbers in the first two columns indicate the extent to which constraints (a) and (b) of Eq. (2) are saturated by the two fits. Evidently, in both cases it is the deep inelastic inequality which is the limiting constraint on the overall neutral current strength. This means, as remarked above, that parameters which give somewhat larger values of $\sigma(\nu p)$, and reduced values of the difference $\sigma(\bar\nu p) - \sigma(\nu p)$, may well also be acceptable. The next two columns give the deep inelastic neutral to the charged current ratios R_ν and $R_{\bar\nu}$ for the two fits. The value of R_ν in fit #2 is somewhat large, but otherwise these are satisfactory, especially since final experimental determination of R_ν and $R_{\bar\nu}$ will require the results of measurements now in progress which will determine the y distributions of deep inelastic neutral current events. (A detailed discussion of the y distribution experiment has been given by B. C. Barish in his talk at this conference.) In Fig. 7 I have plotted the y distribution expected for an S $-\frac{1}{4}$T scalar-tensor mixture (solid line) together with those expected in the Weinberg-Salam model for $\sin^2\theta_W$=0.35 (dashed line). For both incident ν's and $\bar\nu$'s, the S $-\frac{1}{4}$T and Weinberg-Salam curves are remarkably similar - so much so that it will be hard to distinguish them experimentally. The characteristic difference between the two sets of curves is that whereas the Weinberg-Salam model curves are monotonically decreasing functions of y, the S $-\frac{1}{4}$T curves show

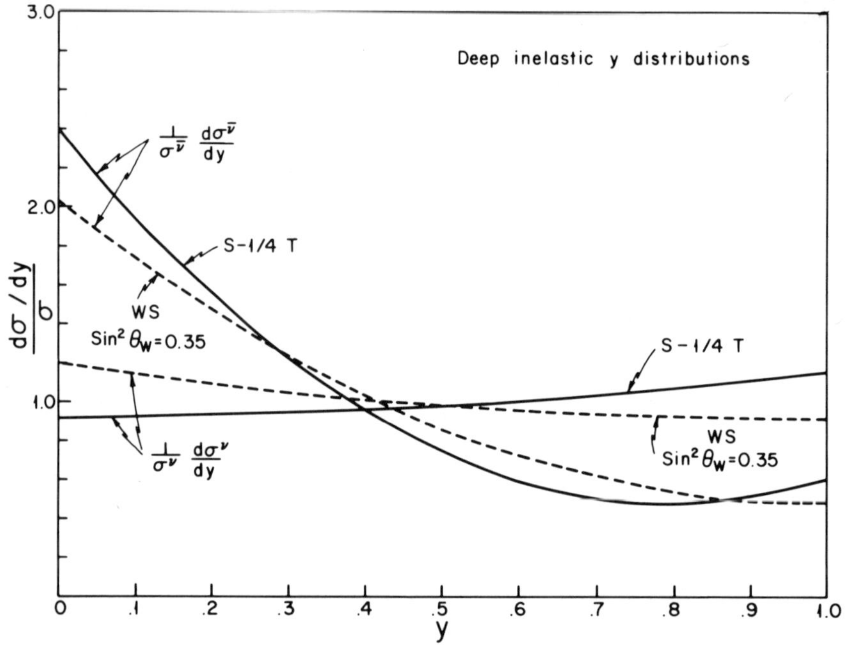

Figure 7

a small increase (arising from the scalar component) near y = 1. For larger scalar admixtures, this effect becomes much more dramatic, as can be seen in Fig. 8, which shows the y distributions for an S- $\frac{1}{10}$T mixture.

Returning to the parameters tabulated in Eq. (30), the final column gives the quantity a_0^2 introduced by Freedman,[9] which measures the strength of coherent scattering neutrino radiation pressure effects, which are of astrophysical importance in the theory of supernova explosions. For comparison, in the Weinberg-Salam model this parameter has the value $a_0^2 \sim 0.5$. The much larger values of a_0^2 found in the S $-\frac{1}{4}$T fits are a feature which appears in general when a sizeable scalar component is present in the neutral current.[10] A closely related effect is that LAMPF cross sections for νp and $\bar{\nu} p$ scattering will be an order of magnitude

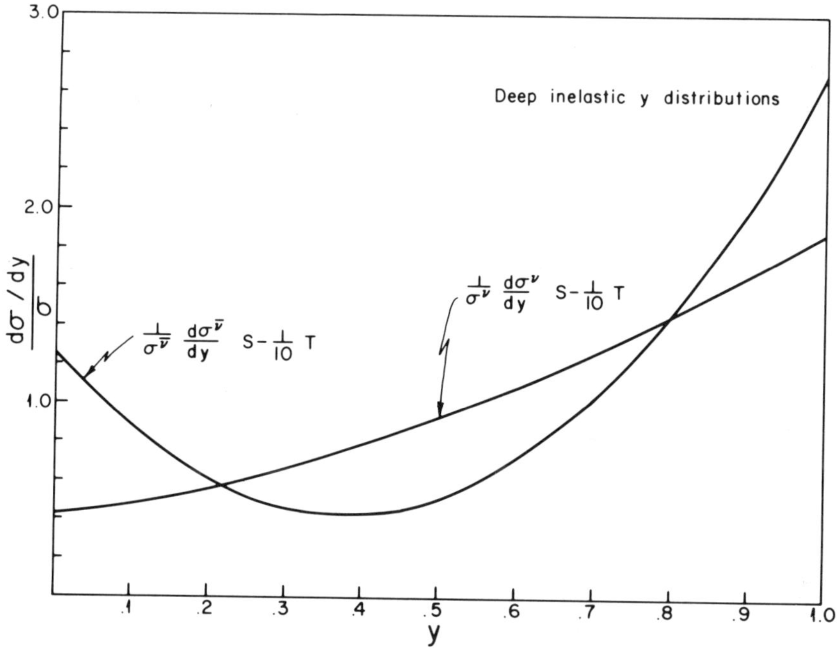

Figure 8

larger for fits #1 and #2 than for the Weinberg-Salam model neutral current.

IV. DISCUSSION

In conclusion, let me make a number of comments and speculative digressions concerning the work discussed above.

(i) First, I wish to emphasize again that our results for the S, P, T case are <u>very preliminary</u> - we have not systematically searched the parameter space and there may be satisfactory fits which are qualitatively different from those described above. We are now adapting our computer programs to work in an interactive mode and then we will do more extensive parameter searching.

(ii) Reasonable scalar-tensor fits are possible for neutral currents of the form S +xT, with the parameter x lying in a range which as yet is not well-determined. While tensor couplings are hard to interpret in terms of a renormalizable field theory, by a suitable Fierz transformation one can always get an effective Lagrangian containing only S and P type terms, which can therefore be given a renormalizable Yukawa field theory interpretation. For example, for the S - ¼T combination used in fits #1 and #2 one finds (with ψ, as before, a quark field)

$$L \propto \overline{\nu}\nu\, \overline{\psi}\psi - \tfrac{1}{4}\overline{\nu}\sigma_{\lambda\eta}\nu\overline{\psi}\sigma^{\lambda\eta}\psi$$

$$= \tfrac{1}{2}[\overline{\nu}\nu\, \overline{\psi}\psi - \overline{\nu}\gamma_5\nu\overline{\psi}\gamma_5\psi] - [\overline{\psi}\nu^c\overline{\nu}^c\psi + \overline{\psi}\gamma_5\nu^c\overline{\nu}^c\gamma_5\psi] \ . \qquad (31)$$

In interpreting Eq. (31) as the effective Lagrangian describing the large boson mass limit of a Yukawa field theory, the first bracketed term will involve scalar and pseudoscalar intermediate bosons without internal quantum numbers, while the second will involve scalar and pseudoscalar bosons of Tanikawa-Wantanabe[11] type carrying both leptonic and quark quantum numbers. Of course, if S, P, T couplings are present it is possible that one should not try to give the effective Lagrangian a simple renormalizable field theory interpretation - it may be that the form of the effective Lagrangian does not indicate, in either direct or Fierz-transformed version, the structure of the presumed underlying local field theory.

(iii) Ruderman[12] has placed an upper limit on the magnitude of neutral tensor couplings $|G_T|$ using an astrophysical limit on the ν_μ magnetic moment induced by the diagram

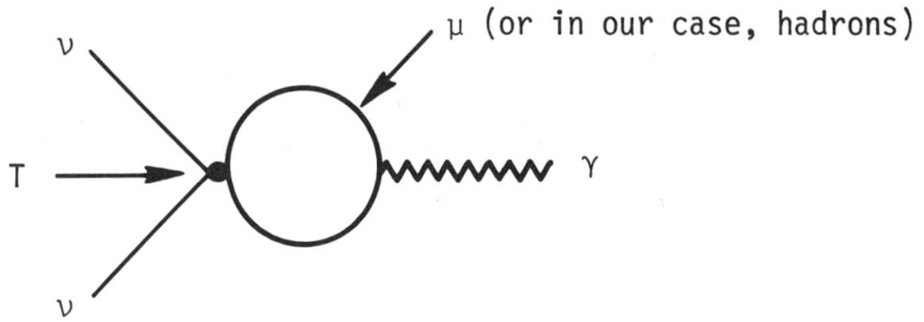

(32)

A rather hand-waving argument gives the limit $|G_T|<.02$. In our case the basic neutrino-hadron tensor coupling is $\frac{1}{2}\sqrt{\frac{2}{3}}|g_T| \sim .2$, but since the coupling of an SU_3-singlet tensor current to the SU_3-octet photon is SU_3-violating another order of magnitude suppression is possible, and so Ruderman's argument poses no clear problem.

(iv) An interesting question is whether there is a simple leptonic extension of the phenomenology examined above to quarks (i.e., if there is lepton-hadron universality), then for $\nu_\mu e$ scattering we have the expression

$$\frac{d}{dE_2} = \frac{G^2 m_e}{2\pi}\left[\frac{1}{2}(G_S^2+G_P^2)\left(\frac{E_2}{E_1}\right)^2 + 16G_T^2\left(1-\frac{1}{2}\frac{E_2}{E_1}\right)^2 - 4G_T(G_S-G_P)\frac{E_2}{E_1}\left(1-\frac{1}{2}\frac{E_2}{E_1}\right)\right], \tag{33}$$

E_1 = initial ν energy, E_2 = scattered e energy, with G_S, G_P, G_T the same couplings as appear in the semileptonic neutrino quark interaction. Taking $G_P=0$,

$$G_S = \frac{1}{2}\sqrt{\frac{2}{3}}\, g_{SO},$$

$$G_T = \begin{cases} \frac{1}{2}\sqrt{\frac{2}{3}}\, g_{to} & \nu \text{ incident} \\ -\frac{1}{2}\sqrt{\frac{2}{3}}\, g_{TO} & \bar{\nu} \text{ incident,} \end{cases} \tag{34}$$

we find the following cross sections:

$$\begin{aligned} \text{fit \#1:}\quad & \sigma(\nu_\mu e) = 0.21 \times 10^{-41}\,\mathrm{cm}^2\ E_1/\mathrm{GeV}, \\ & \sigma(\bar{\nu}_\mu e) = 0.080 \times 10^{-41}\,\mathrm{cm}^2\ E_1/\mathrm{GeV}; \\ \text{fit \#2:}\quad & \sigma(\nu_\mu e) = 0.30 \times 10^{-41}\,\mathrm{cm}^2\ E_1/\mathrm{GeV}, \\ & \sigma(\bar{\nu}_\mu e) = 0.114 \times 10^{-41}\,\mathrm{cm}^2\ E_1/\mathrm{GeV}. \end{aligned} \tag{35}$$

These results are compatible with the current experimental 90% confidence bounds,[13]

$$\begin{aligned} & \sigma(\nu_\mu e) < 0.26 \times 10^{-41}\,\mathrm{cm}^2\ E_1/\mathrm{GeV}, \\ 0.03 \times 10^{-41}\,\mathrm{cm}^2\ E_1/\mathrm{GeV} < {} & \sigma(\bar{\nu}_\mu e) < 0.3 \times 10^{-41}\,\mathrm{cm}^2\ E_1/\mathrm{GeV}, \end{aligned} \tag{36}$$

so a universal neutral coupling of an S, T form is not out of the question. However, with such a coupling one would then have to worry, in the leptonic sector, about Ruderman's astrophysical limit on the tensor coupling strength.

If the leptonic analog of Eq. (31) and the usual effective Lagrangian for charged leptonic processes are given a Yukawa field theory interpretation, the necessary intermediate boson will have dileptonic quantum numbers. That is, one will have $B(\bar{\mu}\,\nu_\mu)$, $B(e\ \nu_\mu)$, $B(\mu^-\nu_e)$, $B(e^-\nu_e)$, which would appear in high energy neutrino reactions induced by ν_μ's with a $\mu^+\mu^-$, e^+e^- or $e^+\mu^-$ dileptonic signature, via the reactions

$$\begin{aligned} & \nu_\mu + \ldots \to \mu^+ + B(\mu^-\nu_\mu) + \ldots \to \mu^+ + \mu^- + \nu_\mu + \ldots\ , \\ & \nu_\mu + \ldots \to e^+ + B(e^-\nu_\mu) + \ldots \to e^+ + e^- + \nu_\mu + \ldots\ , \\ & \nu_\mu + \ldots \to e^+ + B(\mu^-\nu_e) + \ldots \to e^+ + \mu^- + \nu_e + \ldots\ ; \\ & \nu_\mu + \ldots \not\to \mu^+ + e^- + \nu\text{'s} + \ldots \text{ to same order.} \end{aligned} \tag{37}$$

(v) Additional phenomenological work now in progress

includes further parameter search studies, generation of other distributions of experimental interest such as pion polar angle and azimuthal (Treiman-Yang) angle distributions, study of isovector admixtures and (3,) resonance excitation, etc. My collaborators and I are also studying the properties of the Yukawa type models described briefly above, and examining yet another (less appealing) alternative to the presence of S, P, T coupling, the possibility that neutral currents may be of V, A spatial structure but involve wrong G-parity (second class) components. In the meantime the experimentalists will be busy. Experiments which should have results this year should tell us whether the radical departure from conventional ideas about weak interactions which I have discussed above is necessary.

I wish to thank S. F. Tuan for stimulating discussions about the structure of neutral currents. S. B. Treiman for many helpful critical comments in the course of this work, and members of the Argonne bubble chamber group and the Columbia-Illinois-Rockefeller collaboration for conversations about the Argonne and Brookhaven neutrino experiments. <u>Added Note</u>: After the conference I found a programming error which, when corrected, reduces the large $|g|$ wings of the curves in Fig. 1 to $(44 - 48) \times 10^{-41} cm^2$. The corrected figure will appear in a detailed paper describing the V,A current aspects of the work reported above.

REFERENCES

1. P. A. Schreiner, Argonne National Laboratory Report ANL/HEP 7436, presented at the XVII International Conference on High Energy Physics, London, 1974.
2. S. J. Barish, Bull. Am. Phys. Soc. Series II, Vol. 20, #1, p.86 (1975). This number is a preliminary one and may be somewhat modified in the final manuscript being prepared by the ANL group for submission to Phys. Rev. Letters. The actual Argonne measured two bin cross section is $(13.4 \pm 6.7) \times 10^{-41} \mathrm{cm}^2$ for events with $E_\nu < 1.5$ GeV and $|k^2| \leq 0.5$ (GeV)^2. I have estimated the effect of the cuts by assuming the k^2 dependence of the neutral current cross section to be the same as that of the charged current cross section in the reaction $\nu p \rightarrow \mu^- p\pi^+$.
3. S. L. Adler, Phys. Rev. Letters 33, 1511 (1974).
4. This assumption is the same one used to get definite y-distribution predictions in the Weinberg-Salam model case. See B. C. Barish's talk at this Conference and L. M. Sehgal, Nucl. Phys. B65, 141 (1973).
5. D. C. Cundy et al., Phys. Letters 31B, 479 (1970).
6. See, for example, B. Kayser et al., Phys. Lett. B52, 385 (1974); R. L. Kingsley et al., Phys. Rev. D10, 2216 (1974).
7. S. L. Adler, E. W. Colglazier, Jr., J. B. Healy, Inga Karliner, Hudy Lieberman, Yee Jack Ng and Hung-Sheng Tso, "Renormalization Constants for Scalar, Pseudoscalar and Tensor Currents," Phys. Rev. D (1975).
8. J. S. Bell and S. M. Berman, Nuovo Cimento 25, 404 (1962).

9. D. Z. Freedman, Phys. Rev. D0, 1389 (1974).

10. S. L. Adler, "Neutrino Radiation Pressure Arising from a Scalar Weak Neutral Coupling," Phys. Rev. D (1975).

11. Y. Tanikawa and S. Watanabe, Phys. Rev. 113, 1344 (1957). For further references see the review by C. H. Llewellyn-Smith, Physics Reports 3C, no. 5 (1972).

12. M. A. Ruderman, "Neutrinos in Astrophysics," in Proceedings of the Topical Conference on Weak Interactions, CERN 69-7. See especially pp. 128-129.

13. D. H. Perkins, "Experimental Aspects of Neutrino Interactions," in Proceedings of the Fifth Hawaii Topical Conference in Particle Physics, (University Press, Hawaii, 1973), p. 507.

Some of the participants in attendance at the Laser and Laser Fusion Sessions of the Orbis Scientiae II

UNIFIED GAUGE THEORIES

Howard Georgi*

Lyman Laboratory of Physics

Harvard University, Cambridge, Mass. 02138

I don't have anything very new to say about unified theories of weak, electromagnetic, and strong interactions. It is difficult to find time for theological speculations when our experimentalist friends keep us so busy. What I want to do today is to discuss some of the interesting unsolved problems in the field that I intend to study myself if charm is discovered and Shelly gives me time off for good behavior.

Before I start discussing what we don't know about unified theories, let me briefly remind you of what we do know. If the weak, electromagnetic, and strong interactions are due to renormalizable non-Abelian gauge field theories, something like Weinberg's SU(2) × U(1) × color SU(3), and furthermore the strong interactions are asymptotically free, then at some large momentum the effective coupling constants of the various interactions may be the same size and fit into a simple gauge group, with a single gauge coupling constant. The

* Junior Fellow, Harvard University Society of Fellows

simplest example of this is SU(5).[1] The SU(5) gauge symmetry is spontaneously broken down to SU(3) × SU(2) × U(1), say by a Higgs mechanism with a scalar meson developing a vacuum expectation value of the order of M. Because the momentum dependence of the couplings are weak (logarithmic in simple theories) and because at ordinary momenta, the strong interactions are considerably stronger than the electromagnetic interactions, the mass M must be enormous.[2] In SU(5) this is a good thing, because the theory predicts proton decay with a rate proportional to $1/M^4$. The Weinberg angle is determined in principle in terms of the strength of the strong interactions at ordinary energies. This is shown in Table 1[2] for a simple theory where the only scalar mesons are those associated with the superstrong symmetry breaking at M. That is about all we know.

Let me now discuss three questions about unified theories:

I: What is the Role of Gravity?

II: Is Symmetry Breakdown at Ordinary Momenta Higgs or Dynamical?

III: Why are There Muons and Strange and Charmed Particles?

The first question is perhaps the most interesting and I have the least to say about it. The point is that the M which we are led to in unified theories is not small compared to the Planck mass, so we might begin to worry about ignoring gravity. Furthermore, the prediction of proton decay is suggestive, because one might not expect baryon number conservation in a universe in which black holes exist. These things suggest that the superstrong symmetry breaking mechanism which is responsible for the large mass M has something to do

Table 1

$g_3{}^2(10\ \text{Gev})/4\pi$	M(Gev)	$\sin^2\theta_W$
.5	2×10^{17}	.18
.2	2×10^{16}	.19
.1	5×10^{14}	.21
.05	2×10^{11}	.25

with gravity. I have nothing constructive to say about this possibility, but I think it is so attractive that I always mention it in the hope that someone else will be able to do something with it.

The second question I want to discuss is related to the nature of the spontaneous symmetry breaking at ordinary energies which breaks the weak and electromagnetic gauge group down to electromagnetic gauge invariance and gives mass to the leptons and quarks. The problem is that if this symmetry breakdown is due to an explicit Higgs mechanism with a scalar meson field developing vacuum expectation values, it is difficult to understand the appearance of such vastly different expectation values as 300 Gev and 10^{18} Gev, and the analysis of the difference in strength between the strong and electromagnetic interactions and the prediction of the Weinberg angle becomes much more complicated. On the other hand, if the ordinary symmetry breakdown is dynamical, there is a natural, if handwaving, explanation of the large disparity in mass scales, but dynamical symmetry breaking may not work, and anyway it opens a Pandora's box of Goldstone and pseudo-Goldstone bosons. I think I had better elaborate on the last two sentences. With explicit Higgs scalars, the various vacuum expectation values are just phenomenological parameters to be put in by hand. There is nothing wrong with taking one to be 10^{18} Gev and the other 300 Gev, but it is somehow unsatisfying. A more serious problem is that the presence of scalar mesons complicates the renormalization group argument that relates the strength of the strong interactions to M. Indeed, one must be careful not to spoil at least temporary freedom of the strong interaction subgroup, which is necessary for unification. The effective gauge coupling constant of the strong group (or groups) must decrease with momentum from ordinary mass scales to M. I don't really care if the theory is asymptotically free for momenta greater than M. It seems simpler at first glance to assume that the only Higgs mesons in the problem have vacuum expectation values of the order of M, and that the symmetry breakdown at ordinary momenta is dynamical. This makes sense because one might expect dynamical symmetry breakdown to set in at a momentum scale at which the most asymptotically free interaction gets large. In other words, dynamical symmetry breakdown occurs at ordinary momenta because the strong interactions are getting strong. There are two problems with dynamical symmetry breaking. The first is simply that no one knows whether it actually occurs in these theories. (See R. Jackiw's talk in these proceedings, "Quantum Mechanical Approximations in Quantum Field Theory".) The second is that even assuming everything works, it is hard to avoid Goldstone and pseudo-Goldstone bosons.[3] Consider for instance SU(5), where the strong interaction subgroup is color SU(3). The strong interactions in the absence of scalars have a chiral SU(4) × SU(4) × U(1) symmetry which must be spontaneously broken. Some of the consequent Goldstone bosons are associated with generators of the weak and electromagnetic gauge subgroup and are eaten by the Higgs mechanism. Some of them are associated with symmetries and are broken by the weak and electromagnetic gauge couplings and are pseudo-Goldstone bosons which develop ordinary masses because of second-order effects. And some of them are associated with unbroken symmetries of the weak, electromagnetic, and strong couplings. These are either massless or have tiny masses depending on whether they are actually symmetries of the full SU(5) gauge Lagrangian. For instance in SU(5) broken this way, there would be massless Goldstone bosons corresponding to the SU(2) rotation that takes n↔λ (among other things). Clearly such objects must be avoided, and this puts a new kind of constraint on model building if the symmetry breaking is dynamical.[3]

The last question I will talk about is the muon-strangeness-charm puzzle. You will probably remember that in the old days after Glashow, Iliopoulos, Maiani[4] and before gauge theories there was a muon puzzle and a strangness-charm puzzle. Gauge theories changed all that. Bouchiat, Iliopoulos, and Meyer[5] realized that if in a gauge theory of weak and electromagnetic interactions the quarks come in color triplets, and if there is a muon (and ν_μ) in addition to the electron (and ν_e) and the ρ and n quarks, then there must be strange and charmed quarks to cancel the triangle anomalies. But why the entire μ-p'-λ system should exist remains a mystery. This mystery persists in partially unified theories like the Pati-Salam model[6] and also in unified theories like SU(5). The trouble with all these theories is that the fermions split into two equivalent representations of the gauge group, one involving primarily e, p, n, the other μ, p', λ. Now the world may actually work this way, but it would be more fun if all the fermions and antifermions fit into a single irreducible representation of the unifying gauge group. This can actually be done in a simpler world without strangeness, charm, or muons. The electron and the proton and neutron quark triplets and their antiparticles together with the electron neutrino and an extra neutral lepton can be put into the 16-dimensional representation of O(10),[7] as follows. The 16 dimensional representation of O(10) is generated by the matrices σ_i, τ_i, η_i, $\sigma_i\rho_1$, $\tau_i\rho_2$, $\eta_i\rho_3$, $\tau_i\eta_j\rho_1$, $\eta_i\sigma_j\rho_2$, and $\sigma_i\tau_j\rho_3$, where σ, τ, η, and ρ are commuting Pauli matrices and i, j = 1 to 3. A possible assignment of the 16 left-handed fields shown in Table 2. Note that the generators $\eta_i(1 + \rho_3)$, σ_i, τ_i, and $\sigma_i\tau_j\rho_3$ generate an SU(2) × SU(2) × SU(4) subgroup which is just the Pati-Salam model.

If the superstrong symmetry breaking is to SU(2) × U(1) × SU(3), then the relation between M and the Weinberg angle is as shown in Table 1, just as in SU(5). However, there are now other possibilities. For instance if O(10) is broken down to SU(2) × SU(2) × U(1) × SU(3) (with an additional "right-handed" SU(2)), the relations are quite different, as shown in Table 3.

It would be very pleasant to find some similar assignment of all 30 left-handed fermion and anti-fermion fields (possibly with the addition of some extra neutral leptons) to an irreducible representation of some unified gauge group. Unfortunately it seems to be impossible to find such an assignment which reproduces physics. The essential problem is that the representation must be complex because the left-handed quarks participate in charged current weak interactions while the left-handed antiquarks (or right-handed quarks) do not. But the representation must also be anomaly free for renormalizability. I believe that the only theories satisfying these two constraints with four triplets of quarks are the SU(5) and O(17) theories which leave the muon-strangeness-charm puzzle unresolved. With more quarks and leptons, it is possible to satisfy all these constraints, but the variety of possible

Table 2

σ_3	τ_3	η_3	ρ_3	
1	1	1	1	ν_e
-1	1	1	1	p_r
1	-1	1	1	p_w
-1	-1	1	1	p_b
1	1	-1	1	e^-
-1	1	-1	1	n_r
1	-1	-1	1	n_w
-1	-1	-1	1	n_b
1	1	1	-1	$\bar{n}_b$
-1	1	1	-1	$-\bar{n}_w$
1	-1	1	-1	$-\bar{n}_r$
-1	-1	1	-1	e^+
1	1	-1	-1	$\bar{p}_b$
-1	1	-1	-1	$-\bar{p}_w$
1	-1	-1	-1	$-\bar{p}_r$
-1	-1	-1	-1	X^o

Table 3

$g_3^2(10\ \mathrm{Gev})/4\pi$	M(Gev)	$\sin^2\theta_W$
.5	10^{26}	.26
.2	3×10^{24}	.26
.1	10^{22}	.27
.05	10^{17}	.30

models is bewildering, at least to me, and I don't know how to choose the right one.

I hope this talk has not left the audience with the impression that I am pessimistic about the future of unified theories. I expect that the problems I talked about are solvable. Evidence is beginning to pile up that the weak, electromagnetic, and strong interactions all arise from gauge theories. If that is true, then either there is an underlying unified theory or the Creator has played a nasty trick on us. Lenny Susskind asked me at dinner yesterday why I think that God is a group-theorist. The answer is all around us -- in snowflakes, flowers, galaxies. It cannot be such a bad idea to try to take symmetry one step farther.

REFERENCES

1. H. Georgi and S. L. Glashow, Phys. Rev. Letters 32, 438 (1974).
2. H. Georgi, H. R. Quinn, and S. Weinberg, Phys. Rev. Letters 33, 451 (1974).
3. This has been emphasized by S. Weinberg, unpublished.
4. S. L. Glashow, J. Iliopoulos and L. Maiani, Phys. Rev. D2, 1285 (1970).
5. C. Bouchiat, J. Iliopoulos and Ph. Meyer, Phys. Letters B, 38B, 519 (1972).
6. J. C. Pati and A. Salam, Phys. Rev. Letters 31, 661 (1973).
7. H. Georgi, Proceedings of the 1974 meeting of the Division of Particles and Fields of the American Physical Society, at William and Mary College.

MONOPOLE STRINGS AND CHARMONIUM*

A. P. Balachandran, R. Ramachandran,[†]
J. Schecter and Kameshwar C. Wali
(presented by Kameshwar C. Wali)
Department of Physics, Syracuse, New York
and
Heinz Rupertsberger
Institut für Theoretische Physik der
Universität Wien, Wien, Austria

ABSTRACT

We show that the strength of the potential which varies as the distance between quarks can be related to the universal Regge slope parameter α'. This relation is in excellent agreement with the phenomenological analysis of the newly discovered resonances $\psi(3.1)$ and $\psi(3.7)$ by Eichten et al.

---

* Supported in part by the U. S. Atomic Energy Commission

† Department of Physics, Indian Institute of Technology Kanpur, India (Permanent address)

Various considerations have suggested to many authors[1] that a potential of the form

$$V(r) = c_1 \frac{e^{-\mu r}}{r} + c_2 r \quad , \quad \begin{matrix} c_1 < 0 \\ c_2 > 0 \end{matrix} \tag{1}$$

provides a heuristic description of the quark-anti quark binding force.

One realization of this potential is in a model mathematically analogous to that of the magnetic force between 2 monopoles where the vector field acquires a mass, μ. Detailed examination of such a theory by the present authors shows that the constant c_2 can be related to the universal Regge slope parameter α' of the Regge trajectories of the hadrons. More precisely,

$$c_2 = \frac{1}{2\pi\alpha'} \quad . \tag{2}$$

In a suitable quasistatic limit this model gives a potential

$$V = c_1 \frac{e^{-\mu r}}{r} + H_{string} \quad , \tag{3}$$

where H_{string} is the Hamiltonian which follows from the ordinary Nambu-Goto action:

$$S = -\frac{1}{2\pi\alpha'} \iint d\sigma\, d\tau \sqrt{(\dot{y}\cdot y')^2 - \dot{y}^2 y'^2} \quad . \tag{4}$$

In a coordinate frame where $\tau = t$, $y_4 = it$ and t is time, we may follow the usual canonical procedure to find

$$H_{string} = \int d\sigma \sqrt{\underline{p}^2(\sigma) + \underline{y}'^2(\sigma)/(2\pi\alpha')^2} \quad ; \tag{5}$$

$\underline{p}(\sigma)$ = canonical momentum density.

Eq. (5) is to be integrated between the positions of the quark and anti-quark along the string parameterized by σ. When the classical string is unexcited we set $\underline{p} = 0$ so that

$$H_{string} = \frac{1}{2\pi\alpha'} \int d\sigma \sqrt{\underline{y}'^2(\sigma)} = \frac{1}{2\pi\alpha'} \int d\ell$$

$$= \Delta\ell/2\pi\alpha' \ , \qquad (6)$$

where $\Delta\ell$ is the interquark distance measured along the string. It is reasonable to expect that the string geometry is not too different from a straight-line configuration (the exact static limit of our model requires this) so that $\Delta\ell$=r which leads to (2). Thus the static limit of (5) can be related to the second term in (1).

Our formal considerations start from Dirac's action[2] with an additional mass term for the "photon" as suggested by Nambu and others[3]. The Lagrangian we start with is

$$L = -\frac{1}{4} \int d^3x \ F_{\mu\nu}(x)F_{\mu\nu}(x) - \frac{1}{2}\mu^2 A_\mu A_\mu + \text{(kinetic terms)},$$

$$F_{\mu\nu} = \partial_\mu A_\nu - \partial_\nu A_\mu - \frac{i}{2}\varepsilon_{\mu\nu\alpha\beta} G_{\alpha\beta} \ ,$$

$$G_{\alpha\beta}(x) = \sum_N g_N \int d\sigma \frac{\varepsilon(\sigma-\sigma_N)}{2} \delta^3(\underline{x}-y(\sigma))(\dot{y}_\alpha y'_\beta - y'_\alpha \dot{y}_\beta) \ , \qquad (7)$$

where σ_N is the position of the Nth monopole.

Nambu[1] has approximated (7) in a Lagrangian framework. We have on the other hand, proceeded according to the Hamiltonian formalism. This is much more difficult, involving the consideration of both first and second class constraints, but has the advantage of leading directly to an expression for the energy. The quasi-static limit in (3) corresponds to the case when the physical field variables $\underline{E}$ and $\underline{H}$, as well as the potential $\underline{A}$ are taken to have zero time derivative at some fixed time t while the string is not so constrained. After a rather lengthy and complicated calculation, we find

$$V = \sum_{N,N'} \frac{g_N g_{N'}}{8\pi} \frac{e^{-\mu|\underline{y}(\sigma_N)-\underline{y}(\sigma_{N'})|}}{|\underline{y}(\sigma_N)-\underline{y}(\sigma_{N'})|}$$

$$+ \sum_{N,N'} \frac{g_N g_{N'}}{2} \iint d\sigma\, d\sigma' \frac{\varepsilon(\sigma-\sigma_N)}{2} \frac{\varepsilon(\sigma'-\sigma_{N'})}{2} \times$$

$$\left(\frac{\mu^2}{\mu^2-\nabla^2} \partial^3(\underline{y}(\sigma)-\underline{y}(\sigma'))\right) \times$$

$$\times \{\underline{y}'(\sigma)\cdot\underline{y}'(\sigma')(1+\dot{\underline{y}}(\sigma) \cdot\dot{\underline{y}}(\sigma'))-\underline{y}'(\sigma)\cdot\dot{y}(\sigma')\dot{\underline{y}}(\sigma)\cdot\underline{y}'(\sigma')\}. \qquad (8)$$

The first term in (8) evidently represents an inter-quark Yukawa potential. The second term contains, when suitably regularized to get rid of an overall infinity, the string Hamiltonian. To see this, consider for simplicity the large μ limit and set[4]

$$\frac{\mu^2}{\mu^2-\nabla^2} \delta^3(y(\sigma)-y(\sigma')) \to \frac{\delta^2(0)}{|\underline{y}'|} \delta(\sigma-\sigma') .$$

Neglecting self energy effects, the second term gives a quark-anti-quark energy:

$$\sim g^2\delta^2(0) \int \frac{d\sigma}{|y'|} \{\underline{y}'^2(1+\dot{\underline{y}}^2)-(\dot{\underline{y}}\cdot\underline{y}')^2\} \qquad (9)$$

where the integration extends from quark to anti-quark. This is an effective Hamiltonian which corresponds to the Lagrangian

$$g^2\delta^2(0)\int \frac{d\sigma}{|\underline{y}'|}\{-y'^2(1-\dot{\underline{y}}^2)-(\dot{\underline{y}}\cdot\underline{y}')^2\}$$

$$\simeq g^2\iint d\sigma\, d\sigma'\, \delta^3(\underline{y}(\sigma)-\underline{y}(\sigma'))\{\dot{y}_\mu(\sigma)y'_\nu(\sigma)-(\mu\leftrightarrow\nu)\}x$$

$$\times\ \{\dot{y}_\mu(\sigma')y'_\nu(\sigma')-(\mu\leftrightarrow\nu)\} \quad . \tag{10}$$

Note that in (10) we have made use of our coordinate choices $y_4 = it$, $\tau=t$. To show the relation of (10) to the string Lagrangian, we write its integral over t in the manifestly covariant form

$$g^2\int d\sigma\ d\tau\ d\sigma' d\tau' \delta^4[y(\sigma,\tau)-y(\sigma',\tau')][\dot{y}_\mu(\sigma,\tau)y'_\nu(\sigma,\tau)-(\mu\leftrightarrow\nu)]$$

$$\times\ [\dot{y}_\mu(\sigma',\tau')y'_\nu\ (\sigma',\tau')-(\mu\leftrightarrow\nu)] \tag{11}$$

We evaluate (11) by setting[4]

$$\int d\sigma' d\tau'\ \delta^4[y(\sigma,\tau)-y(\sigma',\tau')] \rightarrow \delta^2(0)[(\dot{y}\cdot y')^2-\dot{y}^2y'^2]^{-1/2}$$

which leads to the action (4).

This interesting connection between the dual string and the Dirac monopole string needs really a very careful examination which is currently under study. Our Hamiltonian formalism in the limit when the vector meson has zero mass, leads to the usual QED with monopoles. On the other hand, if we start from the beginning by identifying $G_{\mu\nu}G_{\mu\nu}$ as the dual string Lagrangian[5], it is not clear to us at present whether it leads to a QED with monopoles. In spite of these reservations, it is interesting to see the implications of (2) on the recently discovered new particles.

Eichten et al[6] use a potential

$$V(r) = -\frac{\alpha_s}{r} + \frac{\alpha_s}{a^2} r . \tag{12}$$

By requiring

$$M_{\psi_2} - M_{\psi_1} = 0.59 ,$$

and

$$\Gamma_{e^+e^-}(\psi_1) = 5.5 \text{ kev},$$

they find that $\alpha_s = 0.2$ fm. They also claim that the the first term in (12) plays a relatively small role in phenomenology. Consequently the differences due to the first terms in (1) and (12) are expected to be negligible[7]. With the stated values for α_s and a,

$$\alpha_s/a^2 = 0.19 \text{ (Gev)}^2 . \tag{13}$$

Now from (2)

$$c_2 = .18 \text{ (Gev)}^2 ,$$

where

$$\alpha' = 0.895 \text{ (Gev)}^{-2} . \tag{14}$$

Thus we see that the phenomenological value for c_2 $(=\alpha_s/a^2)$ is remarkably close to $1/2\pi\alpha'$. We think that this agreement is not just a numerical accident, but an indication of the essential correctness of the idea that the quark binding force is string like. Full details of our work will be presented elsewhere.

FOOTNOTES AND REFERENCES

1. See for example: Y. Nambu "Strings, Monopoles, and Gauge Fields", to be published in the Physical Review' T. Appelquist, A. DeRujula, S. L. Glashow and D. H. Politzer, to be published.
2. P.A.M. Dirac, Phys. Rev. 74, 817 (1948).
3. H. Nielsen and P. Olesen, Nucl. Phys. B61, 45 (1973); Y. Nambu, "Report of the Johns Hopkins Workshop on Current Problems in High Energy Particle Theory" (1974); A. P. Balachandran, H. Rupertsberger, and J. Schechter, Syracuse University preprints SU-4205-37 and SU-4205-41. A. Jevicki and P. Senjanovic, to be published.
4. We here omit the arguments leading to such approximations.
5. See Y. Nambu, reference 1.
6. E. Eichten, K. Gottfried, T. Kinoshita, J. Kogut, K. D. Lane and T. M. Yan, "The Spectrum of Charmonium", Cornell preprint CLNS-292 (1974).
7. If we neglect the first terms in (1) and (12), the energy levels of S states are given in terms of the zeros of Airy function. The energy differences between $\psi(4.2)$, $\psi(3.7)$, $\psi(3,1)$ are well fit by the corresponding formula. See reference 6. And also Barry J. Harrington, Soo Yong Park, and Asim Yildiz; Phys. Rev. Lett. 34, 168 (1975).

UNIFIED APPROACH TO MULTIPARTICLE PRODUCTION AT HIGH ENERGY

P. Carruthers*

Theoretical Division, University of California

Los Alamos Scientific Laboratory

Los Alamos, New Mexico 87544

and

F. Zachariasen**

California Institute of Technology

Pasadena, California 91109

INTRODUCTION

Many models have been proposed for the description of multiparticle production in high energy hadronic collisions[1]. The physical assumptions underlying the various models often are unrelated or apparently contradictory. Yet approaches as different as the multiperipheral model and the statistical-hydrodynamic model seem to give partial insights into the nature of the production process. Recently we have proposed[2] a covariant transport equation approach which appears to

*Research Performed under the auspices of the U.S. E.R.D.A.

** Supported in part by the U.S.E.R.D.A. Contract AT (11-1)-68 for the San Francisco Operations Office.

unify many desirable features of the more attractive models. Field theory equations of motion for correlation functions can be cast in a form reminiscent of classical transport theory; in this manner one is led to a natural description of collective motions without making unconvincing hypotheses such as local thermodynamic equilibrium.

The basic object of the theory is the covariant field theoretic analogue of the Wigner phase space distribution function[3], which is in turn the quantum mechanical substitute for the single particle Boltzmann distribution function. By taking the Fourier transform of the correlation function with respect to the relative coordinate (cf. Eq. (21) below) one obtains an object F(p,R) which obeys a transport-like equation with a source term which typically involves higher order correlations (thus generating a coupled hierarchy of such equations for n-particle distribution functions). When various truncations are made one obtains Boltzmann or Vlasov-like equations which can be examined in detail to establish such questions as the existence of collective excitations, local equilibrium, hydrodynamic behavior, etc.

While the Wigner distribution plays a central role in quantum transport theory[4] its utility for scattering and reaction theory has only been appreciated recently[2,5] despite some suggestive remarks in papers by Kirkwood, Zwanzig and collaborators[6,7]. In Section II we review some pertinent definitions in the non-relativistic case and show how one may treat the scattering of a single particle from a potential well using the transport equation method.

The problem of particle production in relativistic field theory is illustrated for scalar field theories involving a c-number potential V(x) ($L_{int} = V\phi$ and $L_{int} = \frac{1}{2} V\phi^2$) and for a ϕ^4 self-interaction. It is observed that the Fourier transform F(p,q) of the generalized Boltzmann function F(p,R) is just the absorptive part of a multiparticle scattering amplitude, giving a more vivid physical significance to generalized unitarity theorems of the sort expounded by Mueller[8]. (This connection is exhibited in some detail for the model with $L_{int} = \frac{1}{2} V\phi^2$.) Exact and approximate transport equations are discussed. We examine the ϕ^4 theory for the existence of a collective mode in a uniform system of temperature T, and find a massive excitation in the Hartree approximation. This question is of interest in relation to the existence of clusters[9].

A more detailed study of the problems raised by the proposed approach will be given elsewhere[10]. The purpose of this talk is to summarize the qualitative ideas of this new method.

II. PHASE SPACE DISTRIBUTIONS IN CLASSICAL AND NON-RELATIVISTIC QUANTUM MECHANICS: SCATTERING FROM A POTENTIAL.

The Boltzmann single particle distribution function $f(\underline{p},\underline{R},t)$ is a familiar object in classical statistical physics. It specifies simultaneously the probability of finding a single particle of momentum p at position x, and can be normalized so that

$$\int d^3R \; f(\underline{p},\underline{R},t) = n(\underline{p},t) \quad , \qquad (1)$$

$$\int d^3p \; f(\underline{p},\underline{R},t) = n(\underline{R},t) \quad , \qquad (2)$$

where $n(\underline{p},t)$, $n(\underline{R},t)$ are respectively the instantaneous momentum and position space densities. Although the true equation of motion for f leads to the introduction of higher order distribution functions there are many cases in which Boltzmann's famous transport equation (which involves f alone) is adequate.

In quantum mechanics it is not possible to specify $\underline{R}$ and $\underline{p}$ simultaneously. However, a suitable phase space distribution having most of the desired properties was introduced by Wigner for non-relativistic quantum mechanics[3]. Consider a single particle wave function $\psi(\underline{R},t)$ for which the probability density in coordinate space is $\psi^*(\underline{R},t)\psi(\underline{R},t)$. Wigner's distribution is now given by Fourier transformation of $\psi^*(\underline{x}_1,t)$ $\psi(\underline{x}_2,t)$ on the relative coordinate $\underline{r} = \underline{x}_2 - \underline{x}_1$:

$$f(\underline{p},\underline{R},t) = \int \frac{d^3r}{(2\pi)^3} e^{-i\underline{p}\cdot\underline{r}} \psi^*(\underline{R} - \tfrac{1}{2}\underline{r},t)\psi(\underline{R} + \tfrac{1}{2}\underline{r},t), \quad (3)$$

where $\underline{R} = \frac{1}{2}(\underline{x}_1 + \underline{x}_2)$.

From (3) we see immediately that in analogy with Eq. (2)

$$\int d^3p \; f(\underline{p},\underline{R},t) = \psi^*(\underline{R},t)\psi(\underline{R},t) \quad . \quad (4)$$

The momentum space amplitude $a(\underline{p},t)$ is defined by

$$\psi(\underline{R},t) = \int \frac{d^3p}{(2\pi)^{3/2}} a(\underline{p},t)e^{i\underline{p}\cdot\underline{R}} \quad . \quad (5)$$

In terms of these coefficients $f(\underline{p},\underline{R},t)$ is given by

$$f(\underline{p},\underline{R},t) = \int \frac{d^3q}{(2\pi)^3} e^{-i\underline{q}\cdot\underline{R}} a^*(\underline{p} + \tfrac{\underline{q}}{2},t)a(\underline{p} - \tfrac{\underline{q}}{2},t) \quad , \quad (6)$$

so that the analogue of Eq. (1) is

$$\int d^3R \; f(\underline{p},\underline{R},t) = a^*(\underline{p},t)a(\underline{p},t) \quad . \quad (7)$$

The restriction to fixed particle number may be removed by using second quantization. Equation (3) becomes simply

$$f(\underline{p},\underline{R},t) = \int \frac{d^3r}{(2\pi)^3} e^{-i\underline{p}\cdot\underline{r}} \left\{ <\psi^*(R - \frac{1}{2}\,\underline{r},t)\psi(R + \frac{1}{2}\underline{r},t)> \right\}, \tag{8}$$

where the bracket means $<A> \equiv Tr(\rho A)$. In the case of a pure state, most often used in this work, we have the usual expression $<A> = <(\underline{\psi}|A|\psi>$. We shall mostly use states normalized to unity because of the space localization characteristic of our approach. (The limit of the continuous spectrum of scattering states will generally be taken at a late stage of the calculation in order to avoid ill-defined quantities). In second quantization the expansion coefficients $a(\underline{p},t)$ in (5) become particle destruction operators normalized so that $[a(\underline{p},t), a^*(\underline{p}',t)] = \delta(\underline{p} - \underline{p}')$.

The general idea of our approach is illustrated by the simple problem of scattering of a wave packet from a potential well $V(\underline{R})$. The initial condition is

$$f(\underline{p},\underline{R},t) \xrightarrow[t \to -\infty]{} f_0(\underline{p},\underline{R},t) , \tag{9}$$

where $f_0(\underline{p},\underline{R},t)$ is the initial distribution calculated from a suitable free-particle wave packet. Since $\int d^3Rf(\underline{p},\underline{R},t)$ is the differential number density dN/d^3p, the differential cross section is

$$\frac{d\sigma}{d^3p} = \frac{\lim_{t \to \infty} \int d^3R\ f(\underline{p},\underline{R},t)}{dN_{inc}/dA} . \tag{10}$$

Here the incident flux is

$$\frac{dN_{inc}}{dA} = \int_{-\infty}^{\infty} dt \int d^3p\ v_z(p)\ f_0(\underline{p},\underline{R},t) , \tag{11}$$

where $\underline{v}(p) = \underline{p}/m$. In the calculation of (10) we will, of course, use a large wave packet (peaked in momentum distribution near $\underline{p} = \underline{p}_0$.) much bigger than the size of the potential well.

The equation of motion for f is easily computed using Schrödinger's equation. The kinetic energy term can be integrated by parts to give the drift term $v \cdot \nabla f$; we find

$$\partial f/\partial t + v \cdot \nabla f = S(\underline{p},\underline{R},t) \quad ; \tag{12}$$

$$S(\underline{p},\underline{R},t) = \frac{1}{i} \int d^3r \, e^{-i\underline{p}\cdot\underline{r}} \left| V(\underline{R} + \frac{1}{2}\underline{r}) - V(\underline{R} - \frac{1}{2}\underline{r}) \right| \psi^* (\underline{R} - \frac{1}{2}\underline{r},t)\psi(\underline{R} + \frac{1}{2}\underline{r},t) \quad .$$

Inverting Eq. (3) gives

$$\psi^*(\underline{R} - \frac{1}{2}\underline{r},t)\Psi(\underline{R} + \frac{1}{2}\underline{r},t) = \int d^3p \, e^{i\underline{p}\cdot\underline{r}} f(\underline{p},\underline{R},t), \tag{13}$$

so that S is linear in f. The full equation of motion for f is thus

$$i\left|\frac{\partial}{\partial t} + \underline{v}\cdot\nabla\right| f(\underline{p},\underline{R},t) = \int d^3r \int d^3p' \, e^{i(\underline{p}' - \underline{p})\cdot\underline{r}} f(\underline{p}',\underline{R},t) \, [V(\underline{R} + \frac{1}{2}\underline{r}) - V(\underline{R}-\frac{1}{2}\underline{r})]. \tag{14}$$

Equation (14) is easily recognized as a close cousin of the ordinary Boltzmann equation for particles moving in an external force field; if V is slowly varying on a scale compared with the overlap of $\psi(\underline{R} + \frac{1}{2}\underline{r})$ with $\psi(\underline{R} - \frac{1}{2}\underline{r})$ then we write $V(\underline{R} + \frac{1}{2}\underline{r}) - V(\underline{R} - \frac{1}{2}\underline{r}) \simeq \underline{r}\cdot\nabla V(\underline{R})$ in (12) and find

$$\frac{\partial f}{\partial t} + \underline{v}\cdot\nabla f + \underline{F}\cdot\nabla_p f = 0 \quad , \tag{15}$$

where $\vec{F} = -\nabla V$ is the classical force function.

Equation (12) or (14) is easily converted to a linear integral equation for f subject to the initial condition (9)

$$f(\underline{p},\underline{R},t) - f_0(\underline{p},\underline{R},t) + \int_{-\infty}^{t} dt' \; S(\underline{p},\underline{R} - \underline{v}_p(t - t')\,). \quad (16)$$

It is instructive to iterate (16) to contrast this approach with the usual one. (Details will be reported elsewhere.) We assume an initial wave packet of the form (5), setting $a(\underline{p},t)$ equal to $C(\underline{p},t)$ to indicate that this state is the special initial packet. For such a state, $C(\underline{p},t)$ has time dependence e^{-iEt}. The initial distribution is

$$f_0(\underline{p},\underline{R},t) =$$

$$\int \frac{d^3q}{(2\pi)^3}\, e^{-i\underline{q}\,(\underline{x} - \underline{v}_p t)}\; C^*(\underline{p} + \tfrac{1}{2}\,\underline{q})C(\underline{p} - \tfrac{1}{2}\,\underline{q}), \quad (17)$$

and the incident flux is

$$\frac{dN_{inc}}{dA} = \int \frac{d^3q}{(2\pi)^3}\,\frac{d^3q'}{}\; C^*\,(\underline{q}')C(\underline{q})2\pi\partial[\hat{v}_0\cdot(\underline{q}' - \underline{q})], \quad (18)$$

when $C(\underline{p})$ is sufficiently sharply peaked that $\underline{p} \simeq \underline{p}_0$ in the integrand. $\hat{v}_0 = \vec{\underline{p}}_0/|p_0|$ is the incident (unit) velocity.

A straightforward calculation now gives to second order

$$\int_{t\to\infty} d^3R f(\underline{p},\underline{R},t) = \int_{t\to\infty} d^3R[f_0 + f_1 + f_2 + \ldots]$$

$$= C^*\,(\underline{p})C(\underline{p}) + \frac{d\sigma^{(2)}}{d^3p}\,\frac{dN_{inc}}{dA} \quad (19)$$

$$- \sigma^{(2)}_{TOT}\int \frac{d^3q}{(2\pi)^3}\; C^*(\underline{p})C(\underline{q})\delta[\hat{v}_0\cdot(\underline{p} - \underline{q})]\;,$$

where $d\sigma^{(2)}/d^3p$ is given by

$$\frac{d\sigma^{(2)}}{d^3p} = \frac{(2\pi)^{-2}}{v_0} |V(\underline{p} - \underline{p}_0)|^2 \delta(E - E_0). \tag{20}$$

Here we have assumed $C(\underline{p})$ to be sharply peaked at $\underline{p}_0$ so that we can factor smooth integrands out of the integrals. Hence when $p \neq \underline{p}_0$ we get agreement with Eq. (10) to second order. It will be noted that in the present problem the normalization is exhausted by $C^*(\underline{p})C(\underline{p})$; the integral $\int d^3p f_2$ vanishes by cancellation. In the simple scattering problem there is little if any practical advantage of using the transport approach. However, in more complex problems involving production of many particles the complexity of the transport theory description of the reaction is not especially increased. More significantly, the method exposes possible collective motions more clearly than approaches involving amplitudes only. Nothing prevents one from applying the present method to nuclear reaction theory. (For this set of problems the use of second quantization is recommended.) A similar method has been developed recently for this purpose by Remler and Sathe[5].

III. FORMULATION OF COVARIANT TRANSPORT THEORY

In relativistic quantum field theory the concept of number density loses its central meaning except when it coincides with an absolutely conserved quantity (e.g., baryon number or charge density for fermion fields). Nevertheless it is possible to construct a useful covariant analogue of the Wigner phase space distribution. We note that Eqs. (3) and (8) are nothing but the Fourier transforms of field correlation functions with equal time labels for the fields. Making the times unequal we define for Bosons the function

$$F(p,R) = \int d^4r\, e^{ip\cdot r} \langle \underline{\psi} | \phi(R - \tfrac{1}{2} r)\phi(R + \tfrac{1}{2} r) | \underline{\psi} \rangle , \quad (21)$$

where $\underline{\psi}$ is a normalized in state; we work in the Heisenberg picture throughout. In the present paper we deal only with real Bose fields, the case of Fermions being treated elsewhere. The metric used here has sign structure (+ - - -). A vacuum subtraction is tacitly understood in the definition (21), if no external fields are present.

The definition (21) is closely related to the observable number distribution of particles created by external potentials or by collisions. Let us suppose that initially there are no quanta of the field ϕ in the state $\underline{\psi}$. The outgoing number distribution dN/d^3p is then given by $\langle \underline{\psi} | a^*_{out}(\vec{p}) a_{out}(\vec{p}) | \underline{\psi} \rangle$. Making use of the reduction formula leads immediately to the result[2] (here $j(x)$ is $(\Box + \mu^2)\phi(x)$)

$$2\omega \frac{dN}{d^3p} = \frac{1}{(2\pi)^3} \int d^4x_1 d^4x_2 e^{ip\cdot(x_2 - x_1)} \Big\{ \langle \underline{\psi} | j(x_1) j(x_2) | \underline{\psi} \rangle \Big\} . \quad (22)$$

The significance of the right hand side depends on the problem under consideration; if $|\underline{\psi}\rangle$ is the incoming vacuum under the influence of an external potential then (5) calculates the number distribution directly. When $|\underline{\psi}\rangle$ represents a scattering state the right hand side is a single particle inclusive differential cross section times a flux factor which can be calculated for wave packets sufficiently sharply peaked in momentum space.

Changing coordinates to R, r (defined by $R = \frac{1}{2}(x_1 + x_2)$, $r = x_2 - x_1$) we find

$$2\omega \frac{dN}{d^3p} = \frac{1}{(2\pi)^3} \int d^4R\, \tilde{F}(p,R) \, , \qquad (23)$$

where $\tilde{F}(p,R)$ is defined by an equation like (21) with ϕ replaced by j. The Fourier transforms $F(p,q) \equiv \int d^4R e^{iq.R} F(p,R)$, $\tilde{F}(p,q) \equiv \int d^4R e^{iq.R} \tilde{F}(p,R)$ are related by

$$\tilde{F}(p,q) = [(p + \tfrac{q}{2})^2 - \mu^2]\,[(p - \tfrac{q}{2})^2 - \mu^2]\, F(p,q), \quad (24)$$

so that (23) can be written as

$$2\omega \frac{dN}{d^3p} = \frac{1}{(2\pi)^3} \tilde{F}(p,q = 0) =$$

$$\frac{(p^2 - \mu^2)^2}{(2\pi)^3} F(p,q = 0) \quad . \qquad (25)$$

The function F, which has a tractable equation of motion, has to have the external legs amputated to get the physical quantity $\tilde{F}$. $F(p,q = 0)$ has a second order pole at $p^2 = \mu^2$.

Equation (22) is basically the same as Mueller's result[8] for the single pion inclusive differential cross section if we let $\underline{\psi}$ be a two-proton state. The only difference lies in our use of normalized wave packet states (useful in studying localizable features of the production process). Therefore in the limit of sharply peaked wave packets in momentum space the right hand side of (22) factors into the inclusive cross section times a flux factor as in the non-relativistic case Eq. (10). Details of this correspondence will be given elsewhere[10].

Evidently (cf. Eqs. (22) and (25)) computation of the Fourier transform $F(p,q)$ of the Boltzmann function provides a means of calculating the absorptive part of a suitable multiparticle amplitude (for forward scattering when $q = 0$). Hence, the solution of a transport

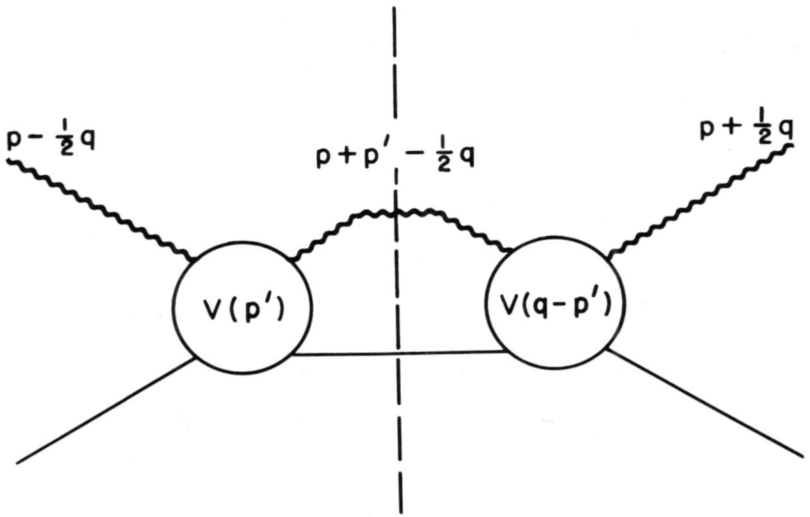

The discontinuity (represented by the vertical dashed line) of the scattering amplitude for meson $p - q/2$ going to meson $p + q/2$ in the presence of the potential V (the latter schematically indicated by straight lines) is indicated in second order. When the external legs are amputated this quantity corresponds to $\tilde{F}_2(p,q)$.

problem is identified with the evaluation of an inclusive differential cross section, much in the spirit of the Landau hydrodynamical model.[11-14] Of course the situation is enormously complicated by the existence of a hierarchy of coupled transport equations for F(p,R) and its multiparticle analogues $F(p_1p_2,R_1R_2)$ etc. Here we only treat cases in which the equations of motion can be sensibly approximated to give closed systems involving F(p,R) alone. (In multicomponent systems there will naturally be distributions for each asymptotic particle species.)

The equations of motion of the correlation function can be cast into a form strongly reminiscent of the non-relativistic transport equation in a straightforward manner. Subtracting the equations of motion

$$\begin{aligned}(\Box_1 + \mu^2)\ \langle\phi(x_1)\phi(x_2)\rangle &= \langle j(x_1)\phi(x_2)\rangle \quad , \\ (\Box_2 + \mu^2)\ \langle\phi(x_1)\phi(x_2)\rangle &= \langle\phi(x_1)j(x_2)\rangle \quad ,\end{aligned} \tag{26}$$

and recognizing the identify

$$\Box_2^2 - \Box_1^2 = 2\ \frac{\partial}{\partial R}\cdot\frac{\partial}{\partial r}\ , \tag{27}$$

we find by Fourier transformation on the relative coordinate r the equation

$$\begin{aligned}2ip\cdot\frac{\partial}{\partial R}\ F(p,R) = \\ \int d^4r\ e^{ip\cdot r}\ \{\langle j(R - \tfrac{1}{2}\ r)\phi(R + \tfrac{1}{2}\ r)\rangle \\ - \langle\phi(R - \tfrac{1}{2}\ r)j(R + \tfrac{1}{2}\ r)\rangle\} \quad .\end{aligned} \tag{28}$$

Clearly this is the equation from which the system of transport equations can be generated. The operator $p\cdot\partial/\partial R$ is the covariant analogue of the usual $\partial/\partial t + \underline{v}\cdot\nabla$

in non-relativistic transport theory. The significance of the right hand side depends on the detailed nature of the interaction assumed. We shall consider here three illustrative cases:

$$\text{(a)} \quad L_{int} = V(x)\phi(x);$$

$$\text{(b)} \quad L_{int} = \frac{1}{2} V(x)\phi^2(x) \text{ and}$$

$$\text{(c)} \quad L_{int} = \frac{1}{2} V(x)\phi^2(x) + \frac{1}{4} \lambda\phi^4(x).$$

The corresponding currents are respectively $j = V$, $j = V\phi$ and $j = V\phi + \lambda\phi^3$. We shall see that in case (a) the right hand is easily evaluated explicitly; in case (b) the expectation value $<\phi\phi>$ appears on the right hand side so that (28) becomes a linear integro-differential equation in $F(p,R)$; in case (c) the ϕ^4 interaction leads to the presence of four-point correlation functions $<\phi^4>$ on the right hand side. In a complete treatment one has to compute the equation of motion for this object, which leads to $<\phi^6>$, etc. This hierarchy, familiarly intractable in all many particle systems, will be analyzed in more detail elsewhere; here we shall only treat the problem by "Hartree" or "random phase approximation"; this amounts to ignoring correlations. Thus $<\phi^4>$ will be approximated to be $<\phi^2> <\phi^2>$ (each bracket involves a vacuum subtraction); this is in turn quadratic in F so that the transport equation reduces to a covariant analogue in the Vlasov equation familiar to workers in plasma physics.

The simplest possible case involves a Lorentz scalar source $V(x)$ coupled linearly to the meson field, i.e., $L_{int}(x) = V(x)\phi(x)$. In this case the current $j(x) = V(x)$ and the formal solution to the equation of motion

$$\phi(x) = \phi_{in}(x) - \int d^4x' \, \Delta(x - x') j(x') \quad , \tag{29}$$

(where $\Delta(x)$ is the retarded Green's function with $\Delta^{-1}(p) = p^2 - \mu^2$) is an explicit solution. We compute particle production from the vacuum by the action of $V(x)$ either by substituting (29) in Eq. (28) and solving by Fourier transformation on R or by substituting (29) directly into the definition (21). The result is expressible as

$$\tilde{F}(p,q) = V(p + \tfrac{q}{2}) V^* (p - \tfrac{q}{2}) \quad , \tag{30}$$

so that the number distribution is, according to (25), the usual result:

$$\frac{dN}{d^3p} = \frac{|V(p)|^2}{2\omega(2\pi)^3} \quad . \tag{31}$$

The problem posed by $L_{int} = \frac{1}{2} V\phi^2$ is just a relativistic Schrödinger problem (of course for the field ϕ, not the state of the system). This example is easily analyzed in perturbation series and gives a detailed illustration of the principles involved in the transport approach to particle production. The transport equation is

$$2ip\cdot\frac{\partial}{\partial R} F(p,R) = \int d^4r \, e^{ip\cdot r} (V(R - \tfrac{1}{2} r) - V(R + \tfrac{1}{2} r)) \langle\phi(R - \tfrac{1}{2} r)\phi(R + \tfrac{1}{2} r)\rangle \quad . \tag{32}$$

The resemblance to the corresponding non-relativistic equation (11) should be noticed. As in this case a slowly varying V permits one to obtain the transport equation for a particle moving in an external field

$$2p\cdot\frac{\partial}{\partial R}F(p,R) = \frac{\partial V}{\partial R}\cdot\frac{\partial F(p,R)}{\partial p} \cong 0 \quad . \qquad (33)$$

The exact equation following form (32) is conveniently written as

$$2p\cdot q\; F(p,q) = \qquad (34)$$
$$\int\frac{d^4p'}{(2\pi)^4}\,V(p')[F(p+\frac{p'}{2},\, q-p') - F(p-\frac{p'}{2},\, q-p')] \;.$$

Again consider particle production by V from an initial vacuum. The unperturbed distribution F_0 is

$$F_0(p,q) = (2\pi)^5\delta_-(p^2-\mu^2)\delta(q) \quad , \qquad (35)$$

where - signifies that only the $p_0 < 0$ root is taken and $\delta(q)$ reflects the spatial homogenity of the initial condition. Equation (34) suggests an iterative scheme; to second order we find

$$F(p,q) = (2\pi)^5\delta_-(p^2-\mu^2)\delta(q)$$
$$-2\pi\left(\frac{\delta_-[(p+\tfrac{1}{2}q)^2-\mu^2]}{(p-\tfrac{1}{2}q)^2-\mu^2} + \frac{_-[(p-\tfrac{1}{2}q)^2-\mu^2]}{(p+\tfrac{1}{2}q)^2-\mu^2}\right) \qquad (36)$$
$$\left(V(q) - \int\frac{d^4p'}{(2\ )^4}\,\frac{V(p')V(q-p')}{(p+p'+\tfrac{1}{2}q)^2-\mu^2}\right)$$
$$+\frac{2\pi}{[(p+\tfrac{1}{2}q)^2-\mu^2][(p-\tfrac{1}{2}q)^2-\mu^2]}$$
$$\int\frac{d^4p'}{(2\pi)^4}\,V(p')V(q-p')\delta_-[(p+p'-\tfrac{1}{2}q)^2-\mu^2] \quad .$$

The physical contribution to $\tilde{F}(p,q)$ is easily computed and gives

$$\frac{dN}{d^3p} = \frac{1}{2\omega(2\pi)^6} \int d^4p' |V(p + p')|^2 \, \delta_+(p'^2 - \mu^2) \quad . \qquad (37)$$

Equation (36) and higher order contributions not exhibited here show that F(p,q) represents a type of absorptive part of a scattering amplitude of mesons $p - q/2$ to $p + q/2$ on a potential V (Fig. 1). $\tilde{F}(p,q)$ is the absorptive part of a scattering amplitude $F'(p,q)$ satisfying the integral equation

$$F'(p,q) = F_2'(p,q) - \int \frac{d^4p'}{(2\pi)^4} \frac{V(p') \, F'(p+\tfrac{1}{2}p', q-p')}{(p+p' - \tfrac{1}{2}q)^2 - \mu^2}, \qquad (38)$$

where $F_2'(p,q)$ is the second-order contribution

$$F_2'(p,q) = -\int \frac{d^4p'}{(2\pi)^4} \frac{V(p') \, V(q-p')}{(p+p' - \tfrac{1}{2}q)^2 - \mu^2} \quad . \qquad (39)$$

The recipe to obtain (36) from (38) is to replace propagators $\frac{1}{p^2-\mu^2}$ one by one by $-2\pi\delta_-(p^2-\mu^2)$.

Finally we are ready for the more meaty problem involving meson self-interaction: $L_{int} = \frac{1}{2} V\phi^2 + \frac{1}{4} \lambda\phi^4$. Writing the current as $j \simeq V\phi + \lambda\phi\langle\phi^2\rangle$ amounts to replacing the potential V(p) by the effective potential

$$V(p) + \lambda \int \frac{d^4p'}{(2\pi)^4} F(p', p) \quad . \qquad (40)$$

The transport equation is similar to a Vlasov equation for a plasma in an external potential:

$$\begin{aligned} 2p\cdot q \; F(p,q) = \int \frac{d^4p'}{(2\pi)^4} \Big\{ \Big[V(p') + \int \frac{d^4p''}{(2\pi)^4} F(p'',p') \Big] \\ \Big[F(p + \tfrac{1}{2} p', q - p') - F(p - \tfrac{1}{2} p', q - p') \Big] \Big\}. \end{aligned} \qquad (41)$$

As is well known such an equation can reveal collective motion in the fluid described by $F(p,q)$. Let us regard V as weak so that a power series solution makes sense. Then the lowest order term satisfies a covariant Vlasov equation

$$2p\cdot q\, F_0(p,q) = \lambda \int \frac{d^4p'}{(2\pi)^4} \int \frac{d^4p''}{(2\pi)^4} F_0(p'',p') \left[F_0(p+\tfrac{1}{2}p',\, q-p') - F_0(p-\tfrac{1}{2}p',\, q-p')\right] . \qquad (42)$$

Consider the simplest case of a spatially homogeneous system of mesons having the unperturbed distribution function

$$F_0(p,q) = (2\pi)^4\, F_0(p)\delta(q) \quad , \qquad (43)$$

where $F_0(p)$ is a function of p^2. The first order correction $F_1(p,q)$ is now computed to be

$$F_1(p,q) = \frac{X(p,q)V(q)}{1 - \lambda \int \frac{d^4p}{(2\pi)^4} X(p,q)} \quad , \qquad (44)$$

where X is defined by

$$X(p,q) = \frac{F_0(p+\frac{1}{2}q) - F_0(p-\frac{1}{2}q)}{(p+\frac{1}{2}q)^2 - (p-\frac{1}{2}q)^2} \qquad (45)$$

The condition that a collective mode exists even as $V \to 0$ is, from (44):

$$1 = \lambda \int \frac{d^4p}{(2\pi)^4} \frac{F_0(p+\frac{1}{2}q) - F_0(p-\frac{1}{2}q)}{(p+\frac{1}{2}q)^2 - (p-\frac{1}{2}q)^2} \qquad (46)$$

We note that classical stability considerations require the constant λ to be negative.

To check for the existence of a collective mode and to examine its nature we must specify the unperturbed ($V = 0$) distribution function more precisely. In a scattering problem $F_0(p,q)$ will be determined by the nonlinear integral equation (42). In a space-time-homogeneous situation F_0 has the form (43) and (42) reduces to zero equals zero. But for a thermalized system F_0 is determined by statistical mechanics. We take $F_0(p)$ to be that appropriate to a system of free bosons in thermal equilibrium[15,16], remembering to subtract out the vacuum expectation value:

$$F_0(p) = 2\pi\delta(p^2 - \mu^2)\left\{\frac{\varepsilon(p_o)}{e^{\beta p_0} - 1} - \theta(-p_0)\right\} . \quad (47)$$

Here $\varepsilon(p_o)$ is ± 1 according to whether p_0 is $\gtrless 0$. Evaluation of the integral (46) now leads to the eigenvalue condition

$$\frac{8\pi^2}{\lambda} = \frac{1}{q}\int_\mu^\infty \frac{dx}{e^{\beta x} -1} \log \left| \frac{(\frac{1}{2}q^2 - \frac{1}{2}q_0^2 + q\sqrt{x^2 - {}^2})^2 - x^2 q_0^2}{(\frac{1}{2}q^2 - \frac{1}{2}q_0^2 - q\sqrt{x^2 - {}^2})^2 - x^2 q_0^2} \right| , \quad (48)$$

where here q means $|\underline{q}|$.

We now examine solutions $q_0 = q_0(\underline{q})$ of Eq. (48). It is simplest to study the long wave length ($q \to 0$) and the low temperature ($\beta\mu >> 1$) limits. (It is not necessary to take these limits simultaneously.) In either case the quantity $q\sqrt{x^2 - \mu^2}$ in the logarithm is small so that one can expand the logarithm. For $q_0 < 2\mu$ we easily find as $\underline{q} \to 0$ the relation

$$1 = \frac{\lambda}{\pi^2} \int_{\mu}^{\infty} \frac{\sqrt{x^2 - \mu^2}}{(e^{\beta x} - 1)(4x^2 - q_0^2)} \, dx \, . \tag{49}$$

Since the right hand side is positive it is evident that no root to (46) exists for $q_0 < 2\mu$ in the long wavelength limit.

For $q_0 > 2\mu$ we find, however, that (46) can be satisfied since (again for $\underline{q} = 0$) the right hand side is now negative. For low temperature ($\beta\mu >> 1$) we get

$$q_0^2 = 4\mu^2 - f(T) \quad , \tag{50}$$

where

$$f(T) = \frac{\lambda}{\pi^2} \int_{\mu}^{\infty} dx \sqrt{x^2 - \mu^2} \Big/ (e^{\beta x} - 1) \; , \tag{51}$$

vanishes exponentially as $T \to 0$.

For finite q it is not difficult to solve (48) for large $\beta\mu$, since the contributing values of x are close to μ. The solution is

$$q_0^2 = \underline{q}^2 + \frac{1}{2} [4\mu^2 - f(T) + \sqrt{(4\mu^2 - f(T))^2 + 16\mu^2 q^2}] \, . \tag{52}$$

As q becomes large (52) $q_0 \cong q$. The sound velocity $\partial q_0/\partial q$ is less than unity, but approaches unity for large q.

The example system, infinite in extent and at constant temperature T, does not accurately imitate the final state in a multiparticle production process. Neither should one imagine that the model Hamiltonian represents the real world. However the general phenomnon of the existence of collective excitations is evidently possible in the real world. It is tempting to speculate that such excitations are at the root of the phenomenon of clustering[9]. In order to do this, one has to examine higher order correlation functions to find evidence for resonant enhancement at the mass of the collective excitation. We shall examine this problem elsewhere.

REFERENCES

1. D. Horn and F. Zachariasen, Hadron Physics at Very High Energies (W.A. Benjamin, Inc., Reading, Massachusetts, 1973).

2. P. Carruthers and F. Zachariasen, p. 481, in AIP Conference Proceedings No. 23, Particles and Fields Subseries No. 10, Ed. Carl E. Carlson (American Institute of Physics, New York [1975] to be published).

3. E. Wigner, Phys. Rev. 40, 749 (1972).

4. L. P. Kadanoff and G. Baym, Quantum Statistical Mechanics, (W. A. Benjamin,Inc., New York 1962).

5. E. Remler and A. P. Sathe (to be published).

6. J. Ross and J. Kirkwood, J. Chem. Phys. 22, 1094 (1954).

7. J. H. Irving and R. W. Zwanzig, J. Chem. Phys. 19, 1173 (1951).

8. A. Mueller, Phys. Rev. D2, 2963 (1970).

9. T. Ludlam and R. Slansky, Phys. Rev. D8, 1408 (1973); W. Kittel, S. Ratti and L. Van Hove, Nuc. Phys. 1330, 333 (1971).

10. P. Carruthers and F. Zachariasen (in preparation).

11. L. D. Landau, Izv. Akad. Nauk SSR 17, 51 (1953).

12. P. Carruthers, Proc. N.Y. Academy of Sciences, Vol. 229, 91 (1974).

13. F. Cooper, p. 499 in AIP Conference Proceedings No. 23, Particles and Fields Subseries No. 10, Ed. Carl E. Carlson (American Institute of Physics, New York, 1975).

14. F. Cooper and D. Sharp (this conference).

15. L. Dolan and R. Jackiw, Phys. Rev. D9, 3320 (1974).

16. Notice that in contrast to the theory of liquid He^4 we do not permit condensation in the ground

state. This possibility will be examined elsewhere; in the usual case of He^4 phonons exist in the system. For the application we have in mind, i.e. to rather transient existence of $10 - 10^2$ mesons, it is not compelling that condensation occurs.

17. In accordance with established tradition the principle value is to be taken (whenever the denominator vanishes) for the purpose of locating the real part of the frequency of the approximate eigenstate.

QUANTUM MECHANICAL APPROXIMATIONS IN QUANTUM FIELD THEORY*

R. Jackiw

Laboratory for Nuclear Science and Department of Physics

Massachusetts Institute of Technology

Cambridge, Massachusetts 02139

I. INTRODUCTION

Covariant perturbation methods, developed over a quarter century ago, have since then dominated dynamical calculations in quantum field theory. Marvelously successful results can be achieved with some problems (especially in electrodynamics); but in many other contexts the technique yields no information. When the coupling constant is large, perturbation theory is useless. Even for weak coupling there remain phenomena, apparently of physical interest, which cannot easily be seen in the perturbative expansion; for example spontaneous symmetry violation, bound states, entrapment of various excitations. These cooperative, coherent effects can only be exposed by approximation procedures which do

*This work is supported in part through funds provided by the Atomic Energy Commission under Contract AT(11-1)-3069.

not rely on analyticity or regularity in the coupling constant. Such approximations are widely used in quantum mechanics (one does not find the properties of a complex atom or nucleus in the Born series!) and it is profitable to extend them to relativistic quantum field theory.

In the last year a group of us in Cambridge[1] has researched some aspects of this topic; in my lectures I shall summarize the results. The application of the following quantum-mechanical procedures to field theory will be described: Rayleigh-Ritz variation, self-consistent (Hartree-Fock) approach, semi-classical approximation, the Kerman-Klein method. (The last category describes generalized Tamm-Dancoff calculations; it includes in a unified way popular many-body techniques--Hartree, Hartree-Fock, Hartree-Fock-Bogolubov, Random Phase Approximation, etc.) With these methods I shall elucidate various interesting physical problems: symmetry behavior at zero and finite temperature, coherent bound states in field theory, dynamical symmetry breaking.

Lack of time prevents me from describing another body of work which certainly falls within the framework of this discussion. A group at Princeton[2] has shown how the WKB approximation can be used for an analysis of the particle spectrum in field theory.

II. VARIATIONAL PRINCIPLE

Any quantum problem, for example, one set in field theory, can be formulated variationally. Given a Hamiltonian H depending on a field operator Φ and on canonical momentum Π, we seek the state $|\psi\rangle$ for which $\langle\psi|H|\psi\rangle/\langle\psi|\psi\rangle$ is stationary. (For the time being theories involving only one spinless field are considered.) It is convenient to implement this variational principle in two steps. Rather than varying $|\psi\rangle$ arbitrarily, we impose two subsidiary conditions: $\langle\psi|H|\psi\rangle/\langle\psi|\psi\rangle$ is to be stationary, but the matrix elements of the quantum field and of the product of two quantum fields are held fixed.

$$\langle\psi|\Phi(t,\underset{\sim}{x})|\psi\rangle/\langle\psi|\psi\rangle = \phi(\underset{\sim}{x}) \quad , \tag{2.1a}$$

$$\langle\psi|\Phi(t,\underset{\sim}{x})\Phi(t,\underset{\sim}{y})|\psi\rangle/\langle\psi|\psi\rangle = \phi(\underset{\sim}{x})\phi(\underset{\sim}{y})+G(\underset{\sim}{x},\underset{\sim}{y}) \quad . \tag{2.1b}$$

The expectation of H in this constrained state depends on ϕ and G; we call that quantity the <u>energy functional</u>, $E(\phi,G)$. The complete variational principle is now implemented by demanding that $E(\phi,G)$ be stationary against variations of ϕ and G.

$$\frac{\delta E(\phi,G)}{\delta\phi(\underset{\sim}{x})} = 0 \quad , \tag{2.2a}$$

$$\frac{\delta E(\phi,G)}{\delta G(\underset{\sim}{x},\underset{\sim}{y})} = 0 \quad . \tag{2.2b}$$

(It is recognized that the constrained state is an eigenstate of the Hamiltonian, modified by Lagrange multipliers J and K, which enforce the subsidiary condition:[3] $H - \int d\underset{\sim}{x}\; J(\underset{\sim}{x})\; \Phi(t,\underset{\sim}{x}) - \frac{1}{2}\int d\underset{\sim}{x}d\underset{\sim}{y} K(\underset{\sim}{x},\underset{\sim}{y})\; \Phi(t,\underset{\sim}{x})\; \Phi(t,\underset{\sim}{y})$. $E(\phi,G)$ is the Legendre transform of the eigenvalue $\varepsilon(J, K)$, where ϕ and G are conjugate to J and K.)[4]

The advantage of this formulation is that approximations to $E(\phi, G)$ can be readily constructed, and the problem of solving the field theory reduces to solving (2.2). Also, once (2.2) is solved, the equilibrium forms of $\phi(\underset{\sim}{x})$ and $G(\underset{\sim}{x}, \underset{\sim}{y})$ are known. These are relevant to spontaneous symmetry violation.

III. RAYLEIGH-RITZ VARIATION

An exact application of the variational principle leads to intractable equations of the complete field theory. The Rayleigh-Ritz approximation allows $|\psi\rangle$ to be of a specific form depending on parameters, and the variational principle is effected approximately by varying these parameters. We chose $|\psi\rangle$ to depend on ϕ and G in way such that eqs. (2.1) are exactly satisfied.

To carry out the program, a fixed time Schrödinger picture for field theory is introduced[5]. We associate with the state $|\psi\rangle$ a "wave-function" which is a functional of a c number field $\Phi(\underset{\sim}{x})$.

$$|\psi\rangle \to \Psi\{\Phi\} \quad . \tag{3.1a}$$

The quantum field operator $\Phi(t,\underset{\sim}{x})$ is replaced by $\Phi(\underset{\sim}{x})$ and the canonical momentum operator by $\frac{1}{i}\frac{\delta}{\delta\Phi(\underset{\sim}{x})}$.

$$\Phi(t,\underset{\sim}{x})|\psi\rangle \to \Phi(\underset{\sim}{x})\Psi\{\Phi\} \tag{3.1b}$$

$$\Pi(t,\underset{\sim}{x})|\psi\rangle \to \frac{1}{i}\frac{\delta}{\delta\Phi(\underset{\sim}{x})}\Psi\{\Phi\} \quad . \tag{3.1c}$$

The inner product is realized by functional integration.

$$\langle\psi_1|\psi_2\rangle \to \int d\Phi \Psi_1^*\{\Phi\}\Psi_2\{\Phi\} \quad . \tag{3.1d}$$

An operator Hamiltonian

$$H = \int d\underset{\sim}{x}\left[\tfrac{1}{2}\Pi^2 + \tfrac{1}{2}(\underset{\sim}{\nabla}\Phi)^2 + U(\Phi)\right] \tag{3.2a}$$

becomes in the Schrödinger picture

$$H = \int d\underset{\sim}{x}\left[-\frac{1}{2}\frac{\delta^2}{\delta\Phi(\underset{\sim}{x})\delta\Phi(\underset{\sim}{x})} + \frac{1}{2}(\underset{\sim}{\nabla}\Phi)^2 + U(\Phi)\right] \quad . \qquad (3.2b)$$

Following Kuti[5], we use the trial wavefunction

$$\Psi\{\Phi\} = \exp\left[-\frac{1}{\hbar}\int d\underset{\sim}{x}d\underset{\sim}{y}[\Phi(\underset{\sim}{x})-\phi(\underset{\sim}{x})]G^{-1}(\underset{\sim}{x},\underset{\sim}{y})[\Phi(\underset{\sim}{y})-\phi(\underset{\sim}{y})]\right] \quad . \qquad (3.3)$$

Since $\Psi\{\Phi\}$ is Gaussian, all functional integrations are elementary. It is clear that eqs. (2.1) are satisfied, and $E(\phi, G)$ is found to be

$$E(\phi,G) = \frac{1}{8}\int d\underset{\sim}{x}\; G^{-1}(\underset{\sim}{x},\underset{\sim}{x}) - \frac{1}{2}\int d\underset{\sim}{x}\; d\underset{\sim}{y}\; G(\underset{\sim}{x},\underset{\sim}{y})\nabla^2\delta(\underset{\sim}{x}-\underset{\sim}{y})$$

$$+ \frac{1}{2}\int d\underset{\sim}{x}(\underset{\sim}{\nabla}\phi)^2 + \int d\underset{\sim}{x}\; \frac{1}{\sqrt{\pi}}\int_{-\infty}^{\infty} da\; e^{-a^2}\, U(a\sqrt{2G(\underset{\sim}{x},\underset{\sim}{x})} + \phi(\underset{\sim}{x})). \qquad (3.4)$$

The variational equations (2.2) are

$$\nabla^2\phi(\underset{\sim}{x}) = \frac{1}{\sqrt{\pi}}\int_{-\infty}^{\infty} da\; e^{-a^2}\, U'(a\sqrt{2G(\underset{\sim}{x},\underset{\sim}{x})} + \phi(\underset{\sim}{x})) \quad , \qquad (3.5a)$$

$$\frac{1}{4}\, G^{-2}(\underset{\sim}{x},\underset{\sim}{y}) = -\nabla^2\delta(\underset{\sim}{x}-\underset{\sim}{y}) + \frac{1}{\sqrt{\pi}}\int_{-\infty}^{\infty} da\; e^{-a^2}\, U''(a\sqrt{2G(\underset{\sim}{x},\underset{\sim}{x})}+\phi(\underset{\sim}{x})) . \qquad (3.5b)$$

For a specific example, we evaluate the energy functional in a theory with interaction $\frac{\lambda}{4!}\,\Phi^4$.

$$E(\phi,G) = E_c(\phi) + \frac{1}{8}\int d\underset{\sim}{x}\; G^{-1}(\underset{\sim}{x},\underset{\sim}{x})$$

$$+ \frac{1}{2}\int d\underset{\sim}{x}d\underset{\sim}{y}\; G(\underset{\sim}{x},\underset{\sim}{y})\, \frac{\delta^2 E_c(\phi)}{\delta\phi(\underset{\sim}{x})\delta\phi(\underset{\sim}{y})}$$

$$+ \frac{\lambda}{8}\int d\underset{\sim}{x}\; G(\underset{\sim}{x},\underset{\sim}{x})G(\underset{\sim}{x},\underset{\sim}{x}) \qquad (3.6a)$$

$E_c(\phi)$ is the classical energy of a static field.

$$E_c(\phi) = \int d\underset{\sim}{x}[\tfrac{1}{2}(\underset{\sim}{\nabla}\phi)^2 + U(\phi)] \quad . \tag{3.6b}$$

Eqs. (3.5) become

$$\nabla^2\phi(\underset{\sim}{x}) = U'(\phi) + \frac{\lambda}{2} G(\underset{\sim}{x},\underset{\sim}{x})\phi(\underset{\sim}{x}) \quad , \tag{3.7a}$$

$$\frac{1}{4}G^{-2}(\underset{\sim}{x},\underset{\sim}{y}) = \frac{\delta^2 E_c(\ )}{\delta\phi(\underset{\sim}{x})\delta\phi(\underset{\sim}{y})} + \frac{\lambda}{2} G(\underset{\sim}{x},\underset{\sim}{x})\delta(\underset{\sim}{x}-\underset{\sim}{y}) \quad . \tag{3.7b}$$

As with all variational approximations, it is difficult to assess corrections. However, since the approximation is variational, it probes the structure of the theory rather more deeply than any systematic coupling constant expansion. Such an expansion will be given in the next Section.

IV. EFFECTIVE ACTION, LOOP EXPANSION, SEMI-CLASSICAL AND HARTREE-FOCK APPROXIMATIONS

A method for calculating the energy functional to arbitrary accuracy is the loop expansion. To derive this, we first generalize the previous fixed-time approach by allowing time variation. The theory is now described by a Lagrangian $L(\Phi)$ and we consider the vacuum persistence amplitude $Z(J,K)$ in the presence of space-time varying sources, $J(x)$ and $K(x,y)$; $J(x)$ couples to $\Phi(x)$ and $K(x,y)$ to $\frac{1}{2}\Phi(x)\Phi(y)$. The generalized effective action $\Gamma(\phi,G)$ is defined by a double Legendre transform of $-i\ln Z(J,K) = W(J,K)$.

$$\frac{\delta W(J,K)}{\delta J(x)} = \phi(x), \quad \frac{\delta W(J,K)}{\delta K(x,y)} = \frac{1}{2}\,[\phi(x)\phi(y)+G(x,y)] \quad , \tag{4.1}$$

$$\Gamma(\phi,G) = W(J,K) - \int dx\phi(x)J(x) \quad ,$$

$$- \frac{1}{2}\int dxdy[\phi(x)\phi(y)+G(x,y)]K(x,y) \quad . \tag{4.2}$$

In the physical theory the sources are absent, hence $\Gamma(\phi,G)$ satisfies

$$\frac{\delta\Gamma(\phi,G)}{\delta\phi(x)} = -J(x)-\int dy\ K(x,y)\phi(y) = 0 \quad ,$$

$$\frac{\delta\Gamma(\phi,G)}{\delta G(x,y)} = -\frac{1}{2}K(x,y) = 0 \quad . \tag{4.3}$$

It is clear from (4.1) that $\phi(x)$ is the expectation of the quantum field and $G(x,y)$ is the propagator of the theory.

For $\Gamma(\phi,G)$ a simple diagrammatic expansion can be given; since $\Gamma(\phi,G)$ is related to the energy functional, see below, this provides an expansion for $E(\phi,G)$. The expansion formula for $\Gamma(\phi,G)$ is[6]

$$\Gamma(\phi,G) = I(\phi)-\frac{i}{2}\ \mathrm{Tr}[\ell n G D^{-1} - G\Delta^{-1}(\phi)+1]+\Gamma_2(\phi,G) \quad . \tag{4.4}$$

Here $I(\phi)$ is the classical action

$$I(\phi) = \int dx\ L(\phi) \quad , \tag{4.5}$$

$\Delta(\phi)$ is a field dependent propagator, while D is its field-free version.

$$i\Delta^{-1}\{\phi;x,y\} = \frac{\delta^2 I(\phi)}{\delta\phi(x)\sigma\phi(y)} \quad ,$$

$$D(x,y) = \Delta\{0;x,y\} \quad , \tag{4.6}$$

$\Gamma_2(\phi,G)$ is the sum of all two-particle irreducible vacuum graphs where the propagator is G and the vertices are given by the interaction part of $L(\Phi+\phi)$. The trace and logarithm in (4.4) are functional.

The connection between the generalized effective action and the energy functional is as follows[4]. In $\Gamma(\phi,G)$ set $\phi(x) = \phi(\underset{\sim}{x})$. Also solve for $G(x,y)$ in terms of $G(\underset{\sim}{x},\underset{\sim}{y}) = G(x_o\underset{\sim}{x},\ x_o\underset{\sim}{y})$, using the equation

$$\frac{\delta\Gamma(\phi,G)}{\delta G(x,y)} = -\frac{1}{2}\,\delta(x_o-y_o)K(\underset{\sim}{x},\underset{\sim}{y}) \quad .$$

[The sources occurring in the calculation of the energy functional are static.] Elimination of $G(x,y)$ in favor of $G(\underset{\sim}{x},\underset{\sim}{y})$ in $\Gamma(\phi,G)$ gives $E(\phi,G)$, except for an overall time integral.

$$\Gamma(\phi,G)\Big|_{\text{static}} = -E(\phi,G)\int dt \quad . \tag{4.7}$$

An alternate reduction is obtained when translation invariant forms are used: ϕ constant and G depending only on coordinate difference. This defines the generalized effective potential,

$$\Gamma(\phi,G)\Big|_{\substack{\text{translation}\\ \text{invariant}}} = -V(\phi,G)\int dx \quad . \tag{4.8}$$

$\Gamma(\phi,G)$ is a generalization of the ordinary effective action $\Gamma(\phi)$. The latter is the generating functional of single-particle irreducible graphs; it is defined by the same procedure as $\Gamma(\phi,G)$ except that no bilocal source $K(x,y)$ occurs. A formula analogous to (4.4) can be given for $\Gamma(\phi)$[7].

$$\Gamma(\phi) = I(\phi)-\frac{i}{2}\,\mathrm{Tr}\ \ell n\Delta(\phi)D^{-1} + \Gamma_2(\phi) \quad , \tag{4.9}$$

$\Gamma_2(\phi)$ is calculated similarly to $\Gamma_2(\phi,G)$, except that one-particle irreducible vacuum graphs are included and the propagator used in the evaluation is $\Delta(\phi)$. In this single-variable formalism, the complete propagator $G(x,y)$ is given by

$$iG^{-1}(x,y) = \frac{\delta^2\Gamma(\phi)}{\delta\phi(x)\delta\phi(y)} \quad . \tag{4.10}$$

When $\Gamma(\phi)$ is evaluated for static $\phi(x) = \phi(\underset{\sim}{x})$, a single variable energy functional is obtained.

$$\Gamma(\phi)\Big|_{\text{static}} = -\,E(\phi)\int dt \quad . \tag{4.11}$$

Finally for constant ϕ, $E(\phi)$ reduces to the effective potential.[8]

$$E(\phi)\Big|_{\substack{\text{translation}\\ \text{invariant}}} = V(\phi)\int d\underset{\sim}{x} \quad . \tag{4.12}$$

The expansion (4.4) can be ordered in terms of loops: $I(\phi)$ is the zero-loop contribution, the term involving the trace is one-loop, $\Gamma_2(\phi,G)$ involves two- and higher- loop graphs. This loop expansion is a systematic coupling constant series when the potential $U(\Phi)$ in the Lagrangian depends on a coupling constant λ in the following way.

$$U(\Phi;\lambda) = \frac{1}{\lambda}\, U(\lambda^{\frac{1}{2}}\Phi;1) \quad . \tag{4.13a}$$

Eq. (4.13a) assures that the Lagrangian also scales.

$$L(\Phi;\lambda) = \frac{1}{\lambda}\, L(\lambda^{\frac{1}{2}}\Phi;1) \quad . \tag{4.13b}$$

Consequently the n-loop term in $\Gamma(\phi,G)$ is of the form

$$\Gamma^{(n)}(\phi,G;\lambda) = \lambda^{n-1}\ \Gamma^{(n)}(\lambda^{\frac{1}{2}}\phi,G;1) \quad . \qquad (4.13c)$$

Therefore if ϕ is taken to be of order $\lambda^{-\frac{1}{2}}$, the loop expansion corresponds to an expansion in powers of λ starting with $I(\phi)$ which is $O(\lambda^{-1})$.

The semi-classical approximation consists of retaining the first two terms in (4.4); the no loop term is classical, the one-loop gives the first quantum correction,

$$\Gamma(\phi,G) = I(\phi) - \frac{i}{2}\mathrm{Tr}[\mathrm{Ln}GD^{-1} - G\Delta^{-1}(\phi)+1] \quad . \qquad (4.14a)$$

Passing to the energy functional we find[4]

$$E(\phi,G) = E_c(\phi) + \frac{1}{8}\int d\underset{\sim}{x}\ G^{-1}(\underset{\sim}{x},\underset{\sim}{x}) + \frac{1}{2}\int d\underset{\sim}{x}d\underset{\sim}{y}\ G(\underset{\sim}{x},\underset{\sim}{y})\ \frac{\delta^2 E_c(\phi)}{\delta\phi(\underset{\sim}{x})\delta\phi(\underset{\sim}{y})} \quad . \qquad (4.14b)$$

The variational equations read

$$\nabla^2\phi(x) = U'(\phi) + \frac{1}{2}\ G(\underset{\sim}{x},\underset{\sim}{x})U'''(\phi) \quad , \qquad (4.15a)$$

$$\frac{1}{4}\ G^{-2}(\underset{\sim}{x},\underset{\sim}{y}) = \frac{\delta^2 E_c(\phi)}{\delta\phi(\underset{\sim}{x})\delta\phi(\underset{\sim}{y})} \quad ,$$

$$= [-\nabla^2 + U''(\phi)]\,\delta(\underset{\sim}{x}-\underset{\sim}{y}) \quad . \qquad (4.15b)$$

The solution of these equations will be further discussed in Section VI.

The Hartree-Fock approximation (in the $\frac{\lambda}{4!}\ \Phi^4$ theory) involves retaining the double bubble depicted in Fig. 1.

$$\Gamma(\phi,G)=I(\phi)-\frac{i}{2}\mathrm{Tr}[\ell n G D^{-1}-G\Delta^{-1}(\phi)+1]$$
$$-\frac{\lambda}{8}\int d\underset{\sim}{x}\; G(\underset{\sim}{x},\underset{\sim}{x})G(\underset{\sim}{x},\underset{\sim}{x}) \quad . \qquad (4.16)$$

This is not systematic in the coupling constant; another two-loop graph, depicted in Fig. 2, also contributes to this order. Nevertheless it is an interesting approximation, since in the static limit, the energy functional which follows from (4.16) agrees exactly with the Rayleigh-Ritz result (3.6)[4]. The present approximations possess another virtue. If the model is extended to include N spinless fields with an O(N) invariant quartic interaction, the Hartree-Fock formula for $\Gamma(\phi,G)$ is the dominant in N contribution, provided λ is $O(N^{-1})$ and ϕ is $O(N^{1/2})$.[9,10,11]

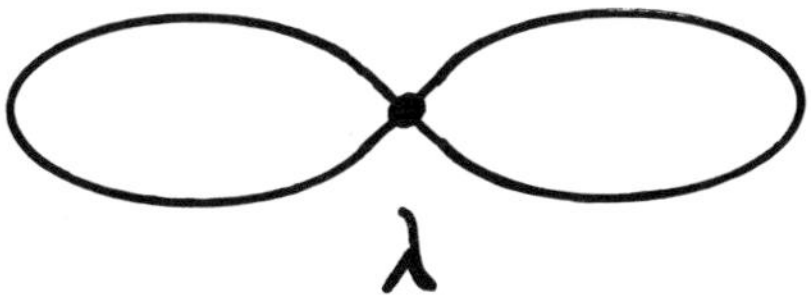

Fig. 1. The two loop diagram which is included in the Hartree-Fock approximation. The vertex is proportional to λ, and so is the entire diagram.

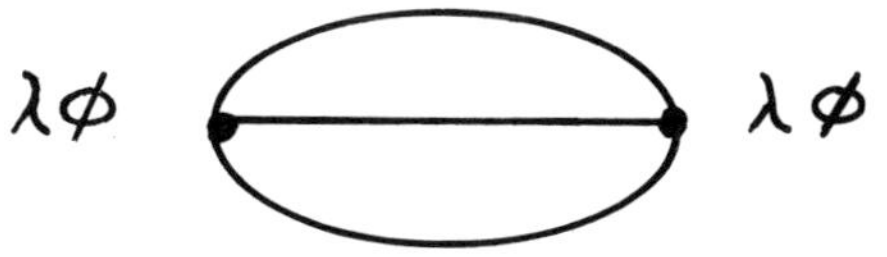

Fig. 2. The two loop graph which is not included in the Hartree-Fock approximation. Each vertex is proportional to $\lambda\phi$ which is $O(\lambda^{1/2})$, and so the entire diagram is $O(\lambda)$.

V. SYMMETRY BEHAVIOR AT ZERO AND FINITE TEMPERATURES

The Hartree-Fock approximation in the Φ^4 theory provides an interesting framework for the study of symmetry behavior at zero and finite temperatures. From (4.3) and (4.16), we have

$$(\Box+\mu^2)\phi(x) + \frac{\lambda}{6}\phi^3(x) + \frac{\lambda}{2}G(x,x)\phi(x) = 0 \ , \qquad (5.1a)$$

$$G^{-1}(x,y) = i[\Box+\mu^2 + \frac{\lambda}{2}\phi^2(x) + \frac{\lambda}{2}G(x,x)]\delta^4(x-y) \ . \qquad (5.1b)$$

To determine whether the symmetry $\Phi\to-\Phi$ is broken (at zero temperature), we seek a solution to (5.1) for constant ϕ in which case G is translationally invariant: $G(x,y) = G(x-y)$. Upon defining the renormalized mass parameter

$$\mu^2 + \frac{\lambda}{2}G(0) = m^2 \ , \qquad (5.2)$$

eqs. (5.1) become

$$[m^2 + \frac{\lambda}{6}\phi^2]\phi = 0 \ , \qquad (5.3a)$$

$$G^{-1}(x-y) = i[\Box + m^2 + \frac{\lambda}{2}\phi^2]\delta^4(x-y) \ . \qquad (5.3b)$$

If m^2 is taken to be a negative number, then the only consistent solution of (5.3) is the symmetry breaking one.

$$\phi^2 = -\frac{6m^2}{\lambda} \ ,$$

$$G^{-1}(x-y) = i[\Box-2m^2]\delta^4(x-y) \ . \qquad (5.4)$$

(The solution $\phi = 0$ is unacceptable, since it leads to

a propagator with imaginary mass.) Similar calculations can be performed in an O(N) invariant Φ^4 theory, (for which the Hartree-Fock approximation dominates when N is large) in different dimensions.[10,11,12] The behavior of spontaneous symmetry breaking with varying dimensionality is thereby exposed: a continuous symmetry can be broken only when the dimension of space-time is greater than 2.

Another interesting question is whether a spontaneously broken symmetry can be restored at finite temperature. Qualitative arguments indicating that this should happen were given by Kirzhnits and Linde[13], and subsequent detailed computations have established the phenomenon.[14,9,15] This topic can be readily analyzed by a straight forward extension of the formalism.

A field theory at a finite temperature, proportional to $1/\beta$, is conveniently described by its finite-temperature Green's functions, which are defined by a statistical average: $\mathrm{Tr}\ e^{-\beta H} T\Phi(x_1)\ldots.\Phi(x_n)/\mathrm{Tr}\ e^{-\beta H}$. These Green's functions satisfy the same differential equations as the corresponding ones at zero temperature. However, the boundary conditions are different: in the complex time interval $(0,-i\beta)$ there are periodicity requirements. It follows that in a theory with interactions, the formulas for temperature Green's functions in terms of the elementary free-field propagator and vertices are the same as at zero temperature, except that the free-field propagators have a "momentum" representation consistent with the periodicity conditions.

$$D_\beta(x) = \int_k e^{-ikx} \frac{i}{k^2-m^2}\ , \qquad \text{(spin 0 fields)}\ ,$$

$$S_\beta(x) = \int_k e^{-ikx} \frac{i}{\not{k}-m}\ , \qquad \text{(spin 1/2 fields)},$$

(5.5)

where $\int_k$ stands for $\frac{1}{-i\beta}\sum_n \int \frac{d^3k}{(2\pi)^3}$, $n = 0, \pm 1 \ldots$; $k^2 = k_o^2 - \underset{\sim}{k}^2$; $k = k_o\gamma^o - \underset{\sim}{k}\cdot\underset{\sim}{\gamma}$; and k_o equals $\frac{2\pi n}{-i\beta}$ for spin 0 fields, $\frac{(2n+1)\pi}{-i\beta}$ for spin 1/2 fields. Consequently symmetry behavior at finite temperature can be studied in terms of solutions to eqs. (5.1) which are also valid at finite temperature.[16]

Only translation invariant solutions of (5.1) need be considered. Introducing the "momentum" representation (5.5), we are led to the system of equations

$$[\mu^2 + \frac{\lambda}{6}\phi_\beta^2 + \frac{\lambda}{2}\int_k G_\beta(k)]\phi_\beta = 0 \quad , \qquad (5.6a)$$

$$G_\beta^{-1}(k) = i[-k^2+\mu^2 + \frac{\lambda}{2}\phi_\beta^2 + \frac{\lambda}{2}\int_k G_\beta(k)] \quad , \qquad (5.6b)$$

$$\phi_\beta = \mathrm{tr}\, e^{-\beta H}\,\Phi(x)/\mathrm{tr}\, e^{-\beta H} \quad ,$$

$$\phi_\beta^2 + \int_k e^{-ik(x-y)}G_\beta(k) = \mathrm{tr}\, e^{-\beta \dot{H}}\, T\Phi(x)\Phi(y)/\mathrm{tr}\, e^{-\beta H} \; .$$

The symmetric solution $\phi_\beta = 0$ will be acceptable if the mass parameter in the propagator is positive.[17]

Eq. (5.6b) is solved by $G_\beta^{-1}(k) = i[-k^2 + m_\beta^2]$ where the temperature dependent mass m_β satisfies [at $\phi_\beta = 0$] the gap equation.

$$m_\beta^2 = \mu^2 + \frac{\lambda}{2}\int_k \frac{i}{k^2-m_\beta^2} \quad ,$$

$$= \mu^2 + \frac{\lambda}{2\beta}\sum_n \int \frac{d\underset{\sim}{k}}{(2\pi)^3} \frac{1}{\frac{(2\pi n)^2}{\beta^2} + \underset{\sim}{k}^2 + m_\beta^2} \quad ,$$

$$= \mu^2 + \frac{\lambda}{2}\int \frac{d\underset{\sim}{k}}{(2\pi)^3}\frac{1}{2\sqrt{\underset{\sim}{k}^2+m_\beta^2}} + \frac{\lambda}{\beta^2} f(m_\beta^2\beta^2) \quad , \qquad (5.7a)$$

$$f(a^2) = \frac{1}{4\pi^2} \int_0^\infty \frac{x^2 dx}{\sqrt{x^2+a^2}} [e^{\sqrt{x^2+u^2}} - 1]^{-1} \quad . \tag{5.7b}$$

The integral occurring in (5.7a) is divergent; the gap equation must be renormalized. It is important that renormalization does not involve any counterterms beyond those of the zero temperature theory. To carry out the renormalization we evaluate the integral in (5.7a) with a cutoff, and rewrite that expression.

$$m_\beta^2 = m^2 + \frac{g}{\beta^2} f(m_\beta^2\beta^2) + \frac{g}{32\pi^2} m_\beta^2 \,\ell n \frac{m_\beta^2}{|m^2|} \quad . \tag{5.7c}$$

Here m^2 is the renormalized mass parameter, taken to be negative, and g is the renormalized coupling constant; they are given in terms of the bare parameters and cut-off Λ.

$$m^2 = \mu^2 + \frac{\lambda}{32\pi^2} [\frac{\Lambda^2}{2} - m^2 \ell n \frac{\Lambda^2}{|m^2|} + m^2] \quad ,$$

$$\frac{1}{g} = \frac{1}{\lambda} + \frac{1}{32\pi^2} [\ell n \frac{\Lambda^2}{|m^2|} - 1] \quad .$$

Eq. (5.7c) is the renormalized gap equation for m_β^2 and we seek solutions for positive m_β^2. At low temperature [$\beta\to\infty$] there is symmetry breaking and no positive solution exists. At high temperature [$\beta\to 0$] one can satisfy (5.7c) with $m_\beta^2 > 0$. The critical temperature β_c^{-1} is that value of the temperature for which m_β^2 vanishes. Therefore from (5.7b) and (5.7c) we have

$$0 = m^2 + \frac{g}{\beta_c^2} f(0) \quad , \tag{5.8}$$

$$\frac{1}{\beta_c^2} = \frac{24|m^2|}{g} \quad .$$

For $\beta^{-1}>\beta_c^{-1}$ symmetry is manifest, for $\beta^{-1}<\beta_c^{-1}$ the symmetry is broken. In this calculation we have ignored higher loop corrections, which are proportional to higher powers of the coupling constant. Hence the entire approach is correct only if the coupling is small, in which case β_c^{-1}, given by (5.8), is indeed large. One can estimate that for small g, the corrections are $O(g^{1/2})$ i.e. $\beta_c^{-2} = \frac{24|m^2|}{g}[1+O(g^{1/2})]$. Eq. (5.7c) can be solved for m_β when $\beta\approx\beta_c$.

$$m_\beta = \frac{2\pi}{3}(\beta^{-1}-\beta_c^{-1}) \quad . \tag{5.9}$$

The computation may be extended to an O(N) invariant Φ^4 theory. (The Hartree-Fock approximation then dominates for large N.) Once again (5.8) and (5.9) are found, except that g is replaced by $g\,\frac{(N+2)}{3}$. Also if gauge fields are included, so that the theory is locally O(N) invariant, one gets

$$\frac{1}{\beta_c^2} = \frac{|m^2|}{g\frac{(N+2)}{72} + e^2\frac{2(N-1)}{4}} \tag{5.10}$$

where e is the gauge coupling strength.[19]

What is the significance of phase transitions in field theory which restore a spontaneously broken symmetry? One answer addresses itself to questions of principle. It may be thought that a theory with a hidden, spontaneously broken symmetry is equivalent to a theory without any symmetry at all, and that the various relationships that exist between masses, coupling constants etc. are merely consequences of perturbative unitary or renormalizability. However, if the physical environment can be arranged so that the symmetry becomes manifest, there can be no doubt about the existence of the symmetry. Practical application of this phenomenon must be confined to speculations about the early universe, since only in that environment were there temperatures sufficiently high to effect a phase transition. (The order of magnitude of β_c^{-1} may be estimated as follows. For global symmetries, we identify the vacuum expectation value of the field with f_π, the pion decay constant. Hence $f_\pi^2 = \frac{6|m^2|}{g}$ and, $\beta_c^{-1} = O(f_\pi) \approx 100$ MeV. For local symmetries, recall that the spontaneously generated vector meson mass is $\sqrt{2}ef_\pi$ and the mass of the Higgs particle is $\sqrt{2|m^2|}$. Hence (5.10) is also given by $\beta_c^{-1} = [\frac{e^2}{m_W^2}\frac{N+2}{6} + \frac{e^2}{m_H^2}\frac{N-1}{2}]^{-1}$. With $e^2 \approx 10^{-2}$ and $m_H < m_W$, we get $\beta_c^{-1} \approx O(10m_H)$.] Thus a temperature environment for field theoretic phase transitions is not readily available. However, one may study other environments which effect phase transitions described by critical parameters that have more immediate experimental consequences.[20]

VI. POSITION DEPENDENT SOLUTIONS, KERMAN-KLEIN METHOD, BOUND STATE BARYONS

Once an explicit, approximate formula for $E(\phi,G)$ has been obtained, it is natural to inquire whether there exist solutions to the variational equations which are position dependent. Unlike the previously discussed translationally invariant solutions, which determine the nature of the vacuum, the translationally non-invariant solutions cannot be associated with vacuum expectation values, since we do not expect translational symmetry to be spontaneously broken. As we shall show below, these solutions should be interpreted as evidence for new states in the theory.[21]

It is in fact quite difficult to solve even the

approximate variational equations exactly. Hence we take the simplest of these, given by the semiclassical approximation of Section IV.

$$E(\phi,G) = E_c(\phi)+\frac{1}{8}\int d\underset{\sim}{x}\; G^{-1}(\underset{\sim}{x},\underset{\sim}{x})+\frac{1}{2}\int d\underset{\sim}{x}d\underset{\sim}{y}\; G(x,y)\frac{\delta^2 E_c(\phi)}{\delta\phi(\underset{\sim}{x})\delta\phi(\underset{\sim}{y})}, \qquad (6.1)$$

$$\nabla^2\phi(\underset{\sim}{x}) = U'(\phi) + \frac{1}{2}\, G(\underset{\sim}{x},\underset{\sim}{x})U'''(\phi) \quad , \qquad (6.2a)$$

$$\frac{1}{4}G^{-2}(\underset{\sim}{x},\underset{\sim}{y}) = [-\nabla^2+U''(\phi)]\delta(\underset{\sim}{x}-\underset{\sim}{y}) \quad , \qquad (6.2b)$$

and solve them sequentially. First the last terms in (6.2a) is ignored since it is $O(\lambda^{1/2})$ while the remaining terms are $O(\lambda^{-1/2})$.

$$\nabla^2\phi(\underset{\sim}{x}) = U'(\phi) \quad . \qquad (6.3a)$$

With $\phi(\underset{\sim}{x}) = \phi_c(\underset{\sim}{x})$ solving (6.3a), the solution of (6.2b) for $\phi(\underset{\sim}{x}) = \phi_c(\underset{\sim}{x})$ is obtained by finding a complete set of functions ψ_n satisfying a Schrödinger-like equation.

$$[-\nabla^2 + U''(\phi_c)]\psi_n = w_n^2\;\psi_n \quad . \qquad (6.3b)$$

This gives to order λ^o

$$G^{-2}(\underset{\sim}{x},\underset{\sim}{y}) = \sum_n 4w_n^2\;\psi_n^*(\underset{\sim}{x})\psi_n(\underset{\sim}{y}) \quad . \qquad (6.3c)$$

Substituting our solutions into (6.1) determines the energy to order λ^o.

$$E = E_c(\phi_c) + \frac{1}{4}\int d\underset{\sim}{x}\; G^{-1}(\underset{\sim}{x},\underset{\sim}{x})$$

$$= E_c(\phi_c) + \frac{1}{2}\sum_n w_n \quad . \qquad (6.4)$$

The meaning of (6.4) is clear: the total energy in this approximation is composed of the classical energy, plus the zero point energy of the field fluctuations.

Before proceeding, we take note of an important stability criterion. The eigenfrequencies ω_n^2 must be non-negative so that the energy be real.[22] There is always a zero-frequency mode: upon differentiation of (6.3a) with respect to $\underset{\sim}{x}$, it is recognized that $\underset{\sim}{\nabla}\phi$ satisfies (6.3b) with $\omega_o = 0$. For stability this must be the lowest mode. However, when the dimensionality of space is greater than one, $\underset{\sim}{\nabla}\phi$ involves several independent functions, and the mode is degenerate. Since a degenerate state is never the lowest level of an ordinary Schrödinger equation, we conclude that stability exists only in one spatial dimension.

I do not at this stage abandon the investigation of stable static solutions, not because one dimension holds any particular interest, but rather because it is possible to construct stable, static models in three-dimensional space, provided something more complicated than a spinless field (or a set of spinless fields) is used; for example fields with spin.[23] Moreover, the formalism and interpretation that we develop works for the realistic situation as well. Therefore I restrict the subsequent discussion to one dimension, where the equation (6.3a) may be integrated once to give

$$\frac{1}{2}\,[\phi'(x)]^2 = U(\phi) \quad , \tag{6.5}$$

and the classical energy becomes

$$\begin{aligned} E_c(\phi_c) &= \int dx\,[\tfrac{1}{2}(\phi_c')^2 + U(\phi_c)] \quad , \\ &= \int dx\,(\phi_c')^2 \;. \end{aligned} \tag{6.6}$$

(The constant of integration is chosen so that $E_c(\phi_c)$ is finite.)

The zero frequency mode $\phi_c'(x)$ is a consequence of translation invariance (we call it the translation mode): if $\phi_c(x)$ solves (6.5), so does $\phi_c(x + a)$. The translation mode produces a singularity in the propagator, since ω_o vanishes.

$$G(x,y) = \sum_n \frac{1}{2\omega_n} \psi_n^*(x)\psi_n(y) \quad . \tag{6.7}$$

This of course is the familiar Goldstone phenomenon when one is dealing with a spontaneously broken symmetry; in the present instance translation invariance appears to be broken. However, we now make the following reinterpretation of our results. We allege that the position dependent solution of the variational equations is an artifact of the approximation; if $E(\phi,G)$ were computed exactly, then only constant solutions would be found. Correspondingly the translation mode does not correspond to an excitation of the system.[24] (As an indication of this, note that even the semiclassical approximation cannot be carried to higher order. The $O(\lambda^{1/2})$ solution to (6.2a) requires $G(x,x)$ which is infinite because of the translation mode.)

What then is the correct interpretation of the solutions we have found? We suggest the following _Ansatz_. In addition to the conventional particles of the theory, (which we call mesons) there exist heavy particles (which we call baryons). The baryon is described by a non-normalizable Poincaré covariant state $|p\rangle$; it carries momentum p and energy $\sqrt{p^2+M^2}$. In weak coupling M is of order λ^{-1}, hence $E \approx M + \frac{p^2}{2M}$. To order λ^o, the energy previously calculated in (6.4), coincides with the mass of the baryon. There exist also baryon, multi-meson states $|p;\{k_n\}>$, with total momentum $p + \sum_n k_n$ and energy $E(p) + \sum_n \omega(k_n)$.

We shall demonstrate the consistency of the Ansatz by calculating matrix elements of Φ between baryon-multimeson states $|p;\{k_n\}>$. For $<p;\{k_n\}|\Phi|p';\{k_m'\}>$ we take a sum of all possible terms of the form $(2\pi)\delta(k_1-k_1')(2\pi)\delta(k_2-k_2')<p;k_3\ldots|\Phi|p';\, k_3'\ldots>_c$, in which any number of mesons is disconnected. The calculation will proceed by the Kerman-Klein method[25]. This involves using the field equations, saturating with intermediate states, and truncating the intermediate state sum. We can make the truncation process a systematic coupling constant approximation by postulating that the connected matrix elements between m and n mesons have an expansion in powers of λ, with leading order $\lambda^{1/2(m+n-1)}$. Thus $<p'|\Phi|p>$ is of order $\lambda^{-1/2}$, $<p'|\Phi|p;k>$, of order λ^{o}; while $<p';k|\Phi|p\,;\ell> = (2\pi)\delta(k-\ell)<p'|\Phi|p> + <p';k|\Phi|p;\ell>_c$ where the connected part is of order $\lambda^{1/2}$. Also the stability of the baryon (which we discuss again below) leads us to set $<p;\{k_n\}|\Phi|\{\ell_m\}>$ to zero.

We begin by studying the equation for the no-meson matrix element of Φ. For definiteness, we pick the potential $U(\phi) = \frac{1}{2\lambda}\,(m^2-\lambda\phi^2)^2$. The exact equation of motion is

$$\{-(p-q)^2 + (E(p)-E(q))^2+2m^2\}<p|\Phi|q> = 2\lambda<p|\Phi^3|q> \quad . \tag{6.8a}$$

To lowest order in λ, that is to order $\lambda^{-1/2}$, the energy difference vanishes, since $E(p)\approx E(q)\approx M$-- we are led to a static approximation. To the same order $<p|\Phi|q>$ depends only on the momentum difference. On the right hand side, complete sets of states are inserted between each of the Φ factors; to lowest order only the no-meson states survive. Thus the equation becomes

$$\frac{d^2}{dx^2} f(x) = -2m^2 f(x) + 2\lambda f^3(x) = U'(f) \quad ,$$

$$f(x) = \frac{m}{\lambda^{1/2}} \tanh mx = \phi_c(x) \quad , \qquad (6.8b)$$

$$\langle p|\Phi|q\rangle = \int dx\, e^{i(p-q)x} f(x) \quad . \qquad (6.9)$$

Therefore the solution to the static, classical field equations emerges not as the expectation of the quantum field, but rather as the Fourier transform of the field formfactor. Observe that f(x) interpolates between the two vacuum solutions the two constant solutions of the classical equation, $\pm \frac{m}{\lambda^{1/2}}$.

The energy may also be calculated in the same approximation.

$$H = \int dx[\tfrac{1}{2}\pi^2 + \tfrac{1}{2}(\Phi')^2 + U(\Phi)], \; \Pi = \frac{d\Phi}{dt} \quad ,$$

$$\langle p|H|p'\rangle = (2\pi)\delta(p-p')E(p) \quad ,$$

$$E(p) = \langle p|\tfrac{1}{2}\Pi^2 + \tfrac{1}{2}(\Phi')^2 + U(\Phi)|p\rangle \quad . \qquad (6.10a)$$

To leading order, λ^{-1}, the left hand side is just M. On the right hand side, we saturate with single baryon states. The matrix element of Π^2 gives zero, since it involves energy differences which vanish in leading order. The remaining terms are easily shown to give $E_c(\phi_c)$. Hence we find consistent with the <u>Ansatz</u>

$$M = E_c(\phi_c) + O(\lambda^o) \quad ,$$

$$= \int dx (f'(x))^2 + O(\lambda^o) \quad . \qquad (6.10b)$$

To calculate the next order in λ, the single-meson matrix element of Φ is required. As before we assume that to lowest order it depends only on the momentum differences of the baryons.

$$<p|\Phi|p';k> \int dx e^{i(p-p'-k)x} f(k;x) \quad . \qquad (6.11)$$

The equation for f(k;x) is obtained analogously to (6.8). The saturation on the right hand side to order λ^o requires the no-meson, one-meson and the disconnected two-meson matrix elements. The latter is just the no-meson matrix element again; hence the equation is

$$[-\frac{d^2}{dx^2} - 2m^2 + 6\lambda f^2(x)] f(k;x) = \omega^2(k) f(k;x) \quad ,$$

$$[-\frac{d^2}{dx^2} + U''(f)] f(k;x) = \omega^2(k) f(k;x) \quad .$$

We have again encountered the Schrödinger-like equation, now the wavefunctions have a physical significance. Inserting the solution (6.8b), we find that for the Φ^4 theory

$$[-\frac{d^2}{dx^2} + 4m^2 - \frac{6m^2}{\cosh^2 mx}] f(k;x) = \omega^2(k) f(k;x). \qquad (6.13)$$

The eigenvalues are non-negative, hence the solution is stable; they are $\omega^2 = 0$, $\omega^2 = 3m^2$ and a continuum begins at $\omega^2 = 4m^2$. Since 2m is the meson mass calculated in the simplest approximation to the vacuum expectation value of Φ, we interpret the continuum states as baryon-meson scattering states. The discrete level at $\omega^2 = 3m^2$ is associated with an excited state of the baryon. The translation mode at $\omega^2 = 0$, with wavefunction $f'(x) = \phi_c'(x)$, is not associated with any state; we show below that it describes the motion of a free baryon, rather than a baryon-meson state. For later use, note that the normalized wavefunction for the translation mode is $\frac{1}{M^{1/2}} f'(x)$, where the normalization factor is determined from (6.10b). Also for convenience, we set $f(k;x) = [2\omega(k)]^{-1/2}\psi_k(x)$, where $\psi_k(x)$ is a normalized solution of the Schrödinger equation.

With f(k;x) we can determine next order corrections to (6.8b) and (6.10b). Proceeding as before, but retaining also the single-meson state gives

$$\frac{d^2}{dx^2} f(x) = -2m^2 f(x) + 2\lambda f^3(x) + m^2\tilde{G}(x,x)f(x) \quad ,$$

$$= U'(f) + \frac{1}{2}\tilde{G}(x,x)U'''(f) \quad , \qquad (6.14)$$

$$M = E_c(f) + \frac{1}{8}\int dx\, \tilde{G}^{-1}(x,x) + \frac{1}{2}\int dx dy\, \tilde{G}(x,y)\frac{\delta^2 E_c(f)}{\delta f(x)\delta f(y)} + O(\lambda) \quad , \qquad (6.15)$$

$$[\tilde{G}(x,y)]^{\pm 1} = \Sigma' [2\omega(k)]^{\mp 1}\, \psi_k^*(x)\psi_k(y) \ . \qquad (6.16)$$

These formulas are quite similar to the corresponding expressions obtained from the action principle approach, eqs. (6.1) and (6.2). There are however important differences. The quantities f and $\tilde{G}$ in (6.15) are not variational parameters; rather they are given by (6.14) and (6.16). The zero-frequency mode does not contribute to $\tilde{G}$, since there is no physical state corresponding to that solution of the Schrödinger equation. (This is indicated by the prime of the summation sign.) Consequently there no longer is any difficulty with the solution of (6.14). Eq. (6.15) may be simplified, to $O(\lambda)$, by inserting the $O(\lambda^{-1/2})$ solution to (6.14); $f = \phi_c$. (The $O(\lambda^{1/2})$ correction does not contribute since $E_c(f)$ is stationary at $f = \phi_c$.) We then get

$$M = \int dx [\phi_c']^2 + \frac{1}{2} \sum_k \omega(k) \quad . \tag{6.17}$$

Is it consistent to exclude the zero-frequency contribution from the intermediate state sums? To demonstrate the correctness of this, we consider the matrix elements of the canonical commutator between baryon states.

$$\langle p | [\Phi(0,x) \; , \; \Pi(0,y)] | p' \rangle = i(2\pi)\delta(p-p')\delta(x-y) \quad . \tag{6.18}$$

Saturate with no-meson and one-meson intermediate states. The contribution of the one-meson states can be shown to be

$$i\sum_k{}' \omega(k) \{ \int dz \, \frac{\psi_k^*(x-z)}{\sqrt{2\omega(k)}} \frac{\psi_k(y-z)}{\sqrt{2\omega(k)}} \, e^{i(p'-p)z} + x \leftrightarrow y \} . \tag{6.19a}$$

If the translation mode were included, we could use completeness of the wavefunctions to perform the sum; since it is excluded, (6.19a) sums to

$$i(2\pi)\delta(p-p')\delta(x-y) - i\int dz \, e^{i(p-p')z} \frac{f'(x-z)}{\sqrt{M}} \frac{f'(y-z)}{\sqrt{M}} \; . \tag{6.19b}$$

In the sum over no-meson states, we retain the energy

difference to order λ; viz.

$$\langle p|\Pi(0,x)|q\rangle = i[E(p)-E(q)]\langle p|\Phi(0,x)|q\rangle$$
$$\approx i\,\frac{p^2-q^2}{M}\langle p|\Phi(0,x)|q\rangle \quad . \qquad (6.19c)$$

It is not difficult to see that the contribution of this term to the commutator, precisely cancels the translation mode term in (6.19b).

Consequently we have verified that the translation mode is not a true state of system; rather it describes the first correction to the motion of the baryon. Moreover, the argument also shows that the energy satisfies the relativistic dispersion formula, to order λ: $E(p) = M + \frac{p^2}{2M} + 0(\lambda^2)$. (The important point is that the mass term of the static limit, also occurs in the kinetic energy.)

In principle the calculations in the one-baryon sector of the theory can be carried out to arbitrary accuracy, by expanding all expressions in powers of λ.

We have taken the baryon to be stable. This may be understood as follows. The theory admits a conserved current $J^\mu = \varepsilon^{\mu\nu}\partial_\nu\Phi$. The matrix elements of the charge, will be proportional to $\langle\Phi(x)\rangle|_{x=-\infty}^{x=\infty}$. In the no-baryon sector the field tends to the same constant as $x\to\pm\infty$, hence the matrix element vanishes. In the one baryon sector, the field tends to different constants (compare (6.8b)) and the charge is non-zero. It is the conservation of this charge that prevents a no-baryon state from connecting to a baryon state. Thus even though the baryons are heavy, they cannot decay into mesons. (One may also use Kuti's wavefunction (3.3) to establish this result. Take $|\psi\rangle_B$-- the baryons state--

to be represented by (3.3) with $\phi(x) = \phi_c(x)$ and $G^{-1}(x,y) = \Sigma 2\omega(k)\psi_k^*(x)\psi_k(y)$; also take $|\psi>_M$ --the meson state-- to be described by $\phi(x)$ = constant and $G^{-1}(x,y) = \int dk 2\sqrt{k^2+\mu^2} e^{ik(x-y)}$. It is then easy to show that ${}_M<\psi|\Phi(0,x_1)\ldots\Phi(0,x_n)|\psi>_B = 0$.]

Another remarkable feature of the baryons is that they appear to be Fermions. We were led to this conclusion by noting that the form factor $<p|\Phi|q> = \int dx e^{i(p-q)x}\phi_c(x)$ is antisymmetric in $p\leftrightarrow q$, since $\phi_c(x) = -\phi_c(-x)$. Presumably this is a feature of two-dimensional field theories, which do not have a spin-statistics theorem.

Evidence for our interpretation, with all its startling aspects, has been recently found in the study of the sine-Gordon equation. Here the potential is $U(\phi) = \frac{m^2}{\lambda}(1-\cos\lambda^{1/2}\phi)$ and one can obtain a stable static solution to the classical equations, $\phi_c(x) = \frac{4}{\lambda^{1/2}}\tan^{-1}\exp xm$. Hence the theory can be developed as above. On the other hand a careful examination of the Green's functions of the sine-Gordon theory reveals that they are identical to those of the massive Thirring model, $L = i\bar{\psi}\gamma^\mu\partial_\mu\psi - M\bar{\psi}\psi - \frac{g}{2}\bar{\psi}\gamma^\mu\psi\bar{\psi}\gamma_\mu\psi$ with the identifications $4\pi/\lambda = 1 + g/\pi$, $\lambda^{1/2}\varepsilon^{\mu\nu}\partial_\nu\phi = 2\pi\bar{\psi}\gamma^\mu\psi$, $(m^2/\lambda)\cos\lambda^{1/2}\phi = -M\bar{\psi}\psi$.[26] Hence it is very plausible to associate the Fermion field of the Thirring model with the massive baryons of the sine-Gordon equation.

Do these new, remarkable states have any significance for practical physics? Of course the question can only be addressed to models in 4-dimensional space-time, where we have shown that fields with spin must be necessarily used. Various such candidates have been proposed but their consequences are not yet completely understood.[23] For example techniques for multi-baryon states have yet to be developed. Only then will it be possible to assess theory. It may be, as has been long speculated,[27] that the baryons occuring in nature will be found to coincide with the mathematical baryons which I have here discussed.

VII. DYNAMICAL SYMMETRY BREAKING

The last application of our techniques is to study the dynamical symmetry violation. For a variety of reasons, it is attractive to suppose that a symmetry is spontaneously broken, not by a vacuum expectation of a canonical field, but by dynamical bound state formation. In a now familiar fashion this can happen if a zero mass bound excitation violates a global symmetry. Furthermore when gauge fields are present, the local symmetry is also destroyed, if the bound state couples to them. The massless gauge field acquires a mass, and the massless excitation decouples from the theory. When the coupling of the massless excitation to the conserved currents is called f, then the mass of the vector meson is given by f times the gauge coupling constant.[28]

When symmetry breaking does not occur for the one-point function (vacuum expectation values of a field) but can happen for the two-point function, then the generalized effective potential, $V(\phi,G)$, described in Section IV, provides a convenient formalism for the studying this possibility. Upon defining $V(G) = V(0,G)$, we seek symmetry breaking solutions of

$$\frac{\delta V(G)}{\delta G} = 0 \quad . \tag{7.1}$$

Even in the Hartree-Fock approximation to $V(G)$, (7.1) is

an untractable non-linear integral equation. An obvious next step is to approximate further by linearizing. A more interesting procedure is to use the Rayleigh-Ritz idea: an expression for $G(x-y)$ is postulated which depends on symmetry breaking parameters; $V(G)$ is evaluated with this form and then varied with respect to the parameters. This yields tractable algebraic equations.[29]

We illustrate the procedure for a simple model which has in the past served an (unrealistic) paradigm for dynamical gauge symmetry breaking.[30] The Lagrangian is

$$L = \bar{\psi}(i\partial\!\!\!/ - m - g_A \gamma_\mu A^\mu - g_B \tau_2 \gamma_\mu B^\mu)\psi$$
$$- \frac{1}{4} A^{\mu\nu} A_{\mu\nu} - \frac{1}{4} B^{\mu\nu} B_{\mu\nu} \quad ,$$
$$A^{\mu\nu} = \partial^\mu A^\nu - \partial^\nu A^\mu \quad ,$$
$$B^{\mu\nu} = \partial^\mu B^\nu - \partial^\nu B^\mu \quad , \qquad (7.2)$$

where ψ is a two-component spinor field in "iso-spin" space and τ_2 is the usual Pauli matrix. If the gauge symmetry

$$\psi \to e^{i\theta\tau_2}\psi$$
$$B_\mu \to B_\mu - \frac{1}{g_B}\partial_\mu \theta \qquad (7.3)$$

is spontaneously broken, so that the Fermion masses split from the symmetric value m by an amount $\pm\delta m$, the B meson picks up a mass M_B.

The generalized effective potential is given by (4.4) and (4.8), except the following modifications are made. A field dependence is not included and the effective potential depends on three propagators: G for Fermions and Δ_i, i = A, B, for the vector mesons. As a consequence of Fermi statistics, the factor - 1/2 is replaced by 1. Moreover, since we seek only translation-invariant solutions, a momentum representation may be used. Thus for our problem

$$V(G,\Delta_i) = - i\int \frac{d^4p}{(2\pi)^4} \operatorname{tr} [\ell n\, S^{-1}(p)G(p) - S^{-1}(p)G(p) + 1]$$
$$+ \frac{i}{2} \sum_{i=A,B} \int \frac{d^4p}{(2\pi)^4} \operatorname{tr} [\ell n D^{-1}_{\mu\nu}(p)\Delta_i^{\mu\nu}(p) - D^{-1}_{\mu\nu}(p)\Delta_i^{\mu\nu}(p) + 1]$$
$$+ V_2(G,\Delta_i) \quad . \qquad (7.4)$$

The free propagators are

$$S(p) = \frac{i}{\not p - m} \quad , \qquad (7.5)$$

$$D^{\mu\nu}(p) = \frac{-i}{p^2}\left(g^{\mu\nu} - \frac{p^\mu p^\nu}{p^2}\right) \quad .$$

In the Hartree-Fock approximation, we keep just the lowest order contributions. Hence $V_2(G,\Delta_i)$ is given by the graphs of Fig. 3, where the solid lines represent G(p); the wavy line, $\Delta_A^{\mu\nu}(p)$; and the zigzag line, $\Delta_B^{\mu\nu}(p)$. The analytic expression is

$$V_2(G,\Delta_i) = \frac{i}{2} \sum_{i=A,B} \int \frac{d^4p\, d^4q}{(2\pi)^8} \operatorname{tr} \Gamma_i^\mu G(p) \Gamma_i^\nu G(p+k) \Delta_{i,\mu\nu}(k) \quad ,$$

$$\Gamma_A^\mu = g_A \gamma^\mu \quad , \qquad \Gamma_B^\mu = g_B \gamma^\mu \tau_2 \quad , \qquad (7.6)$$

$V_2(G,\Delta_i) = \Gamma_A$ 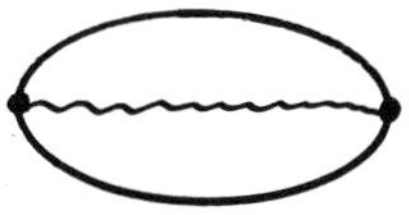 $\Gamma_A + \Gamma_B$ 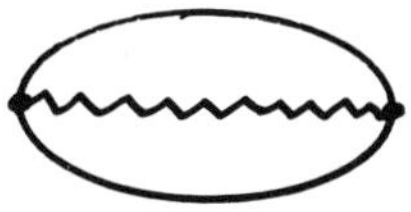 Γ_B .

Fig. 3. Hartree-Fock approximation to $V_2(G,\Delta_i)$.

Stationarity of V with respect to variations of G and Δ_i requires (we use a symbolic notation)

$$G^{-1} = S^{-1} + \sum_{i=A,B} \Gamma_i \, G \, \Gamma_i \, \Delta_i \quad ,$$

$$\Delta_i^{-1} = D^{-1} - \Gamma_i \, G \, \Gamma_i \, G \quad . \tag{7.7}$$

A possible symmetry breaking term in G^{-1} will be proportional to τ_3; since S^{-1} has no such contribution, the symmetry-breaking part satisfies a homogeneous, non-linear integral equation. That equation is intractable, hence a further approximation is made by linearizing it. The solutions of the linearized theory for weak coupling show that the Fermion self-energy Σ has a symmetry violating part Σ_v.

$$\Sigma_v = \left\{ \begin{array}{l} -i \ \delta m \left(\dfrac{-p^2}{m^2}\right)^{-\varepsilon} \tau_3 \ , \ |-p^2| >> m^2 \\ -i \ \delta m \ \tau_3 \ , \ |-p|^2 \leq m^2 \end{array} \right\} \ ,$$

$$\varepsilon = \frac{3}{16\pi^2} \left(g_A^2 - g_B^2\right) \quad . \tag{7.8}$$

Similarly the self-energy of the B meson Π^B, also exhibits a gauge symmetry violating mass term, Π_v^B.

$$\Pi_v^B = \begin{cases} M_B^2\left(\frac{-p^2}{m^2}\right)^{-2\varepsilon} & , |-p^2| \gg m^2 \\ M_B^2 & , |-p^2| < m^2 \end{cases}$$

$$M_B^2 = \frac{g_B^2}{2\pi^2\varepsilon} (\delta m)^2 \quad . \tag{7.9}$$

Thus a symmetry breaking solution ($\delta m \neq 0$) is found. The surprise, in the linearized theory, is that the symmetry breaking parameter δm is not determined. Indeed the only condition for the existence of the solutions (7.8) and (7.9) is that ε be positive, viz. that the attractive coupling dominate over the repulsive coupling.

In order to survey the non-linear aspects of the theory the following procedure may be followed. We substitute in $V(G,\Delta_i)$ the expressions for the propagators determined by the linear theory, with δm an undetermined parameter. Subtracting from the formula the analogous symmetric ($\delta m = 0$) expression, gives a potential which depends on δm, and the idea is that the minimum of this potential as a function of δm should determine δm. The calculation, though lengthy, is straightforward, and yields

$$V(\delta m) = \frac{(\delta m)^4}{32\pi^2\varepsilon} - \frac{(\delta m)^4}{6\pi^2\varepsilon(r^2-1)^2}$$

$$- \frac{m^4}{8\pi^2}\left[(1+\frac{\delta m}{m})^4 \ell n(1+\frac{\delta m}{m}) + (1-\frac{\delta m}{m})^4 \ell n(1-\frac{\delta m}{m}) - 7(\frac{\delta m}{m})^2\right] ,$$

$$r^2 = \frac{g_A^2}{g_B^2} > 1 \quad . \tag{7.10}$$

(Contributions to $V(\delta m)$ which are negligible for weak coupling have been dropped.)

Various aspects of eq. (7.10) deserve comment. There are no divergences; possible logarithmic infinities have been replaced by ε^{-1}, as a consequence of the power behavior (7.8) and (7.9). The form of $V(\delta m)$ is reminiscent of the effective potential in a theory with scalar mesons, with δm playing the role of the scalar fields: there is a quartic term in δm, followed by a logarithmic one. The main differences are the appearance of inverse powers of the coupling constant, present in ε, and the fact that $V(\delta m)$ becomes complex for $|\delta m/m|>1$.

Because the underlying physical model is unrealistic, a detailed analysis of $V(\delta m)$ will not be presented. Note however, that $V(\delta m)$ does possess a minimum, which determines $\delta m/m$ in terms of ε and r, provided ε is not vanishingly small. Hence our Rayleigh-Ritz analysis of the non-linear theory provides information not previously determined by the linear theory: δm is calculable and there are constraints on the coupling constants.

Dynamical symmetry breaking is an attractive theoretical alternative to explicit spontaneous symmetry breaking by scalar fields. For it to be a practical idea for model building, say in weak interactions, computational techniques must be developed which bypass ordinary perturbation theory. Some suggestions for effective Lagrangians have been given.[31] These can be used for low energy computations; they give non-linear realizations of the underlying symmetry.

Another question is whether models based on dynamical symmetry breaking give predictions significantly different from those that utilized scalar fields.

In the context of a certain class of unified theories of weak and electromagnetic interactions, the answer is yes. In these models, dynamical symmetry violation necessitates the existence of "pseudo-Goldstone" bosons, with masses of the order of a few GeV, but with no strong interactions.[32]

Finally let me observe that although a zero mass Goldstone excitation, which is associated with spontaneous violation of a global symmetry, will necessarily induce a mass for vector gauge mesons, it is also possible that masses for gauge fields arise without spontaneous violation of any global symmetry.[33] As is well known, the crucial element in mass generation is the Schwinger mechanism - i.e. the presence of a pole at zero momentum in the vacuum polarization tensor $\Pi^{\mu\nu}(k)$. The vacuum polarization tensor is related to the vertex function $\Gamma^{\mu}(p, p + k)$ by Dyson's equation, see Fig. 4. Certainly if $\Gamma^{\mu}(p, p + k)$ has a longitudinal part proportional to k^{μ}/k^2, which signals violation of a global symmetry and exhibits the Goldstone pole, then also $\Pi^{\mu\nu}(k)$ will possess a pole and the vector meson will acquire a mass. However it may be that the vertex function has a pole in its transverse part, $(g^{\mu\nu} - k^{\mu}k^{\nu}/k^2)\tilde{\Gamma}_{\nu}(p,p+k)$. This would not interfere with a Ward identity -no global symmetry is violated- yet $\Pi^{\mu\nu}(k)$ retains a pole and a mass is generated. Alternatively it could also happen that no poles are present in $\Gamma^{\mu}(p,p+k)$, but the loop integral in p, which must be performed to obtain $\Pi^{\mu\nu}(k)$, diverges at $k = 0$. Indeed this is precisely the state of affairs in Schwinger's classical example. It is not yet known whether mass generation without symmetry violation is a useful concept for physical theory.

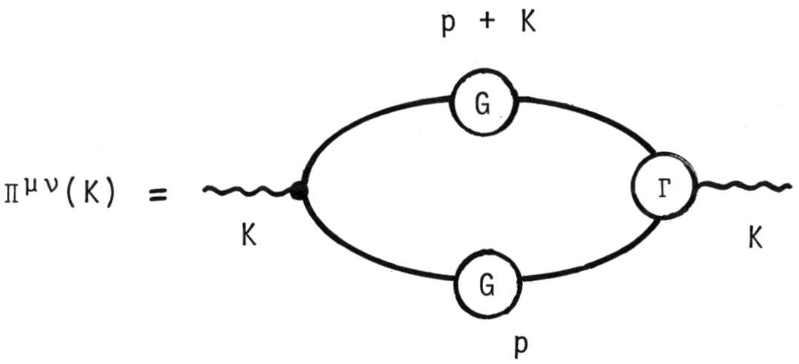

Fig. 4. Dyson Equation for Vacuum Polarization Tensor

REFERENCES

1. Colleagues include S. Coleman, J. Cornwall, L. Dolan, J. Goldstone, J. Kuti, L. Jacobs, K. Johnson, H. Politzer, R. Root, H. Schnitzer, E. Tomboulis, S. Weinberg.
2. R. Dashen, B. Hasslacher and A. Neveu, Phys. Rev. D (in press).
3. The symbols x, dx, etc. refer to space-time coordinates, while $\underset{\sim}{x}$, $d\underset{\sim}{x}$, etc. refer to space coordinates. However in Section VI, when models in two-space time dimensions are discussed, x and dx refer to the single spatial coordinate.
4. For details see J. Cornwall, R. Jackiw and E. Tomboulis, Phys. Rev. D 10, 2428 (1974).
5. J. Kuti, unpublished. Kuti's work is summarized in Ref. 4. See also G. Rosen, Phys. Rev. 160, 1278 (1967).
6. In statistical mechanics, analogous expressions were obtained by T.D. Lee and C.N. Yang, Phys. Rev. 117, 22 (1960); J.M. Luttinger and J.C. Ward, Phys. Rev. 118, 1417 (1960). In relativistic field theory the expansion was derived in Ref. 4.
7. R. Jackiw, Phys. Rev. D 9, 1686 (1974).
8. The effective potential was introduced into field theory by Euler, Heisenberg and Schwinger. It was used in the pioneering works on symmetry breaking by Goldstone, Jona-Lasinio, Weinberg and Salam. More recent discussions are given in Ref. 7; also S. Coleman and E. Weinberg, Phys. Rev. D 7, 1888 (1973); S. Weinberg, Phys. Rev. D 7, 2887 (1973); A. Salam and J. Strathdee, Phys. Rev. D 9, 1129 (1974).
9. L. Dolan and R. Jackiw, Phys. Rev. D 9, 3320 (1974).

10. H. Schnitzer, Phys. Rev. D 10, 1800 (1974).
11. S. Coleman, R. Jackiw and H. Politzer, Phys. Rev. D 10, 2491 (1974).
12. $O(N^{-1})$ corrections to the Hartree-Fock approximations have been computed by R. Root, Phys. Rev. D 10, (1974).
13. D. Kirzhnits and A. Linde, Phys. Lett. 42B, 471 (1972).
14. S. Weinberg, Phys. Rev. D 9, 3357 (1974).
15. D. Kirzhnits and A. Linde, Lebedev Institute preprint.
16. This brief synopsis of field theory at finite temperature is of course an inadequate summary of the beautiful work of Martin, Schwinger and others. For a fuller account see for example L.P. Kadanoff and G. Baym Quantum Statistical Mechanics, (W.A. Benjamin, Menlo Park, 1962). Discussions of this topic which focus on the present application are also given in Refs. 9, 14 and C. Bernard, Phys. Rev. D 9, 3312 (1974).
17. The mass parameter in the propagator is also the second derivative of the effective potential, see (4.10) and (4.12). Hence when it is positive for a solution to the equilibrium equations, we know that we are at a minimum.
18. The approximation and results of this section are familiar in statistical mechanics, where they are known as "spherical model", "mean-field theory" etc. For a review see E. Stanley, Introduction to Phase Transitions and Critical Phenomena (Oxford Univ. Press, New York, 1971).
19. Temperature initiated phase transitions in field theory have been examined also by L. Jacobs, Phys.

Rev. D (in press); A. Yildiz and B. Harrington, Phys. Rev. D. (in press); R. Dashen, R. Rajaraman and S.-K Ma, Phys. Rev. D (in press); H. Wada, Tokyo University preprint.

20. That phase transitions can be induced by high matter density has been shown by T.D. Lee and G.C. Wick, Phys. Rev. D 9, 2291 (1974). A. Salam and J. Strathdee, Nature 252, 569 (1974) and ICTP preprint, have studied field theoretic phase transitions in electromagnetic environments.

21. J. Goldstone and R. Jackiw, Phys. Rev. D (in press). Similar results are obtained by R. Dashen, B. Hasslacher and A. Neveu, Phys. Rev. D (in press).

22. Since $\frac{1}{4}G^{-2}(\underset{\sim}{x},\underset{\sim}{y}) = \frac{\delta^2 E_c(\phi)}{\delta\phi(x)\delta\phi(y)}$, the stability criterion assures that ϕ_c is not a maximum of the classical energy. The eigenfrequencies ω_n control the time variation of small perturbations about ϕ_c: if we set $\phi(t,\underset{\sim}{x}) = \phi_c(\underset{\sim}{x}) + \psi_n(\underset{\sim}{x})e^{i\omega_n t}$, and demand that $\phi(t,\underset{\sim}{x})$ satisfy the classical time dependent field equation, then to first order, ψ_n solves (6.3b).

23. H.B. Nielsen and P. Olesen, Nucl. Phys. B61, 45 (1973); G.'t Hooft, Nucl. Phys. B79, 276 (1974); L.D. Faddeev, Max-Planck Institute preprint; A.M. Polyakov, Landau Institute preprint; S. Mandelstam, Berkeley preprint.

24. This is analogous to the analysis of the polaron problem or the Hartree-Fock model of the nucleus. There too a lowest order calculation violates translation invariance, which is an exact symmetry.

25. A. Kerman and A. Klein, Phys. Rev. 132, 1326 (1963).

26. S. Coleman, Harvard University preprint.

27. Some of the present results have been anticipated

by T. Skyrme, Proc. Roy. Soc. A, 247, 260 (1958); 262, 237 (1961).

28. Dynamical symmetry violation was first discussed by Y. Nambu and G. Jona-Lasinio, Phys. Rev. 122, 345 (1961), for global symmetries; and by J. Schwinger, Phys. Rev. 125, 397 (1962); 128, 245 (1962), for local symmetries. In the context of modern gauge theories, this has been explored by R. Jackiw and K. Johnson, Phys. Rev. D 8, 2386 (1973); as well as J.M. Cornwall and R.E. Norton Phys. Rev. D 8, 3338 (1973).
29. This strategy is advocated by J.M. Cornwall, R. Jackiw and E. Tomboulis, Phys. Rev. D 10, 2428 (1974).
30. R. Jackiw and K. Johnson, Phys. Rev. D 8, 2386 (1973); J.M. Cornwall and R.E. Norton, Phys. Rev. D 8, 3338 (1973). J.M. Cornwall, Phys. Rev. D 10, 500 (1974); see also H. Pagels, Phys. Rev. D 7, 3689 (1973).
31. R. Jackiw and K. Johnson, Phys. Rev. D 8, 2386 (1973); J.M. Cornwall, Phys. Rev. D 10, 500 (1974); S. Coleman and S. Weinberg, unpublished.
32. S. Weinberg, Harvard University preprint.
33. R. Jackiw and K. Johnson, Ref. 28, footnote 12.

ON THE PROBLEM OF CAUSALITY IN CONFORMAL INVARIANT THEORIES

H. A. Kastrup

Technische Hochschule Aachen

Aachen, FR Germany

This is a short review on the considerable progress made in the last year or so in the field of conformal invariant theories, especially as far as the problem of causality is concerned.

I. STATEMENT OF THE PROBLEM

Let $M^4 = \{E\}$ be the Minkowski space of events E with coordinates $x^j(E)$, $j = 0,1,2,3$, and the metric form

$$g(\ x(2),x(1)\ ) = (x^{\circ}(2)-x^{\circ}(1))^2 - (\vec{x}(2)-\vec{x}(1))^2$$
$$= (x(2)-x(1))^2;\ x(i)=x(E_i),i=1,2$$

A causal ordering of two timelike events: $E_2>E_1$ ("E_2 later than E_1") is defined by the functions

$$g(x(2),x(1)) > 0,\ \text{sign}(x^{\circ}(2)-x^{\circ}(1)) > 0 \qquad (1)$$

This notion of causal ordering is invariant under the orthochronous Poincaré group

$$P_{10}(a,\Lambda):\ x^j \rightarrow \hat{x}^j = \Lambda^j{}_k\, x^k + a^j \quad ,$$

(the index "10" denotes the number of independent parameters) and the dilations

$$D_1(\rho): \hat{x}^j \to x^j = \rho x^j, \ \rho>0.$$

Under very general assumptions it can be shown[1] that these transformations of M^4 onto M^4 are also the most general ones which leave the causal ordering (1) invariant.

Quantized fields F(x) are operator-valued distributions and transform like

$$U(a,\Lambda)F(x)U^{-1}(a,\Lambda) = S(\Lambda^{-1})F(\Lambda x+a),$$

where $S(\Lambda^{-1})$ is a finite matrix, depending on the spin of F. Systems which are also dilation-invariant:

$$U(\rho)F(x)U^{-1}(\rho) = \rho^{d_F} F(\rho x),$$
$$d_F: \text{ dimension of } F,$$

are much more restricted, because $U(\rho)P^2U^{-1}(\rho) = \rho^{-2}P^2$, i.e. either $P^2=0$ or the mass spectrum is continuous!

<u>Problems</u> arise in connection with the "special conformal" transformations of M^4.

$$SC_4(c): x^j \to \hat{x}^j = (x^j - c^j x^2)/\sigma(x;c) \ ,$$
$$\sigma(x;c) = 1-2c\cdot x+c^2x^2$$

As σ (x;c) is not positive definite, the mapping (2) is illdefined for $\sigma = 0$. In addition we have

$$x^2 \to \hat{x}^2 = x^2/\sigma(x;c) \quad .$$

which means $\hat{x}^2 < 0$ for $x^2 > 0$, $\sigma < 0$, i.e. the group SC_4 can change the geometrical (global) causal ordering (1) of two events! Because of

$$dx^j dx_j \rightarrow (\Lambda/\sigma^2)\, dx^j dx_j$$

it leaves invariant a local causal ordering, however.

As conformal invariant theories appear to have interesting properties[2], it seems to be worthwhile to look for remedies for these diseases.

It should be mentioned that in the case $P^2=0$ (free mass zero particles) and arbitrary helicities it is possible[3] to have a well-defined field theory on M^4 even for finite conformal mappings, the reason being the special transformation properties of test functions under $SC_4(c)$.

II. SOLUTION OF THE GEOMETRICAL PROBLEM

The first step is, to extend the Minkowski space in a minimal way, so that the action of SC_4 or of the 15-parameter group $C_{15}(a,\Lambda,\rho,c)$ is well-defined on the new manifold.[4] This is being achieved by introducing projective coordinates such that

$$x^j = \frac{\eta_j}{\eta^4 + \eta^5}, \quad x^j \varepsilon M^4, \quad \eta^4 + \eta^5 \neq 0.$$

The coordinates η^μ, $\mu=0,\ldots,5$, are restricted by the relation

$$\eta^\mu . \eta_\mu \equiv (\eta^o)^2 - (\eta^1)^2 - \ldots - (\eta 4)^2 + (\eta 5)^2 = 0, \eta \neq 0.$$

The points E of the extended Minkowski space, called M_c^4, are in one-to-one correspondence to the rest classes

$$[\eta] = \{\eta, \eta(2) = \lambda\eta(1),\ \lambda \neq 0\}.$$

Taking special representatives of these classes:

$$(\eta^1)^2 + .. + (\eta 4)^2 = \Lambda = (\eta 0)^2 + (\eta 5)^2,$$

we see that

$$M_c^4 \sim (S^1 \times S^3)/Z_2,$$

where S^n is the n-dimensional unit sphere and Z_2 means identification of opposite points, S^1 being the compactification of the time line R^1 and S^3 the compactification of R^3. (M_c^4 being compact cannot be described by a single coordinate system, actually one needs at least four[4]!)

If we define $x = \eta^4 + \eta^5$, we have on M^4

$\operatorname{sgn}[x^o(2)-x^o(1)] = \operatorname{sgn}[(\eta^o(2)\eta^5(1)-\eta^5(1)\eta^o(2)/x(1)x(2)]$

for $(x(2)-x(1))^2 = -2(\eta^\mu(2)\eta_\mu(1))/x(1)x(2) > 0,$

and $\qquad dx^j\, dx_j = (\Lambda|x^2)d\eta^\mu\, d\eta_\mu$

$$\text{and } dx^u dx_j = (\Lambda|x^2)\, d\eta\mu\, d\eta\mu. \qquad (3)$$

The twofold covering group $0^\uparrow(2,4)$ of $C_{15}^\uparrow$ acts linearly on the coordinates η^μ:

$$\eta_\mu \to \hat{\eta}^\mu = w^\mu{}_V \eta^V, \quad W^T g W = g, \quad W=(w^\mu{}_V), \quad \text{diag.}\ (g) = (1,-1,-1,-1,-1,1).$$

The orthochronous part of $O(2,4)$ is defined by $\operatorname{sgn}(w^o{}_o w^5{}_5 - w^o{}_5 w^5{}_o) > 0$. One can show[4] that it leaves the function

$$\operatorname{sgn}[\eta^o(2)\eta^5(1) - \eta^o(1)\eta^5(2)]$$

$$\text{invariant if } \eta^\mu(2)\, \eta_\mu(1) = 0.$$

In connection with Eqs. (3) this gives us a C_{15}-invariant <u>local</u> causal ordering on M_c^4, but not a global one. The impossibility of a global causal ordering on M_c^4 follows also immediately from the topological structure $S^1 \times S^3$: there is no <u>global</u> ordering of points on S^1! <u>The way out globally</u> is the following[5)-8)]: The manifold M_c^4 is not simply connected. Its universal covering space is $\tilde{M}^4 \sim R \times S^3$, the points $\tilde{E}$ of which can be described by the coordinates

$$\tilde{x}(\tilde{E}) = (\tau \in R, \underset{\sim}{n} = (n^1,\dots,n^4; \underset{\sim}{n}^2 = 1)).$$

The projection $\tilde{M}^4 \to M_c^4$ is given by

$$\eta^o = \lambda \sin\tau,\ \eta^5 = \lambda\cos\tau,\ \eta^\mu = \lambda\eta^\mu,\ \mu=1,\dots,4;\ \lambda\neq 0$$

From this one sees immediately the infinitely sheeted covering of M_c^4. On $M^4 \subset M_c^4$ we have

$$x^o = \frac{\sin\tau}{\cos\tau + n4},\ \vec{x} = \frac{\vec{n}}{\cos\tau + n4},$$

$$-\frac{1}{2}\pi < \tau < \frac{1}{2}\pi,\ n4 \geq 0.$$

The metric on $\tilde{M}^4$ is given by

$$d\tau^2 - (d\underset{\sim}{n})^2 = \frac{1}{(\eta^o)^2 + (\eta^5)^2} \tag{4}$$

$$d\eta^\mu\, d\eta^\mu,\ \underset{\sim}{n}d\underset{\sim}{n} = 0,\ \eta^\mu d\eta_\mu = 0.$$

or, globally,

$$(\tau_2-\tau_1)^2 - \text{across}\ (\underset{\sim}{n}(2)\cdot\underset{\sim}{n}(1)).$$

A global causal ordering, $\tilde{E}_2 > \tilde{E}_1$, can now be defined for time-like events by

$$\tau_2-\tau_1 > 0,\ (\tau_2-\tau_1)^2 - \text{arcoss}\ (\underset{\sim}{n}(2)\underset{\sim}{n}(1))>0. \tag{5}$$

Projected on M^4 this definition coincides with that of Eq. (1)!

It remains the problem, whether the notion (5) is invariant under the groups discussed above. For this purpose we have to deal with the universal covering group of $C^{\uparrow}_{15}$: the group SU(2,2) is a 2-fold covering of $SO^{\uparrow}(2,4)$ and a 4-fold covering of $C^{\uparrow}_{15}$. It has the topological (not group theoretical!) structure

$$SU(2,2) \sim U(1) \times SU(2) \times SU(2) \times R^8,$$

implying[9] the structure

$$\widetilde{SU}(2,2) \sim R \times SU(2) \times SU(2) \times R^8$$

for the universal covering group. The action of SU(2,2) on $\tilde{M}^4$ can be computed explicitly[7] and it can be shown to leave the ordering (5) invariant!

Two further remarks:

1. The center $\tilde{Z}$ of $\widetilde{SU}(2,2)$ is an infinite, discrete abelian group, isomorphic to $Z_\infty \times Z_2$, where Z_2 corresponds to the center of one of the SU(2)-groups and distinguishes between fermions and bosons. The other factor Z_∞ is given by

$$Z_\infty = \{z^n, \ n=0, \pm 1, \pm 2, \ldots, \ z = R_{05}(\pi)\Pi\},$$
$$R_{05}(\pi): \tau \to \tau + \pi, \quad \Pi: \underset{\sim}{n} \to -\underset{\sim}{n}$$

The center $\tilde{Z}$ seems to play an important role <u>dynamically</u> (see the following paragraph)!

2. The group of motions for the metric $d\tau^2 - (dn)^2$ is the group $T(\sigma) \times O(4)$, where $T(\sigma): \tau \to \tau + \sigma$.

III. PROPERTIES OF FIELDS

Let $\tilde{g} \varepsilon \widetilde{SU}(2,2)$, $U(\tilde{g})$ a unitary representation of $\widetilde{SU}(2,2)$ and $A(\tilde{x})$ a scalar field[10] on $\tilde{M}^4$:

$$U(\tilde{g})\, A(\tilde{x})\, U(\tilde{g})^{-1} = A(\tilde{g}\tilde{x})$$

If locality holds on $\tilde{M}^4$:

$$[A(\tilde{x}(2)), A(\tilde{x}(1))] = 0, \ \tilde{x}(2), \tilde{x}(1) \ \varepsilon \ \tilde{M}^4 \text{ and relatively spacelike,}$$

then it holds for arbitrary spacelike points on $\tilde{M}^4$, because $\widetilde{SU}(2,2)$ acts transitively on pairs of relatively spacelike points:

$$0 = U(\tilde{g}) \, [A(\tilde{x}(2)), A(\tilde{x}(1))] \, U^{-1}(\tilde{g}) = [A(\tilde{g}\tilde{x}(2)), A(\tilde{g}\tilde{x}(1))].$$

Conformal invariant field theories, especially in the Euclidean region, have been studied intensely by Mack and others[2]. An interesting physical problem is the following[11,12,2]: In which way do fields $A(\tilde{x})$ on $\tilde{M}^4$ differ "over" ("under") the same points $x \varepsilon M^4$? Examples show that they differ in an essential way (i.e. not just by a phase), <u>if</u> the dimension of the field has an anomalous (dynamical!) part! This can best be seen by looking at the transformation of $A(\tilde{x})$ under the center $\tilde{Z}$, because $\tilde{Z}$ takes a sheet of $\tilde{M}^4$ to the next one, but acts as the identity on M^4.

As the fields with anomalous dimensions are <u>not</u> observables, their behavior under $\tilde{Z}$ seems to be acceptable. On the other hand, <u>observable</u> quantities like currents do not have anomalous dimensions and, therefore, do not appear to differ in an essential way in different sheets over the same point E of M^4. This means that the physics in different sheets is the same, as one would expect it to be! However, this problem needs further investigation!

REFERENCES AND FOOTNOTES

1. E. C. Zeeman, J. Math. Phys. 5, 490 (1964); for a more refined version see: H. J. Borchers and G. C. Hegerfeldt, Comm. Math. Phys. 28, 259 (1972).

2. M. Lüscher and G. Mack, Global Conformal Invariance in Quantum Field Theory, Univ. of Bern Preprint, Aug. 1974; this paper contains further references to the substantial work on conformal invariant field theories by Mack and others. See also: I. T. Todorov, Conformal Invariant Field Theories with Anomalous Dimensions, CERN Preprint TH1697 (1973), to be published in the Proceed. of the Cargèse Summer Institute 1973.

3. G. Post, Properties of Massless Relativistic Fields under the Conformal Group, Aachen Preprint, Dec. 1974.

4. T. H. Go, H. A. Kastrup, D. H. Mayer, to be published in Reports on Math. Physics 6.3.

5. I. Segal, Bull. Am. Math.Soc. 77, 958 (1971).

6. I. T. Todorov, see ref. 2.

7. T. H. Go, Some Remarks on Conformal Invariant Theories on 4-Lorentz manifolds, to be published in Comm.Math.Physics.

8. D. H. Mayer, Conformal Invariant Causal Structures on Pseudo-Riemannian Manifolds, Aachen Preprint, April, 1974.

9. M. Schaaf, Reports on Math. Physics 4, 275 (1973).

10. As to the existence of such fields see Mack and Lüscher, ref. 2.

11. B. Schroer and J. A. Swieca, Phys. Rev. D10, 480 (1974).

12. J. Kupsch, W. Rühl and B.C. Yunn, Ann. Physics (N.Y.) 89, 115 (1975).

TRANSPORT AND HYDRODYNAMIC ASPECTS OF MULTIPARTICLE PRODUCTION

F. Cooper*

Belfer Graduate School of Science

Yeshiva University, New York, New York 10003

and

Theoretical Division

University of California

Los Alamos Scientific Laboratory

Los Alamos, New Mexico

and

D. H. Sharp*

Theoretical Division

University of California

Los Alamos Scientific Laboratory

Los Alamos, New Mexico 87544

I. INTRODUCTION

Landau's phenomenological model of particle production[1] is based on a simple picture of the energy flow following a collision process.[2,3] The model

* Work supported by the Energy Research and Development Administration.

assumes that as a result of the collision a large amount of energy is deposited in a small region of space-time. The initial energy density ε_0 of this "pre-hadronic" matter is of order E_{CM}/V_0, where V_0 is the collision volume [essentially that of a Lorentz contracted proton in the center of mass frame; $V_0 \sim \pi a^3 \gamma$, $a = m_\pi^{-1}$, $\gamma = (2m_p/E_{CM})$]. Since the comoving energy density of ordinary hadronic matter is of order $\varepsilon_h = m_\pi/V_\pi$, where $V_\pi = (4/3)\pi a^3$, the pre-matter produced in the collision must expand conserving energy and momentum until $\varepsilon \sim \varepsilon_h$ at which time physical pions, the outstates of the usual S-matrix description, appear.

Conservation of energy and momentum during the expansion is insured by requiring that

$$\partial_\mu T_c^{\mu\nu}(x) = 0 \tag{1.1}$$

where

$$T_c^{\mu\nu}(x) = \langle f_1 f_2 | T^{\mu\nu}(x) | f_1 f_2 \rangle$$

is the expectation value of the energy-momentum tensor in the initial state $|f_1 f_2\rangle$ consisting of two hadron wave packets. Landau assumed that $T_c^{\mu\nu}(x)$ could be written in the form

$$T_c^{\mu\nu}(x) = [\varepsilon(x) + p(x)]u^\mu u^\nu - p(x)g^{\mu\nu} , \tag{1.2}$$

which describes an ideal fluid. In Eq. (1.2), $\varepsilon(x)$ is the comoving energy density, $p(x)$ is the pressure, and $u^\mu(x)$ is the collective 4-velocity field. This assumption means that in the comoving frame, defined as the frame in which $T^{0k}(\bar{x}) = 0$ (or, equivalently, in which $u^i(\bar{x}) = 0$ and $u^0(\bar{x}) = 1$), the distribution of matter is isotropic.[4]

By solving the eigenvalue problem

$$T_c^{\mu\nu}(x) v_\nu^{(\alpha)}(x) = \lambda^{(\alpha)}(x) v^{(\alpha)\mu}(x) \quad , \quad \alpha = 1,4 \tag{1.3}$$

one can write an arbitrary symmetric c-number tensor $T_c^{\mu\nu}(x)$ in the form

$$T_c^{\mu\nu}(x) = \varepsilon(x)u^\mu u^\nu + \sum_{i=1}^{3} p_i(x)v^{(i)\mu}v^{(i)\nu} \quad , \tag{1.4}$$

where one defines the energy density $\varepsilon(x)$ as the eigenvalue of the time-like normalized eigenvector u^μ ($u^\mu u_\mu = 1$) and the three pressures $p_i(x)$ as the eigenvalues of the space-like eigenvectors $v_\mu^{(i)}$. If the pressures $p_i(x)$ are degenerate, then the Landau form results.

If, upon diagonalization of $T_c^{\mu\nu}(x)$, it turns out that the pressures are degenerate and if in addition one can write an equation of state $p = p(\varepsilon)$, then one can introduce an entropy density $s(x)$ and a temperature T which satisfy the usual thermodynamic relationships:

$$\varepsilon = Ts - p \tag{1.5}$$

and

$$d\varepsilon = Tds \ . \tag{1.6}$$

Thus,

$$\ell n\ s = \int d\varepsilon / \left[\varepsilon + p(\varepsilon)\right] \quad . \tag{1.7}$$

Using these relationships one can easily show for an ideal fluid that

$$\begin{aligned} u_\mu \partial_\nu T_c^{\mu\nu} &= (\varepsilon + p)\partial_\mu u^\mu + u^\mu \partial_\mu \varepsilon \\ &= T\partial_\mu (su^\mu) = 0 \quad . \end{aligned} \tag{1.8}$$

Thus there is an entropy current $(su^\mu)(x)$ which satisfies a local conservation law, with

$$S = \int_\sigma (su^\mu) d\sigma_\mu \tag{1.9}$$

being the conserved quantity.

The breakup criterion $\varepsilon(x,t) = \varepsilon_h$ defines a surface of constant energy density, pressure, temperature and entropy. If one can identify the fluid velocity $\underset{\sim}{v}$ [$u^\mu = \gamma(1,\underset{\sim}{v})$] with the velocity of the outgoing pion $\underset{\sim}{v}_\pi$, and if one parametrizes the breakup surface by $\underset{\sim}{v}$ so that, on the surface σ, $x = x(\underset{\sim}{v})$ and $t = t(\underset{\sim}{v})$, then one finds that the energy and entropy distributions are given as functions of $\underset{\sim}{v}$ by

$$\frac{\partial^3 E}{\partial v_x \partial v_y \partial v_z} = T^{0\mu}\bigg|_\sigma \frac{\partial^3 \sigma_\mu}{\partial v_x \partial v_y \partial v_z} = \left[(\varepsilon + p)_h\, u^0 u^\mu - p_h g^{0\mu}\right] \frac{\partial^3 \sigma_\mu}{\partial v_x \partial v_y \partial v_z} \tag{1.10}$$

and

$$\frac{\partial^3 S}{\partial v_x \partial v_y \partial v_z} = s_h u^\mu \frac{\partial^3 \sigma_\mu}{\partial v_x \partial v_y \partial v_z} .$$

One obtains particle distributions from Eq. (1.10) by assuming either that

$$\frac{\partial^3 N}{\partial v_x \partial v_y \partial v_z} = \frac{1}{E_\pi} \frac{\partial^3 E}{\partial v_x \partial v_y \partial v_z} = \frac{1}{m_\pi \left(1 - v^2\right)^{-1/2}} \frac{\partial^3 E}{\partial v_x \partial v_y \partial v_z} \tag{1.11}$$

or that $N \propto S$, in which case

$$\frac{\partial^3 N}{\partial v_x \partial v_y \partial v_z} \propto \frac{\partial^3 S}{\partial v_x \partial v_y \partial v_z} \tag{1.12}$$

Details of such calculations are summarized in Refs. (2) and (3). As an example, suppose one assumes that the equation of state is that of an ultrarelativistic gas, $p = (\varepsilon/3)$. Then $\frac{dN}{dy_{CM}}$, the distribution of particles in the center of mass rapidity variable $y_{C.M.} = \frac{1}{2} \ln\left(\frac{1 + v_{||}}{1 - v_{||}}\right) \approx \ln \tan(\theta/2)$, is typically of the form shown in Fig. 1.

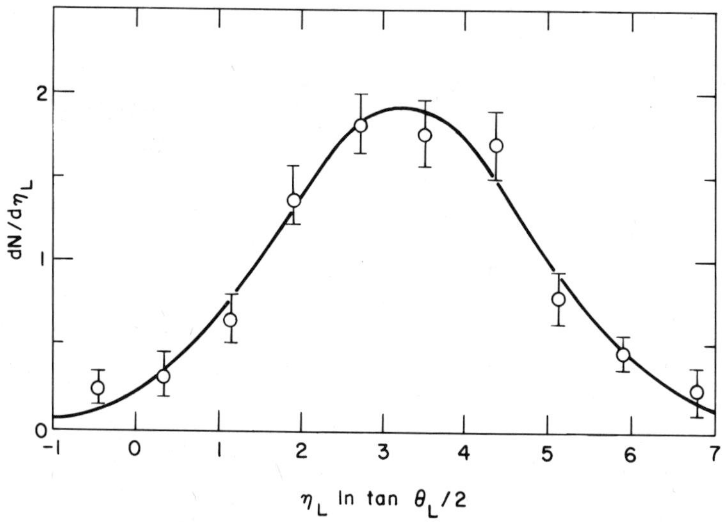

Fig. 1 The laboratory distribution $\frac{dN}{d\eta_L}$ computed in Ref. 5 and compared to the 205-GeV data of Ref. 6 (the lab distribution η_L is shifted from $y_{C.M.}$ by a constant).

The fact that this simple picture of particle production due to Landau leads to reasonable results for the single particle distribution function raises several interesting questions.

The first question is whether there exists a transport theory from which the Landau model, or more general hydrodynamical models, can emerge as approximations. Once we have such a transport theory we can investigate the question of the existence of collective motions and local thermodynamic equilibrium, properties assumed in Landau's original work.

The second question is how transport theory and a hydrodynamic description of multiparticle production can be derived from relativistic field theory.

We have recently studied[7,8] these questions in the case where the pion field is produced by a classical source. Our main conclusions are as follows. Applying the relativistic transport theory recently developed by Carruthers and Zachariasen,[9,10] we show that the expectation value of the normal ordered energy-momentum tensor is determined by the second moment of the single particle relativistic Wigner distribution function. The resulting expression for $T_c^{\mu\nu}(x)$ can be shown to be that of an ideal fluid. Furthermore, the distribution function satisfies an equation of the Boltzmann type. Similar conclusions can be established for a $\lambda\phi^4$ theory, treated in Hartree approximation.

Instead of going from quantum field theory to transport theory, and then constructing moments of the distribution function to arrive at a hydrodynamic description, one can pass directly from quantum field theory to a hydrodynamic description. We find that when pions are produced in a coherent quantum state, as they are by a classical source, the hydrodynamic properties of the pion field are those of an ideal fluid. We also verify, for pion production by a classical source, that the hydrodynamic fluid velocity is equal to the particle velocity, and that one can introduce a formal entropy S. We find $\frac{\partial^3 N}{\partial v_x \partial v_y \partial v_z} \propto \frac{\partial^3 S}{\partial v_x \partial v_y \partial v_z}$, as assumed by Landau. We have applied our results to study the effect of source geometry on the predictions of the Landau model.[8]

In the following sections we present some of these conclusions in greater detail without, however, giving derivations.

II. TRANSPORT APPROACH TO MULTIPARTICLE PRODUCTION

Wigner[11] has shown how a function sharing many of the properties of the Boltzmann distribution function can be defined for quantum mechanical systems, and that this function can be used to formulate a quantum mechanical transport theory. In generalizing these results to quantum field theory, Carruthers and Zachariasen[9] proceed as follows. To be definite, consider a charged pion field. One starts with the Green's function for this field, defined as

$$G^<(x_1,x_2) = {}_{in}\langle f_1 f_2|\phi^*(x_2)\phi(x_1)|f_1 f_2\rangle_{in} \quad , \tag{2.1}$$

where $|f_1 f_2\rangle_{in}$ is the initial 2 proton state. We introduce relative and center of mass coordinates

$$r = x_1 - x_2 \quad , \quad x = (x_1 + x_2)/2 \quad .$$

The relativistic single particle distribution function $G^<(x,p)$ is then defined, in analogy to the nonrelativistic case, as

$$\begin{aligned} G^<(x,p) &= \frac{1}{(2\pi)^4}\int d^4r\, e^{ip.r}\, G^<(x + r/2,\, x - r/2) \\ &= \frac{1}{(2\pi)^4}\int d^4r\, e^{ip.r} \langle\phi^*(x - r/2)\phi(x + r/2)\rangle \; . \end{aligned} \tag{2.2}$$

Using the definition (2.2), $G^<(x,p)$ can be shown to have properties that are reasonable relativistic generalizations of those of the Wigner distribution function $f(\underset{\sim}{x},\underset{\sim}{p},t)$. For instance,

$$\begin{aligned} \int G^<(x,p)p^\mu d^4p &= i\langle\phi^*(x)\, \overleftrightarrow{\partial^\mu}\, \phi(x)\rangle \\ &= \langle j^\mu(x)\rangle \quad . \end{aligned} \tag{2.3}$$

To obtain the momentum space number density we have to wait until we have outstates, because the number of particles is not conserved while they are interacting. But then we find

$$\left\langle E\frac{\partial^3 N}{\partial p_x \partial p_y \partial p_z}\right\rangle = {}_{in}\langle f_1 f_2 | a_{out}(p) a^\dagger_{out}(p) | f_1 f_2 \rangle_{in} \qquad (2.4)$$
$$= \int d^4x \left| \frac{1}{4} \Box^2 + m^2 - p^2 - ip^u \partial_\mu \right|^2 G^<(x,p) \ .$$

Thus we obtain $n_{out}(p)$ by integrating $G^<(x,p)$ over all space and time.

Since we are in the Heisenberg representation, $G^<(x_1,x_2)$ obeys the same equation of motion as the usual vacuum two point function. Only the boundary conditions are different. It also obeys the same equation as the finite temperature Green's function of the usual relativistic many body theory. The distinction is that in the finite temperature problem one assumes the density matrix is one of global thermodynamic equilibrium so that $\rho = e^{-\beta H}$. Here, $\rho = |f_1 f_2\rangle_{in}\ {}_{in}\langle f_1 f_2|$ and it remains to be seen whether local statistical equilibrium is established after the two particles collide.

Next we consider the energy momentum tensor:

$$T^{\mu\nu}(x) = \partial^\mu \phi^* \partial^\nu \phi - g^{\mu\nu} \left\{ \frac{1}{2}\, \partial_\lambda \phi^* \partial^\lambda \phi - \frac{1}{2}\, m^2 \phi^* \phi + L_{int} \right\} , \qquad (2.5)$$

where L_{int} contains the interactions. The expectation value of $:T^{\mu\nu}(x):$ in the state $|f_1 f_2\rangle_{in}$ is

$${}_{in}\langle f_1 f_2 | :T^{\mu\nu}(x): | f_1 f_2 \rangle_{in} = {}_{in}\langle f_1 f_2 | T^{\mu\nu}(x) | f_1 f_2 \rangle_{in}$$
$$- \langle 0 | T^{\mu\nu}(x) | 0 \rangle$$
$$= \mathrm{Tr}\ \tilde{\rho}\ T^{\mu\nu}(x) \ , \qquad (2.6)$$

where $\tilde{\rho} = |f_1 f_2>_{in}\ {}_{in}<f_1 f_2| - |0<>0|$. Thus we find:

$$<:T^{\mu\nu}(x):> \quad \lim_{x_1 \to x_2 = x} \left\{ \frac{1}{2}\left(\partial_1{}^{\mu}\partial_2{}^{\nu} + \partial_1{}^{\nu}\partial_2{}^{\mu} \right) - \frac{1}{2} g^{\mu\nu}\left(\partial_{1\lambda}\partial^{2\lambda} - m^2 \right) \right\} \mathrm{Tr}\ \tilde{\rho}\phi^*(x_2)\phi(x_1) - g^{\mu\nu}<:L_{int}:> \quad , \tag{2.7}$$

or

$$<:T^{\mu\nu}(x):> \int \left[p^{\mu}p^{\nu} - \frac{1}{2} g^{\mu\nu}(p^2 - m^2) \right] \hat{G}^<(x,p)d^4p \tag{2.8}$$
$$+ \frac{1}{4}\left[\partial^{\mu}\partial^{\nu} - \frac{1}{2} g^{\mu\nu} \square^2 \right] \int \hat{G}^<(x,p)d^4p$$
$$-g^{\mu\nu}<L_{int}:> \quad ,$$

where

$$\hat{G}^< (x,p) = \frac{1}{(2\pi)^4} \int d^4r\ e^{ip.r}\ \hat{G}^< (x + r/2,\ x-r/2)$$
$$= \frac{1}{(2\pi)^4} \int d^4e\ e^{ip.r} \{ {}_{in}<f_1 f_2|\phi^*(x - r/2)\phi(x + r/2)$$
$$|f_1 f_2>_{in} - <0|\phi^*(x - r/2)\phi(x + r/2|0>\} \quad .$$

For an interacting theory, one will not be able to express the term involving L_{int} in terms of the 2-point function alone. However, after the interactions have stopped

$$G^<(x,p) \to \delta(p^2 - m^2)\ G(p)$$

and

$$<:T^{\mu\nu}(x):> \to <:T^{\mu\nu}_{out}(x):> \int p^{\mu}p^{\nu}\ \hat{G}^<(x,p)d^4p \quad . \tag{2.9}$$

Thus $<:T^{\mu\nu}_{out}(x):>$ is related to the distribution function in the expected manner.

As an illustration of the above results, we consider the transport equations and their solution for the simplest model of pion production, in which neutral pions are produced by a classical source. Here

$$L = \frac{1}{2} \partial_\lambda \phi \partial^\lambda \phi - \frac{1}{2} m^2 \phi^2 + j_{ext} \phi \tag{2.10}$$

and the field ϕ satisfies the equation of motion

$$(\Box^2 + m^2)\phi(x) = j_{ext}(x) \quad . \tag{2.11}$$

The initial state of two protons is represented by $j_{ext}(x)$, and thus the density matrix is $\rho = |0\rangle_{in\ in}\langle 0|$, $|0\rangle$ being the in-vacuum.

From Eq. (2.11) one obtains

$$\left(\Box^2_{x_1} + m^2\right) G^<(x_1,x_2) = \left(\Box^2_{x_1} + m^2\right) {}_{in}\langle 0|\phi(x_2)\phi(x_1)|0\rangle_{in}$$

$$= j_{ext}(x_1)\ {}_{in}\langle 0|\phi(x_2)|0\rangle_{in} \ . \tag{2.12}$$

Thus, letting ${}_{in}\langle 0|\phi(x)|0\rangle_{in} \equiv \phi_c(x)$, we obtain the c-number equation

$$(\Box^2 + m^2)\phi_c(x) = j_{ext}(x) \quad ,$$

whence

$$\phi_c(x) = \int D_{ret}(x - y)\ j_{ext}(y) d^4y \quad , \tag{2.13}$$

where

$$(\Box^2_x + m^2)\ D_{ret}(x - y) = \delta^4(x - y)$$

and $D_{ret}(x)$ satisfies the retarded boundary conditions.

Using these results, one can easily show that $G^<(x,p)$ satisfies the following Boltzmann-type equation:

$$p^\mu \frac{\partial}{\partial x^\mu} G^<(x,p) = \frac{2i}{(2\pi)^4} \int d^4r\ e^{ip\cdot r} \tag{2.14}$$

$$[j_{ext}(x + r/2)\phi_c(x-r/2) - j_{ext}(x - r/2)\phi_c(x + r/2)]$$

The solution of the homogeneous equation ($j_{ext} = 0$) is

$$G_0^<(x,p) = \frac{1}{(2\pi)^4} \int d^4r\, e^{ip.r}\, {}_{in}\langle 0|\phi_{in}(x_2)\phi_{in}(x_1)|0\rangle_{in}$$
$$= \theta(-p_0)\, \frac{\delta(p^2 - m^2)}{(2\pi)^3} \qquad (2.15)$$

Assuming that Eq. (2.14) has a solution of the form

$$G^<(x,p) = G_0^<(x,p) + \qquad (2.16)$$
$$\frac{1}{(2\pi)^4} \int d^4r\, e^{ip.r}\, f(x + r/2)\, f(x - r/2),$$

we find

$$(\Box^2 + m^2)\, f(x) - j_{ext}(x) \quad ,$$

or

$$f(x) = \phi_c(x) \quad .$$

Thus we obtain

$$G^<(x,p) = G_0^<(x,p) + \qquad (2.17)$$
$$\frac{1}{(2\pi)^4} \int d^4r\, e^{ip.r}\, \phi_c(x - r/2)\phi(x + r/2) \quad .$$

Using Eq. (2.4), one finds

$$\left\langle E\, \frac{\partial^3 N}{\partial p_x \partial p_y \partial p_z} \right\rangle = |j_{ext}(p,\omega_p)|^2 \qquad (2.18)$$

where

$$j_{ext}(p,\omega_p) = \int \frac{d^4x}{\sqrt{2}\,(2\pi)^{3/2}}\, e^{-ip.x} j_{ext}(x).$$

This is the usual result.(12)

Next, using Eq. (2.8) with $\langle :L_{int}:\rangle = j_{ext}(x)\phi_c(x)$ and $\hat{G}^<(x,p) = G^<(x,p) - G_0(x,p)$, one obtains

$$<:T^{\mu\nu}(x):> = \partial^{\mu}\phi_c \partial^{\nu}\phi_c -$$

$$g^{\mu\nu}\left[\frac{1}{2}\,\partial_{\lambda}\phi_c\partial^{\lambda}\phi_c - \frac{1}{2}\,m^2\phi_c^2 + j_{ext}\phi_c\right] \quad . \qquad (2.19)$$

$$= T^{\mu\nu}(x)$$

The diagonalization of $T_c^{\mu\nu}(x)$ will be discussed in the next section, where it is shown that $T_c^{\mu\nu}(x)$ can be written in a form identical to that used for describing an ideal fluid.

We have also studied a self-interacting pion field produced by an external source, treating the $\lambda\phi^4$ self-interaction in Hartree approximation. It can be shown that the distribution function for this problem also satisfies an equation of Boltzmann type:

$$p^{\mu}\frac{\partial}{\partial x^{\mu}}G^{<}(x,p) + \frac{\lambda}{2i(2\ \ )^4}\int e^{(i/h)(p-p'').r}\ [$$

$$\rho(x + r/2) - \rho(x - r/)]G^{<}(x,p)d^4p'\,d^4r$$

$$= \frac{1}{2i(2\pi)^4}\int e^{(i/h)p.r}[j_{ext}(x + r/2)\phi_c(x - r/2)$$

$$- j_{ext}(x - r/2)\phi_c(x + r/2)]d^4r \quad , \qquad (2.20)$$

where $\rho(x) = \int G^{<}(x,p)\ d^4p$, and that the expectation value of $:T^{\mu\nu}(x):$ is determined by $G^{<}(x,p)$. Furthermore, in the $h \to 0$ limit, Eq. (2.20) can be cast in a form resembling the transport equation for a single specie plasma, treated in the Vlasov approximation. Details of these calculations can be found in Ref. (7).

III. HYDRODYNAMIC ASPECTS OF MULTIPARTICLE PRODUCTION

In Section II we outlined the basic machinery of relativistic transport theory and its application to the determination of $<:T^{\mu\nu}(x):>$. If we are only interested in the flow of energy and momentum following a collision, one can dispense with the transport theory machinery and instead consisider directly $T^{\mu\nu}(x) = \mathrm{Tr}\rho T^{\mu\nu}(x)$, where $T^{\mu\nu}(x)$ is the energy momentum tensor of the field theory to be studied, and ρ is the density matrix appropriate to the collision process.

Since $T_c^{\mu\nu}(x)$ is a symmetric c number tensor, one can always find a frame where it is diagonal (provided it does not describe massless particles). In this frame, called the comoving frame and denoted by barred variables, $T^{0k}(\bar{x}) = 0$. That is, by solving the eigenvalue problem

$$T_c^{\mu\nu}(x)v_\nu^{(\alpha)}(x) = \lambda^{(\alpha)}(x)v^{(\alpha)\mu}(x) \quad , \quad \alpha = 1,4 \tag{3.1}$$

one can write

$$T_c^{\mu\nu}(x) - \varepsilon(x)u^\mu u^\nu + \sum_{i=1}^{3} P_i(x)v^{(i)\mu}v^{(i)\nu} \quad , \tag{3.2}$$

where one defines $\varepsilon(x)$ as the eigenvalue of the time-like normalized eigenvector $u^\mu(x)$, and the three pressures as the eigenvalues of the space-like eigenvectors $v_\mu^{(i)}$. The four-velocity of the fluid is $u^\mu(x)$.

In plasma physics, one often has symmetry reasons (azimuthal symmetry) to choose at least two of the pressures $p_i(x)$ to be the same, even on time scales much shorter than those required to establish equilibrium. Likewise in pp scattering, where there is also azimuthal symmetry, one expects there to be at most two different pressures $p_{||}$ and $p_\perp$. If all three space-like eigenvalues are the same, we obtain

$$T_c^{\mu\nu} = (\varepsilon + p)u^\mu u^\nu - g^{\mu\nu}p \quad , \tag{3.3}$$

which is the energy momentum tensor of an ideal fluid.

Let us look at a simple example where the ideal fluid result is obtained. If we suppose that the pions which are produced when hadrons collide are in a coherent state, then we can take the density matrix to be[13]

$$\rho = |\phi_c\ \pi_c><\phi_c\ \pi_c| \quad , \tag{3.4}$$

where

$$|\pi_c\ \phi_c> = \exp\left\{i\int \phi(x)\pi_c(x) - \pi(x)\phi_c(x)d^3x\right\}|0> \equiv U|0> \quad . \tag{3.5}$$

In Eq. (3.5), ϕ_c and π_c are c number square integrable solutions to the classical field equations for ϕ_c and ϕ and π are the pion field and its canonical momentum obeying the usual equal time commutation relations

$$[\pi(\underset{\sim}{x},t),\phi(\underset{\sim}{x}',t)] = -i\delta^3(\underset{\sim}{x} - \underset{\sim}{x}') \quad . \tag{3.6}$$

Using the properties of the Weyl group, one can show that

$$U^\dagger f(\phi,\pi)U - f(\phi + \phi_c, \pi + \pi_c), \tag{3.7}$$

where U is the unitary operator defined in Eq. (3.5). Thus we find that:

$$\begin{aligned} \mathrm{Tr}\rho :T^{\mu\nu}(x): &= <\pi_c\ \phi_c| :T^{\mu\nu}(x): |\pi_c\ \phi_c> \\ &= <0| :T^{\mu\nu}(\phi + \phi_c, \pi + \pi_c)|0> \qquad (3.8) \\ &= T_c^{\mu\nu}(\phi_c, \pi_c) = \partial^\mu\phi_c\ \partial^\nu\phi_c - g^{\mu\nu}L(\phi_c,\pi_c) \quad , \end{aligned}$$

which is the energy momentum tensor for a classical

pion field with arbitrary self-interactions specified by a Lagrangian L. But $T_c^{\mu\nu}(\phi_c, \pi_c)$ can be written in the form (3.3), describing an ideal fluid, if the following identifications are made:

$$u^\mu(x) = \partial^\mu \phi_c(x)/(\varepsilon + p)^{1/2} \qquad (3.9)$$

and

$$\varepsilon + p = \partial_\lambda \phi_c \, \partial^\lambda \phi_c \quad , \qquad p = L(\phi_c, \pi_c) \quad . \qquad (3.10)$$

These results can all be seen explicitly for the case of pion production by a classical source. For this example, the density matrix is $\rho = |0\rangle_{in\ in}\langle 0|$ and the in-vacuum $|0\rangle_{in}$ can easily be shown to be a coherent state, i.e., an eigenstate of $a(k,t)$. Application of Eqs. (3.8)-(3.10) then results in an ideal fluid description for ${}_{in}\langle 0| :T^{\mu\nu}(x): |0\rangle_{in}$, with

$$L(\phi_c, \pi_c) = \frac{1}{2} \partial_\lambda \phi_c \partial^\lambda \phi_c - \frac{1}{2} m^2 \phi_c^2 + j_{ext} \phi_c \quad . \qquad (3.11)$$

We have investigated the behavior of the hydrodynamic quantities ε, p and $u^\mu(x)$ for several different classical sources appropriate to Landau model calculations.[8] Some of the results are summarized in Section IV. Here we shall show that for the simple model in which the source is $j_{ext}(x) = \lambda\delta^4(x)$, several of the basic assumptions of the Landau model can be derived from field theory.

From Eqs. (2.13) and (3.9)-(3.11), it is clear that all the hydrodynamic quantities are determined once $j_{ext}(x)$ and $D_{ret}(x - y)$ are known. The explicit form of D_{ret} is [14]

$$D_{ret} = \theta(x_0) \left\{ \frac{1}{2\pi} \delta(\tau^2) - \frac{m^2}{4\pi} \theta(\tau^2) \frac{J_1(m\tau)}{m\tau} \right\}, \qquad (3.12)$$

where $\tau = \sqrt{t^2 - |\underset{\sim}{x}|^2}$. Thus, using (2.13) we find

$$\phi_c(r,t) = -(\lambda m/4\pi)\left[J_1(m\tau)/m\tau\right] \quad ,$$
$$\partial_0\phi_c(r,t) = (\lambda m^2 t/4\pi\tau)\left[J_2(m\tau)/m\tau\right] , \tag{3.13}$$

and

$$\partial_r\phi_c(r,t) = -(\lambda m^2 r/4\pi\tau)\left[J_2(m\tau)/m\tau\right] ,$$

inside the forward light cone.

Since the fluid velocity $v^r = u^r/u^0 = \partial^r\phi_c/\partial^0\phi_c$, via Eq. (3.9), we obtain using (3.13)

$$v^r = r/t \quad . \tag{3.14}$$

Thus the fluid velocity is the same as the particle velocity in this model, since the particles move freely after they are produced at the origin at time $t = 0$.

For $\varepsilon(\underset{\sim}{x},t)$ and $p(\underset{\sim}{x},t)$ we obtain

$$\varepsilon(r,t) = (m^4\lambda^2/32\pi^2)\left[\frac{J_2^2(m\tau) + J_1^2(m\tau)}{(m\tau)^2}\right]$$

and (3.15)

$$p(r,t) = (m^4\lambda^2/32\pi^2)\left[\frac{J_2^2(m\tau) - J_1^2(m\tau)}{(m\tau)^2}\right]$$

Making use of the asymptotic behavior of the Bessel functions, one finds for large τ that

$$\lim_{\tau\to\infty} \varepsilon(r,t) = (m^4\lambda^2/16\pi^2)[1/(m\tau)^3] \quad ; \tag{3.16}$$

a reasonable result for an expanding spherical cloud of particles. The pressure $p(r,t)$ oscillates but, since $p = p(\tau)$ and $\varepsilon = \varepsilon(\tau)$, in regions where $p(\tau)$ is monotonically increasing or decreasing one has an "equation of state":

$$p = p\left(\tau(\varepsilon)\right) = p(\varepsilon) \quad . \tag{3.17}$$

Using this equation of state and the thermodynamic relationships

$$\varepsilon + p = Ts \quad , \quad d\varepsilon = Tds \quad , \tag{3.18}$$

one can define an "entropy" current s(x) and a "temperature" T. For example, the entropy current turns out to be

$$s(\tau) = (\varepsilon + p)^{1/2}\, H(m\tau) \quad , \tag{3.19}$$

where

$$\ell n\, H(m\tau) = -\int_{m\tau_0}^{m\tau} J_1(x)/J_2(x)\, dx \quad .$$

For an ideal fluid, the parallel component of the energy-momentum conservation equation $u^\mu \partial^\nu T_{\mu\nu} = 0$ reads

$$(\varepsilon + p)\partial_\mu u^\mu + \partial_\mu \varepsilon = 0 \quad . \tag{3.20}$$

Thus, when the thermodynamic relations (3.18) are satisfied, we have the conservation of entropy law

$$\partial_\mu S^\mu(x) \equiv \partial_\mu\, s\, u^\mu(x) = 0 \quad , \tag{3.21}$$

or

$$S = \int_\sigma (su^\mu)(x) d\sigma_\mu \quad .$$

The outstate number current is defined by

$$N^\mu(x) = i\ {}_{in}\langle 0|\phi^{(-)}_{out}(x)\ \overleftrightarrow{\partial_\mu}\ \phi^{(+)}_{out}(x)|0\rangle_{in} \quad . \tag{3.22}$$

Evaluating this matrix element, we find

$$N^{\mu}(x) = n(\tau)u^{\mu}(\underset{\sim}{x},t) \quad , \tag{3.23}$$

where

$$n(\tau) = (\lambda^2 m^3/16\pi^2) \left[\frac{J_1(m\tau)Y_2(m\tau) - Y_1(m\tau)J_2(m\tau)}{(m\tau)^2}\right]$$

Thus we see that along the iso-energy density surfaces $\varepsilon(r,t)$ = constant, τ = constant and

$$S^{\mu}(\underset{\sim}{x},t) = (su^{\mu})(\underset{\sim}{x},t) \propto N^{\mu}(\underset{\sim}{x},t). \tag{3.24}$$

Since we have shown that $\underset{\sim}{v}_{fluid} = \underset{\sim}{v}_{particle}$, we expect to find, on the basis of Eq. (3.24), that

$$E\frac{\partial^3 S}{\partial p_x \partial p_y \partial p_z} \propto \frac{\partial^3 N}{\partial p_x \partial p_y \partial p_z} = \text{constant} \quad . \tag{3.25}$$

It follows immediately from Eq. (2.18) that the right hand side of Eq. (3.25) is a constant if $j_{ext}(x) = \lambda\delta^4(x)$. Likewise, a short calculation using the results of this section shows that $E\frac{\partial^3 S}{\partial p_x \partial p_y \partial p_z}$ is also constant on an isoenergy surface, establishing Eq. (3.25). Thus we find in this simple model that one can determine the single particle distribution from the entropy distribution of a "fluid". The foregoing results provide a direct realization of Landau's model in field theory.

IV. THE EFFECT OF SOURCE GEOMETRY ON THE PREDICTIONS OF THE LANDAU MODEL

In Ref. (8) we have analyzed how the choice of the current $j_{ext}(x)$ influences the predictions of the Landau model. Here we shall give a résumé of our results for the case of a Lorentz contracted disk source:

$$j_{ext}(x,\rho.t) = (\bar{\lambda}/a\Delta)\delta(t)$$

$$\left[\theta\left(x + \frac{\Delta}{2}\right) - \theta\left(x + \frac{\Delta}{2}\right)\right]\theta(a - \rho) \quad , \qquad (4.1)$$

where $a = m_\pi^{-1}$, $\rho = \sqrt{y^2 + z^2}$ and $\Delta = a(2M/E_{CM})$. This might be a reasonable approximation for the pionic source in the case of pp collisions, if the source can be modelled by a c-number current at all.

When the current is given by Eq. (4.1), the single particle distribution is given, according to Eq. (2.18), by

$$\frac{\partial^2 N}{2\rho p_\perp \partial p_\perp \partial y} = \frac{1}{m^2}\left(\frac{M}{m}\right) \qquad (4.2)$$

$$\left[\frac{\sin \frac{m\Delta}{2} \cosh \beta \sinh y}{\frac{m\Delta}{2} \cosh \beta \sinh y}\right]^2 \left[\frac{J_1(\sinh \beta)}{\sinh \beta}\right]^2 \quad ,$$

where

$$p_\perp = m \sinh \beta \quad , \quad \tanh y = (p_{||}/E)$$

and we have used $\int E dN = E_{CM}$. Integrating over $p_\perp$, we find

$$\frac{dN}{dy} = \frac{1}{\pi}\left(\frac{M}{m}\right)\left[\frac{\sin\left(\frac{\tilde{m}\Delta}{2} \sinh y\right)}{\frac{\tilde{m}\Delta}{2} \sinh y}\right]^2 \qquad (4.3)$$

where $\tilde{m}$ is the weighted average of $\left(p_\perp^2 + m^2\right)^{1/2}$.

We note that

$$\left(\frac{dN}{dy}\right)_{y=0} = \frac{1}{\pi}\left(\frac{M}{m}\right) , \qquad (4.4)$$

independent of energy. The distribution (4.3) is essentially flat for small y. (For example if $E_{CM} = 25$ GeV, $\frac{dN}{dy}$ is essentially constant for $y \leq 2$.) The flatness of $\frac{dN}{dy}$ for small y results for any source which has the property that

$$j_{ect}(x,\rho,t) \to \delta(x)F(\rho,t) \text{ as } E_{CM} \to \infty \quad . \qquad (4.5)$$

Hydrodynamically, once $j_{ext} \propto \delta(x)$ one has $v_x = x/t$ which automatically leads to dS/dy = constant, using Eqs. (1.10) and (1.12).

On the other hand, the transverse particle distribution depends critically on the ρ dependence of j_{ext} (x,ρ,t) and does not approach a limiting form as $E_{CM} \to \infty$. For the case of a uniform disk we obtain the values for $\langle N\rangle$ and $\langle p_\perp\rangle$ given in Table I. We also notice from Eq. (4.3) that $N \sim \ell n\, E_{CM}$ and $\frac{dN}{dy} \approx$ constant for small y. Thus the Lorentz-contracted disk source model, which is a realization of the Landau model for a particular equation of state, displays a number of properties of the multiperipheral model.

ACKNOWLEDGEMENTS

The authors wish to thank J. R. Klauder for a helpful discussion on the use of coherent states.

TABLE I

Average multiplicity <N> and transverse momenta $\langle p_\perp \rangle$ for the disk model as functions of E_{CM}.

E_{CM} (GeV)	<N>	$\langle p_\perp \rangle$ (MeV)
10	14.34	312.7
20	15.57	352.8
30	15.97	377.6
40	16.16	395.0
50	16.28	408.8

REFERENCES

1. L. D. Landau, Izv. Akad. Nauk SSR 17, 51 (1953). For recent reviews of the Landau model see Refs. (2) and (3).

2. P. Carruthers, Annals of the N.Y. Academy of Sciences 229, 91 (1974).

3. F. Cooper, "Landau's Hydrodynamic Model of Particle Production" in Particles and Fields - 1974, AIP Conference Proceedings, No. 23, C. E. Carlson, Ed. (American Institute of Physics,New York, 1975) pp. 499-531.

4. For a discussion of relativistic ideal fluids see: S. Weinberg, Gravitation and Cosmology (J. Wiley & Son, New York, 1972) p. 47 ff.

5. P. Carruthers and Minh Duong-Van, Phys. Rev. D8, 859 (1973).

6. G. Charlton et al. Paper contributed to the XVI International Conference on High Energy Physics, Batavia, Ill. (1972).

7. F. Cooper and D. H. Sharp, "Pion Production from a Classical Source: Transport and Hydrodynamical Properties" (to be submitted for publication).

8. F. Cooper, E. Schonberg and D. H. Sharp, "Effect of Source Geometry on the Predictions of Landau's Hydrodynamic Model" (to be submitted for publication).

9. P. Carruthers and F. Zachariasen, "Transport Equation Approach to Multiparticle Production Processes" in Particles and Fields - 1974, AIP Conference Proceedings No. 23, C. E. Carlson, Ed. (American Institute of Physics, New York, 1975) pp. 481-498.

10. P. Carruthers, these Proceedings.

11. E. P. Wigner, Phys. Rev. 40, 749 (1932). For a recent discussion of quantum transport theory see: G. Baym and L. P. Kadanoff, Quantum Statistical Mechanics (W. A. Benjamin, N.Y., 1962).

12. For the usual treatment of particle production from an external source see: B. J. Bjorken and S. Drell, Relativistic Quantum Fields, (McGraw-Hill, N.Y., 1965) pp. 202-207.

13. This discussion is due in part to J. Klauder. See also: J. Klauder, J. Math. Phys. 8, 2392 (1967).

14. A derivation of this formula can be found in: N. N. Boglubov and D. Shirkov, Theory of Quantized Fields, (Interscience, N.Y., 1959).

THE LARGE NUMBERS HYPOTHESIS AND ITS CONSEQUENCES

P. A. M. Dirac

Florida State University

Tallahassee, Florida 32306

From the constants of nature one can construct some dimensionless numbers, independent of what units one uses. Some of these are not so far from unity, for example, hc/e^2 equal to approximately 137, and the ratio of the mass of the proton to that of the electron, m_p/m_e, equal to approximately 1840. Others are extremely large, for example the ratio of the electric to the gravitational force between the electron and the proton in the hydrogen atom, e^2/Gm_pm_e. This is about 2×10^{39}.

Physicists believe that ultimately an explanation will be found for all these numbers. In the case of the very large numbers, the only reasonable hope for an explanation lies in connecting them with the present age of the universe, the epoch t. Recent values for the Hubble constant give this to be about 18×10^9 years. If one expresses it in terms of an atomic unit, say e^2/m_ec^2, it becomes 7×10^{39}, very close to the previous large number.

It is hard to believe that this closeness is just

a coincidence. It would seem that the two numbers must be connected, with a coefficient close to unity that one will be able to calculate when one knows more about atomic theory and about cosmology. Such a connection implies

$$e^2/Gm_p m_e :: t.$$

As the universe gets older, the expression on the left must increase in proportion. Thus quantities that were previously considered constant are not really constant.

A convenient way of picturing this result is to adopt an atomic system of units for quantities with dimensions, so that e, m_p, m_e are constants. Then G is decreasing, proportional to t^{-1}. We have

$$\dot{G}/G = -1/t = -6 \times 10^{-11}/\text{year}.$$

The effect is too small to show up in ordinary experiments, but it might show up in astronomical observations.

The LNH (Large Numbers Hypothesis) extends this argument to any large dimensionless number that appears in the general laws of physics and cosmology. If such a number K is roughly $10^{39\alpha}$, the LNH would require that K is proportional to t^{α} with some coefficient close to unity. From the magnitude of the large number one can infer its dependence on the epoch.

The LNH, if one accepts it, is a powerful tool for developing cosmology and atomic theory. There are two restrictions in its use that one must bear in mind. (i) It applies only to dimensionless numbers. (ii) It gives information only about the asymptotic behavior of K for large values of t. It gives no information about the very early stages of the universe. If the true dependence of K on t is

$$K = c_1 t^{\alpha_1} + c_2 t^{\alpha_2} \qquad \alpha_1 > \alpha_2$$

the LNH would refer only to the first term. It always gives a simple power law for the dependence of K on t (except that we might have a logarithemic dependence).

The LNH requires that G, expressed in atomic units, shall vary. How can one fit this in with Einstein's theory of gravitation, which demands that G shall be constant? The successes of the Einstein theory are so great that we must retain them in any modification that we make in the fundamental laws of nature.

Many people who work with varying G adopt a primitive theory in which gravitational and inertial mass are different and their ratio varies with the epoch. This involves adopting a pre-Einstein view of gravitation and spoils the successes of the Einstein theory. I consider such a theory unacceptable.

One can develop a reasonable theory if one assumes that classical mechanics, including the Einstein theory, is valid only when applied with suitable units, which differ from the atomic units. Let us call the former <u>mechanical units</u>. With both systems of units we take the velocity of light to be unity, so the units of distance and time are changed in the same ratio.

The assumption that different units are needed for classical and quantum mechanics I shall call Milne's Hypothesis, as the basic idea was introduced by E. A. Milne before the war.

I feel strongly that the LNH is correct. I am not so sure about Milne's Hypothesis, because of its interference with the Correspondence Principle connecting classical and quantum mechanics, and I would be willing to accept an alternative assumption for reconciling the variation of G with Einstein's theory if a natural one could be found. I shall here continue to discuss the consequences of adopting both the LNH and Milne's Hypothesis.

Let us consider the total mass of the universe, expressed in units of the proton mass. (If the universe is infinite, we use instead the total mass of that part of the universe that is receding from us with a velocity $<\frac{1}{2}c$). The total mass is not known very accurately, because one does not know how much dark matter there is in the form of intergalactic gas and black holes and dark stars. But making reasonable estimates, one gets a value about 10^{78}. From the LNH this number must increase in proportion to t^2.

We can infer that there is continuous creation of new matter. This must be a cosmological process, a new kind of radioactivity independent of anything that is observed in the laboratory, and violates conservation of mass and conservation of barions.

We must face the question: Where is this new matter created? There are two reasonable assumptions one might make. (i) The new matter is created uniformly throughout space, and hence mainly in intergalactic space. I call this additive creation. (ii) The new matter is created where matter already exists in proportion to the amount existing, and presumably of the same kind as the existing matter. I call this multiplicative creation.

I do not know which alternative to prefer. One should consider both and see which one better fits the observations.

An element ds of distance or of time, as used in the Einstein theory, must be referred to mechanical units and will then be denoted by ds_E. The same quantity in atomic units will be denoted by ds_A. The connection between them can easily be worked out, by considering an elementary example such as the motion of the earth around the sun. The details of this calculation are given in my talk of last year.* The result is

$$ds_E = t\, ds_A \quad \text{additive creation}$$

$$ds_E = t^{-1} ds_A \quad \text{multiplicative creation.}$$

EXPERIMENTAL TESTS FOR VARYING G

The orbits of the planets, expressed in mechanical units, will be fixed, with neglect of their perturbations and Einstein corrections. Expressed in atomic units the distances would all be contracting, proportional to t^{-1}, if there is additive creation, and all expanding, proportional to t, if there is multiplicative creation. These effects are of a cosmological nature and are to be superposed on all other effects arising from known physical causes. By making accurate observations of distances in the solar system referred to atomic apparatus, we have a chance of checking the variation of G and also of distinguishing between the two kinds of creation. In the case of the moon, its distance would vary at the rate of 2 cms per year, approaching with additive creation and receding with multiplicative creation.

---

*Studies in the Natural Sciences Vol 5. Fundamental Theories in Physics pages 11, 12.

The moon's distance can be measured with great accuracy, because astronauts have placed reflectors for laser beams on the moon, enabling one to determine the time taken for laser light to go to the moon and back. Jim Williams at the J.P.L. is working on this lunar ranging and he told me last September that he could then get the moon's distance to an accuracy of 6 cms. But he did not hold out much hope of being able to check on the variation of G by this method, because the effect of the tides on the moon's distance is not known with sufficient accuracy.

Another method is to use the moon's motion. The moon's angular velocity is suffering a deceleration owing to tidal action, which causes an increase in the moon's distance. This deceleration has been observed for centuries on the basis of ephemeris time, which is time marked out by the motion of the earth around the sun. Since 1955 people have made accurate observations of the moon's motion with atomic time. The difference of the lunar deceleration, as observed with atomic time and with ephemeris time, may be ascribed to the variation of G. Tidal effects cancel out from this difference.

Van Flandern has worked out this method.* With n denoting the lunar angular velocity, Van Flandern gets the result

$$\left(\frac{\dot{n}}{n}\right)_{\text{atomic}} - \left(\frac{\dot{n}}{n}\right)_{\text{ephemeris}} = \left(\frac{\dot{n}}{n}\right)_{\text{diff}} = (-16\pm10)\times10^{-11}/\text{year}$$

*Van Flandern's paper will appear shortly in Monthly Notices R.A.S.

Van Flandren used the primitive theory for varying G which I alluded to earlier. This gives

$$\dot{G}/G = \frac{1}{2}(\dot{n}/n)_{diff} = (-8\pm5)x10^{-11}/year$$

which is in rather good agreement with the value deduced at the beginning of my talk.

But this primitive theory is not satisfactory. If one uses instead Milne's Hypothesis, one gets

$$\dot{G}/G = -(\dot{n}/n)_{diff} \quad \text{additive creation}$$

$$\dot{G}/G = (\dot{n}/n)_{diff} \quad \text{multiplicative creation.}$$

We see that Van Flandern's result supports multiplicative creation, and gives a rather too large value for $\dot{G}$. The discrepancy need not worry us at present, because there are considerable inaccuracies in the observations and it is not yet certain that all the possible sources of error have been taken into account.

One may also get information about the variation of G from observations of radar waves reflected by the planets. This method has the advantage that it is not disturbed by tidal effects, but of course the interaction between the planets has to be taken into account. I. I. Shapiro is working on this method. His results so far not sufficiently accurate to assure that $\dot{G}$ is not zero, but one may hope that his observations will decide the question in the near future.

THE MICROWAVE RADIATION

I would like now to consider another application of the LNH. Microwave radiation is observed to be continually falling on the earth, with a constancy and uniformity which show it is not a local phenomenon, arising from the solar system or the galaxy, but is of cosmological origin.

Only a small part of the spectrum has been observed. The observations are consistent with the radiation being black-body radiation at a temperature $T = 2.8^\circ K$. It thus consists of photons with energies centered around the value $h\nu = kT$.

According to the usually accepted theory, this radiation comes from a primordial fireball that existed in the early stages of the universe. To begin with, this fireball was strongly interacting with the matter and was roughly in temperature equilibrium with it. At a certain stage in the evolution of the universe it became decoupled from the matter. Then, with the radiation on its own, it became red-shifted according to the standard formula

$$\lambda :: t \qquad \nu :: t^{-1}.$$

With such red-shifting, black-body radiation remains black-body, but its temperature falls according to the law

$$T :: \nu :: t^{-1}.$$

Thus the microwave radiation is cooling according to this law.

Let is now look at the problem from the point of view of the LNH. The temperature T of $2.8^\circ K$ gives us an energy kT. Let us express it in terms of a natural unit of energy, the rest-energy of the electron. We have

$$k = 1.38 \times 10^{-16} \text{ erg/°K.}$$

For $T = 2.8°K$, we get the energy

$$kT = 4 \times 10^{-16} \text{ erg.}$$

The rest energy of the electron is

$$m_e c^2 = 8 \times 10^{-7} \text{ erg.}$$

The ratio is

$$\frac{kT}{m_e c^2} = 5 \times 10^{-10}.$$

From the LNH this cannot be a constant, but must vary roughly in proportion to $t^{-\frac{1}{4}}$, giving $T::t^{-\frac{1}{4}}$. We might have used the proton mass instead of the electron mass and would then have obtained

$$\frac{kT}{m_p c^2} = 2.5 \times 10^{-13}.$$

This must vary roughly in proportion to $t^{-\frac{1}{3}}$, giving $T::t^{-\frac{1}{3}}$.

We are thus led to a law for the cooling of the microwave radiation $T::t^{-\frac{1}{4}}$ or $T::t^{-\frac{1}{3}}$. The theory is not good enough to distinguish between these two alternatives. But in any case the cooling is much slower than the $T::t^{-1}$ law required by the primordial fireball theory.

We can conclude that the microwave radiation was not decoupled from matter such a long time ago. It must be in continual interaction with some form of matter that is cooling according to the law $T::t^{-\frac{1}{4}}$ or $t^{-\frac{1}{3}}$. This matter may be in the form of intergalactic ionized hydrogen, sufficiently tenuous not to interfere with ordinary astronomical observations, yet sufficiently dense for the microwaves, interacting with the free electrons by the Compton effect, to take on essentially the temperature of the intergalactic gas.

To discuss in more detail the temperature of the microwaves, let us take the case when the mean free path of a photon through the intergalactic electrons is the distance corresponding to the red-shift $z = 1$. In travelling through this distance the epoch t is doubled. The Compton scattering of the photons will then not seriously disturb the observation of even the most distant objects that can be seen by visual or radio telescopes, for which z may amount to 2 or even 3. But the microwave radiation that we see would then have originated from the intergalactic electrons at the epoch $\frac{1}{2} t_p$, if t_p denotes the present epoch. Assuming that the intergalactic gas is cooling according to the law $t^{-\frac{1}{3}}$, we find that the microwave radiation originates as black-body radiation at the temperature $T_e = 2^{\frac{1}{3}} T_p$ (T_p being the present temperature of the intergalactic gas). After it has originated it cools according to the t^{-1} law, so we see it as black-body radiation at the temperature $T_d = 2^{-\frac{2}{3}} T_p$.

The diagram gives three full curves showing, on logarithmic scales, the black-body law for the temperatures T_p, T_e and T_d.

A further effect has to be taken into account. A photon of low frequency, travelling through the intergalactic gas, has its probability of being scattered increased by the stimulation effect of the photons already existing with the frequency of the scattered photon. Thus for the low frequency photons the intergalactic gas is more opaque. The low frequency microwaves thus originate closer to us. They originate where the gas is a little cooler, but they do not have so much time to cool in travelling to us, so we see them as somewhat warmer, corresponding to a temperature nearer to T_p, instead of T_d. This is shown in the diagram by the lower dotted curve. For very low frequencies the temperature of the microwaves would be T_p (corresponding to very opaque intergalactic gas) and for higher frequencies the curve goes over to the black-body curve for T_d.

The above argument holds with additive creation. If we work with multiplicative creation, a further factor has to be taken into account. Corresponding to the multiplication of atomic particles in a piece of matter, we must have a multiplication of the photons in a beam of light, so as to make the energy of the beam, expressed in atomic units, increase in proportion to t^2. Only in this way can we preserve the usual laws of mechanics, expressed in mechanical units.

The photons of the microwaves will then get multiplied as they travel to us from the time they originated. This will lead to a result as shown by the upper dotted curve in the diagram.

We thus see that the microwave radiation that falls on the earth should depart from the black-body law in two different ways for the two kinds of creation.

Unfortunately the only accurate observations that can be made at present are for the longer wave lengths, where the curves for the two kinds of creation and the black-body curve for the temperature T_p all merge together. For higher frequencies, observations cannot be made from the earth's surface because of absorption by the earth's atmosphere. Some observations have been made from rockets and balloons, but the results are not reliable because of contaminating effects by the radiation from the earth. I have heard that plans are being considered for making microwave observations from a space platform. Thus we may hope some day to have an experimental check on this theory and an independent way of deciding between the two kinds of creation.

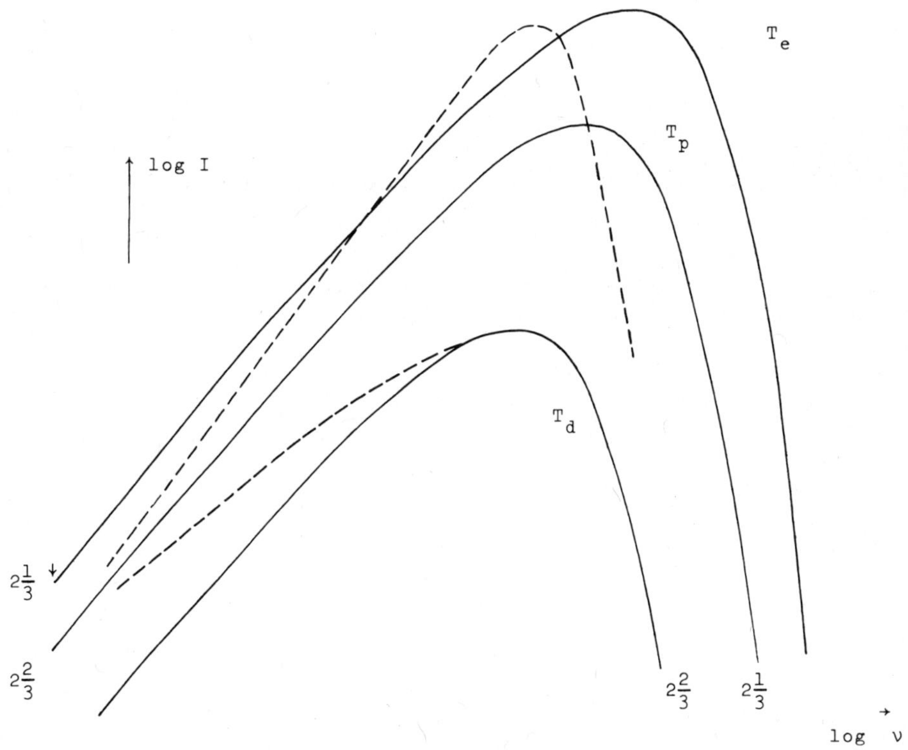

T_p = present electron temp, time t_p

T_e = originating electron temp, time $\frac{1}{2}\, t_p$

T_d = present temp of radiation if decoupled at time $\frac{1}{2}\, t_p$

$$T_e = 2^{\frac{1}{3}}\, T_p$$

$$T_d = 2^{-\frac{2}{3}}\, T_p$$

ARE QUSARS LOCAL?*

James Terrell

Los Alamos Scientific Laboratory

University of California

Los Alamos, New Mexico 87544

Although quasars were discovered in 1963, their nature is still not understood, nor their distance agreed upon. Astronomers are much less happy with them than with such strange phenomena as pulsars, believed to be neutron stars, or fluctuating X-ray sources such as Cygnus X-1, believed to be gravitationally-collapsed black holes. The trouble is that quasars refuse to yield the expected observations in far too many cases.

When quasars were first found to have large red shifts, the estimate of their distance was at once raised from thousands of light years (because of their resemblance to ordinary stars) to billions of light years (because of Hubble's law, which applies to galaxies). This made them the brightest objects in the universe, by orders of magnitude, and satisfied our needs, both for spectacular or even incredible discoveries and for a

*Research supported by the U. S. Energy Research and Development Administration.

tool with which to probe the furthest parts of the universe.

When rapid fluctuations in brightness were discovered in quasars, presumably many thousands of light-years in size, astronomers and cosmologists were aghast and perhaps at first reluctant to accept the observations. Figure 1 shows the data for 3C 273, the archetype of quasars, as taken by Harlan Smith and others and evaluated by Kunkel.[1] These observations extend back to 1887, because the unusual brightness of 3C 273 makes it visible in old sky survey plates, and give a record of changes in brightness which would be embarrassing to a respectable galaxy. In 1929, for example, the luminosity

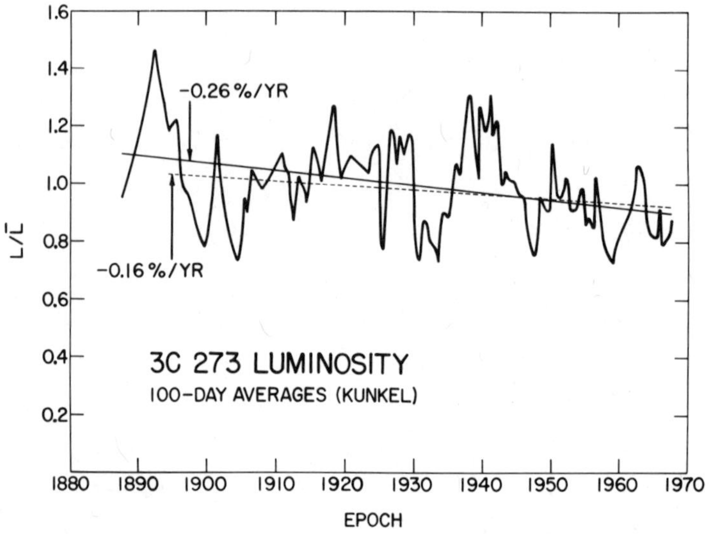

Fig. 1 Luminosity data for the quasar 3C 273, relative to average luminosity $\bar{L}$ (which corresponds to magnitude 12.78), based on photographic magnitudes averaged over 100-day intervals by Kunkel. Least-square linear trends are shown, both for full data (1887-1967) and for truncated data (1894-1967) which omits the less reliable early data. (J. Terrell and K. H. Olsen, Ap. J. 161 399 (1970).)

fell precipitously, by about 0.4 magnitudes (40%) in a period of weeks.

An analysis of the power spectrum of these fluctuations by Olsen and myself[2,3] indicates that these fluctuations are probably shot noise, random outbursts of brightness, with individual outbursts lasting for about three years on the average. Thus 3C 273, or at least the brightest parts, could only be at most a few light-years in size, and some of its fluctuations would make light-weeks a more likely limit. Other quasars give evidence of being only light-days in size or less, resembling the solar system more than a galaxy in size.

This ungalactic behavior poses another and more serious problem for the assumption of cosmological distance -- the problem of surface brightness. The small size indicated by the rapid fluctuations of most quasars,[4-7] combined with the incredible brightness required by Hubble's law if quasars are galaxies, leads to a surface brightness more like that of a laser than that of a star. This non-thermal radiation poses a special problem in the radio spectrum. The quasar CTA 102, for example, is now known to fluctuate on time scales of the order of a year at low radio frequencies.[8] Synchroton radiation, emitted by high-energy electrons circling in magnetic fields, is believed to be the source of such intense emission at low frequencies. Although synchroton radiation is much more intense at such frequencies than the thermal radiation from ordinary stars, it is too feeble to account for the surface brightness of CTA 102,[5] by a factor of about 10^6. Needless to say, the first reports of radio fluctuations in CTA 102 were greeted with considerable skepticism. To accept them was to accept the unthinkable -- that CTA 102, a quasar, was at least a thousand times closer than believed, more like a million light-years than a billion! Many other quasars pose the same problem in less extreme form.

Another difficulty with cosmological quasars has continued to plague astronomers. If quasars have the nature of galaxies, they would be expected to be found in the neighborhood of other galaxies, to cluster as most galaxies do. They should be found in groups rather than as lonesome, isolated objects. Quasars refuse to behave like galaxies in this respect also, in almost all cases. The bright quasar 3C 48, for example, is shown in Fig. 2 as photographed by Sandage and Miller[9] with especially sensitive plates, in order to show up any cluster of galaxies around 3C 48. None showed up. The same is true of 3C 273, which has a much lower red shift and is presumably much closer, and of other quasars.[9]

Observational astronomers have naturally not been lying asleep nights with such a challenge facing them. Gunn,[10] for example, has investigated some faint objects appearing near the quasar PKS 2251+11, as seen in Fig. 3. Are these faint blurs a cluster of galaxies at the same distance as the quasar, or are they much further away? Ordinary galaxies at the distance given

Fig. 2 (a) 3C 48 (quasar) taken on an experimental type plate with the 200-inch Hale reflector. The angular dimensions of the photograph are 4'35" in the east-west direction and 3'40" in the north-south direction. There is no evidence of a cluster of galaxies around 3C 48 (arrow), which shows a faint nubulosity. The limiting magnitude of the plate is probably B = 24.5. (b) Same fields on a conventional 103a0 plate exposed to the sky limit. (A. Sandage and W. C. Miller, Ap. J. 144, 1238 (1966).)

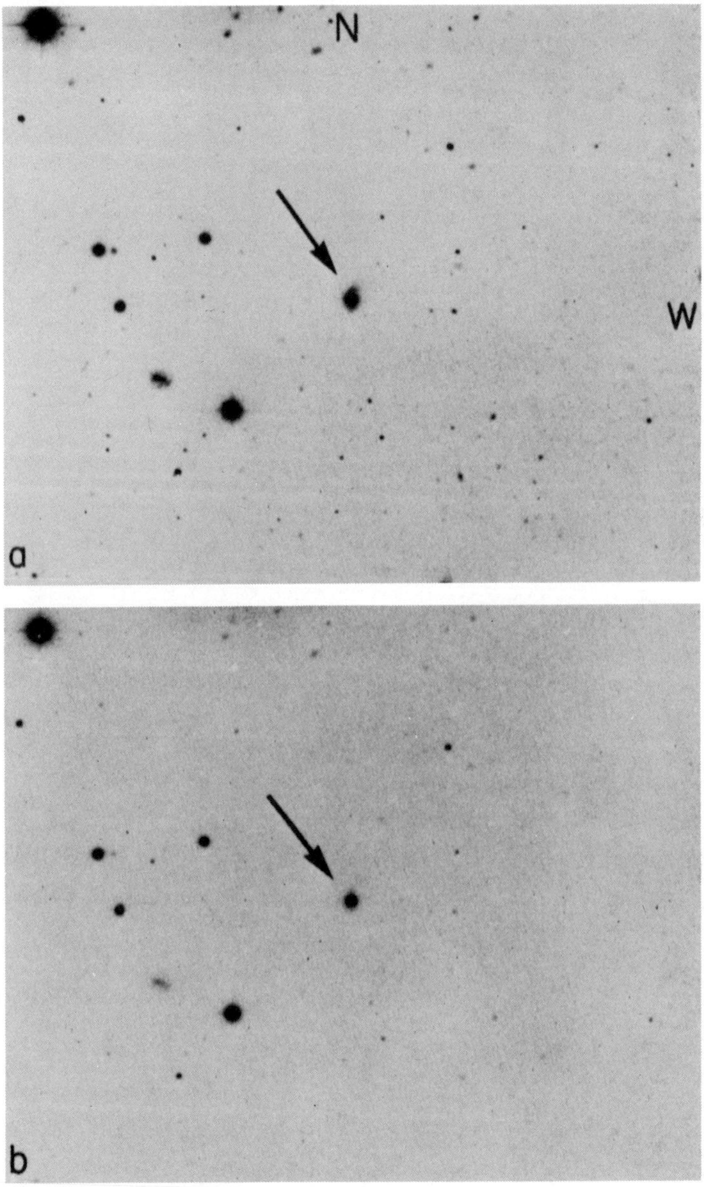
N
W
a
b

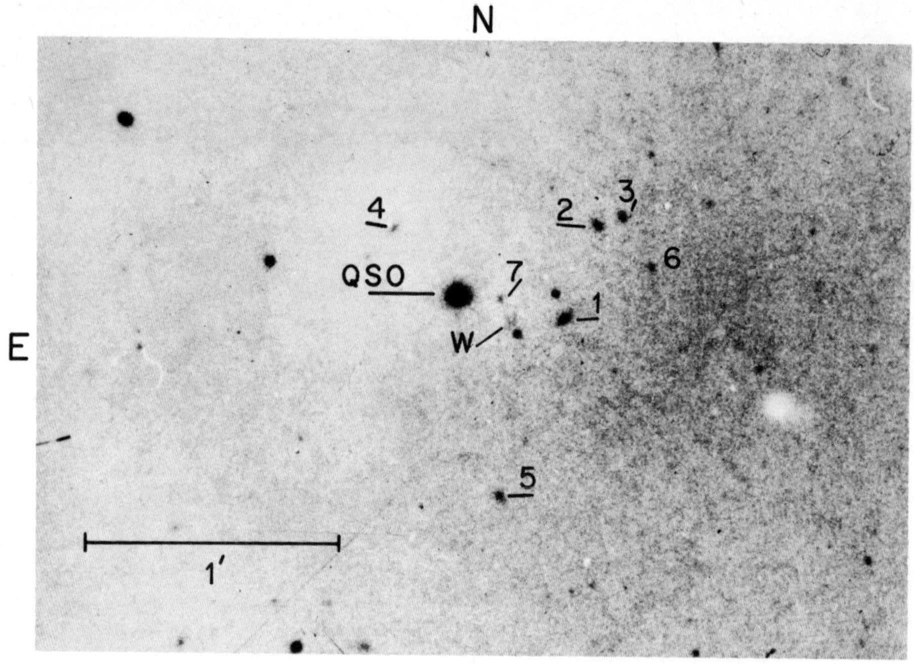

Fig. 3 PKS 2251+11 (quasar) and associated objects, taken with the 200-inch Hale telescope. (J. E. Gunn, Ap. J. 164, L113 (1971).)

by the red shift of PKS 2251+11 (z = 0.323) would be much brighter and much further apart, instead of extending over a distance comparable to the separation of our own galaxy and its nearest neighbors, the Magellanic Clouds. For reasons such as these Arp had concluded that these objects were not an associated cluster of galaxies.[11] They may be background galaxies, much further away than the quasar. Gunn, however, found evidence that one of the objects (no. 1 in Fig. 3) associated with this quasar had precisely the same red shift, indicating that the quasar was indeed in a cluster of galaxies.[10] The spectroscopy of such faint objects is a very difficult, marginal, enterprise, and later work did not support Gunn's spectrum, although other evidence was found for this same red shift, still troubled by signal-to-noise ratio.[12]

Several other cases have been found in which quasars and very distant galaxies appear in the same plate, but it is not clear that the number is more than coincidence could account for.[13] Arp[14] and Burbidge[15] have found a few cases of a different sort, in which quasars appear to be associated with relatively nearby galaxies of quite different red shift. Some few cases would be expected by chance, and it is not clear how many are genuine and not coincidental. Direction is easy for astronomers to measure, of course, but distance is often extraordinarily difficult and sometimes impossible to infer. It is at least clear that quasars do not associate much, if at all, with galaxies, contrary to expectation.

A further difficulty for distant quasars has appeared in recent years. Very-long-baseline interferometry, using radio telescopes which are greatly separated, even on different continents, has made it possible to observe the fine structure of radio-emitting quasars with incredibly good resolution. In several cases relative separation speeds which appear considerably larger than the speed of light have been found for radio sources within the quasars.[16-18] Such speeds amount to approximately 10 times the speed of light in two cases, 3C 273 and 3C 279. These results assume, of course, that these quasars are at Hubble's law distances, as the measurements are of angular separation, and much closer distances would result in much more modest speeds. The Christmas Tree or Theater Marquee model, in which various stationary objects blink on or off at opportune moments in order to give the appearance of motion, has been invoked to explain these extraordinary speeds. The number of radio sources required to explain each case seems to be increasing with time. Cohen, describing these results at the recent Texas Symposium, found it puzzling (on this basis) that the apparent motion is expansion in each case, and never contraction.[18] Thus he invoked the explanation given by Rees and others, in terms of objects approaching us very nearly along the line of sight, and thus appearing to separate much faster than they really are. This explanation, however, has various difficulties of its own, such as the probability of such coordinated motions and directions.

Quasars were originally expected to show very obvious absorption on the blue side of the red-shifted Lyman-α line, due to intergalactic hydrogen atoms at cosmological distances. Although such expected absorption was at first reported, further work has made it clear that there is no evidence for absorption by intergalactic hydrogen, even in the three cases of quasars with red shift greater than 3.0 where it should plainly show up.[19] Although this unexpected lack of absorption could have cast some doubt on the great distances assumed for quasars, it appears to have resulted only in the lowering of estimates of intergalactic neutral hydrogen density, by a factor of perhaps 10^6.

Perhaps the most serious difficulty of all for models of cosmologically-distant quasars is the energy problem.[20] Energy sources are needed for objects of very small size -- light-days, perhaps -- which radiate much more power than large galaxies, probably over millions of years. No suitable model with these properties appears to have been found. Although many quasar models were discussed in the first years after their discovery in 1963, each new discovery of an unexpected and sometimes unwelcome property and each new conflict with theoretical prediction and even apparently with known physical laws reduced the number of viable models, so that now quasar models are hardly mentioned.

Furthermore, data which at first supported the conventional thinking as to quasar distance has on several occasions been found not to be supported by further investigation, or simply to be in error. One such example[5] is the absorption line in the radio spectrum of 3C 273, thought to be due to hydrogen in the Virgo cluster of galaxies, which was reported in 1965 as evidence that 3C 273 lay beyond the cluster but was later found to be instrumental in nature.

A number of other difficulties for the conventional Hubbel's law distance for stubbornly ungalactic quasars could be discussed, but it is already clear that quasars consistently fail to yield the expected properties when tested by observation, resulting in strained explanations, improbable coincidences, and doubts that the laws of physics as we understand them hold in the vicinity of quasars. Why should nature be trying so hard to fool us and puzzle us whenever quasar observations are made? Is it possible that we are over-estimating their distance?

I have suggested, in a number of papers dating back to 1964, that perhaps observed quasar are much closer in most cases, and were emitted by our own galaxy a few millions years ago.[4-7, 21-25] They might then obey a law similar to Hubble's law relating distance and red shift, but with a different constant. This would put them thousands of times closer, of the order of a million light-years, and would solve or greatly ease all the vexing problems discussed above, especially the energy problem. Very local quasars would be of brightness similar to Type O stars,[26] 10^4 to 10^5 times the luminosity of the sun, and would probably not be optically visible from another galaxy unless it were very close or they were unusually bright.[7, 24-25] Rarely if ever, then, would any blue shifts -- or red shifts -- be observable for quasars emitted by other galaxies, as they would be much too faint. Objections to the very local quasar model on the basis that blue shifts have not been observed seem thus to be based on a misunderstanding.

Quasars thrown out with relativistic speed from the center of our galaxy would stir up great quantities of radio noise, synchroton emission, simply by moving through the intergalactic gas and magnetic fields.[5] This explanation of quasars has the virtue of perhaps accounting for some of the strange properties of radio galaxies, as will be discussed below. The energy source for the ejection of the quasars could only be, reasonably, a gravitational collapse at the center of our galaxy.[4] There is much other evidence for strange and powerful events taking place at the center of our galaxy, and other galaxies. A gravitational collapse involving 10^8 or 10^9 solar masses would easily be able to eject large numbers of relativistic quasars, whether before or after condensation into stellar objects.[5,21] The relativistic speed would on this basis be the source of most of the radio emission and would eventually be reduced by interaction with matter.[5] The optical emissions could easily be produced by the same processes that operate in Type O stars, and would require only a few solar masses.[7]

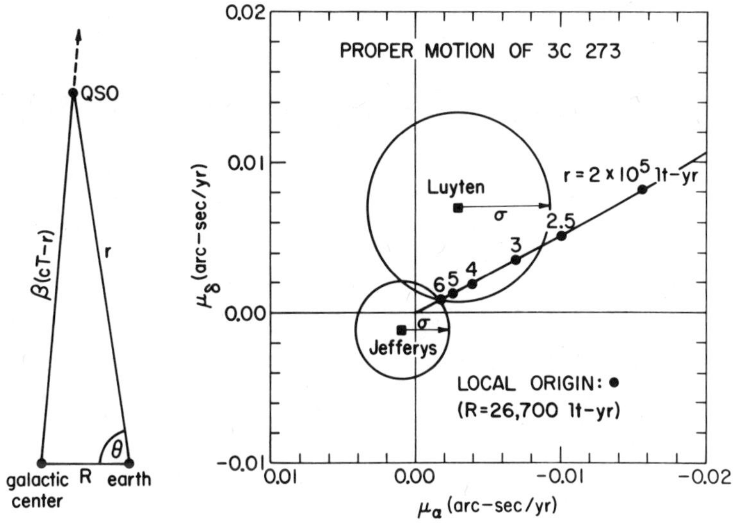

Fig. 4 Proper motion of 3C 273, as measured by Luyten and Jefferys, and as expected for ejection from the galactic center (local origin of quasars), for various observed distances r. Estimated standard deviations (σ) are the same for both components of proper motion, μ_α and μ_δ. (J. Terrell, Phys. Rev. Lett. 21, 637 (1968).)

But what about the proper motion of such relativistically-moving stars? Would not the motion be detectable by astronomers if quasars are that close and that fast? Surprisingly, perhaps, the answer is no! Figure 4 illustrates the situation for a local quasar thrown out in a direction nearly perpendicular to the plane of our galaxy. After it had gone only a few hundred thousand light-years we would see only a small component of the true speed, and the proper motion would be unobservably small.[7] This would agree with the observations of 3C 273, which is seen in such a direction. In the case of this brightest quasar, with observations of position dating back to 1887, we have by far the best chance to observe proper motion. The results of Luyten[27] and of Jefferys[28] are shown in Figure 4 together with their estimates of error. These are two-dimensional (circular) standard deviations, with a probability of 60.7% that the true value lies at a greater distance from the measured value. Also shown are the calculated proper motions for 3C 273 if it is a locally-ejected quasar with presently-observed (retarded) distance r. Luyten's result is readily consistent with a distance as small as 200,000 light-years, with a probability of 13% that the error of measurement can be this large. Jefferys' result is consistent with r as small as 400,000 light-years, with a probability of 18%, and he has informed me that the uncertainty of his measurement may actually be similar to that of Luyten's. Such distances of a local quasar would correspond to ejection from the center of our galaxy a few million years ago,[7] and there is other evidence in the form of approaching gas clouds that an explosion did take place there at such a time.[29]

Such distances of less than a million light-years are very much less than the tens or hundreds of millions of light-years which are suggested for local or at least non-cosmological quasars by Arp[14] and Burbidge.[15] Their models have some of the same problems with energy and other matters that plague cosmological quasars, and should be clearly distinguished from the very local quasar model discussed here.

If our galaxy has emitted great numbers of radio-emitting local quasars, we would naturally expect it not to be unique and would look for such clouds of radio sources around other distant galaxies. Cygnus A, shown in Fig. 5, is a radio galaxy of this sort. It is one of the brightest radio sources in the sky and was originally thought to be two colliding galaxies until

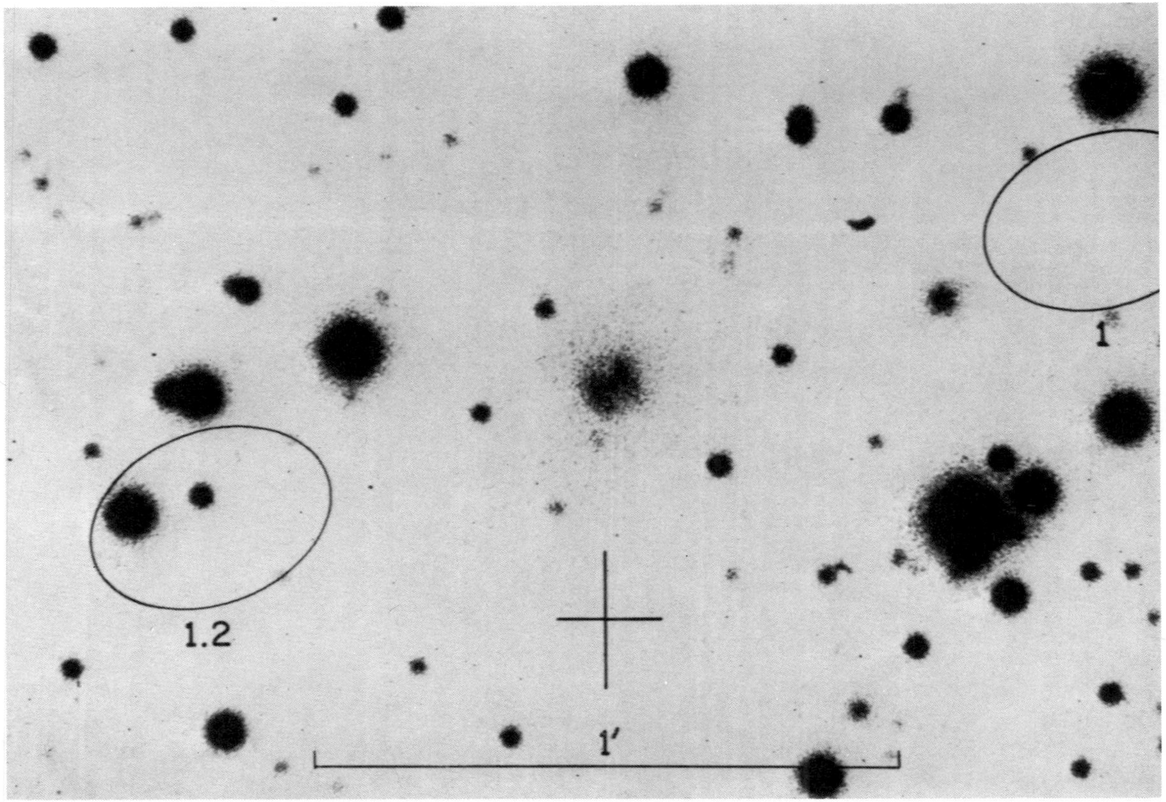

Fig. 5 The radio galaxy Cygnus A = 3C 405. Print from a 200-inch plate by Baade. The cross represents the mean error in the radio position. The curves are half-intensity radio contours. (T.A. Matthews, W. W. Morgan, and M. Schmidt, Ap. J. 140, 35 (1964).)

it was found that the radio emission came not from the bright center but from two other areas about 100,000 light-years out, one on each side of the galactic plane.[30] A somewhat similar situation holds for the radio galaxy Centaurus A, shown in Fig. 6, except that there are at least four radio sources, indicating perhaps two separate explosions and extending out to a million light-years.[30] The improving angular resolution of radio astronomy is giving evidence that these radio clouds are somewhat lumpier than indicated in these figures.

The energy source for such powerful and long-lived radio sources is not at once obvious and has been a serious problem for astronomical theory. It would probably take massive objects thrown out with high, probably relativistic, speed from the galactic center to furnish sustained radio emission of this sort.[5,25,31] Thus we may have to assume the existence of local quasars in order to explain the mysterious properties of radio galaxies, and to go through the reasoning given in this paper in the opposite order.

We should ask ourselves, finally, what explanation would appeal to hypothetical astronomers living in the galaxies Cygnus A or Centaurus A, observing the bright radio sources on each side of their galactic planes and perhaps finding them to correspond to red-shifted astronomical objects resembling stars. Would they call them quasi-stellar objects, and deduce from their red shifts that they are at cosmological distances?

→

Fig. 6 The radio galaxy Centaurus A. The outer radio contours are taken from Bolton and Clark (P.A. S.P. 72, 29 (1960)). The model of the inner double source was determined by Maltby (Nature 191, 793 (1961)). (T. A. Matthews, W. W. Morgan and M. Schmidt, Ap. J. 140, 35 (1964).)

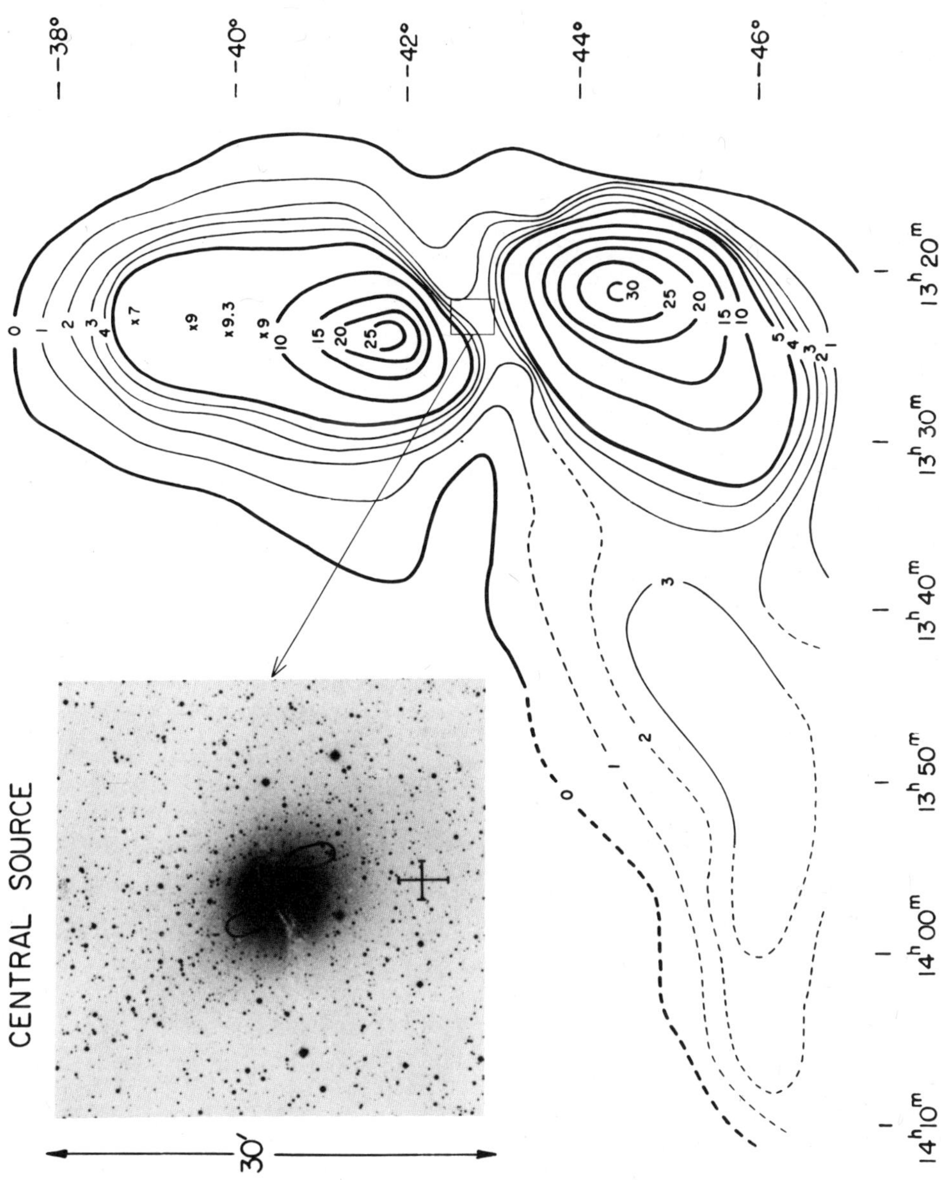
CENTRAL SOURCE
30′
−38°
−40°
−42°
−44°
−46°
13h20m
13h30m
13h40m
13h50m
14h00m
14h10m

REFERENCES

1. W. E. Kunkel, Astron. J. 72 1341 (1967).

2. J. Terrell and K. H. Olsen, Ap. J. 161, 399 (1970).

3. J. Terrell and K. H. Olsen, pp. 179-187 in External Galaxies and Quasi Stellar Objects (I.A.U. Symposium No. 44), edited by D. S. Evans (I.A.U., 1972).

4. J. Terrell, Science 145, 918 (1964); reprinted as pp. 227-228 in The Redshift Controversy, by G. B. Field, H. Arp, and J. N. Bahcall (Benjamin, Reading, 1973).

5. J. Terrell, Science 154, 1281 (1966).

6. J. Terrell, Ap. J. 147, 827 (1967).

7. J. Terrell, Phys. Rev. Lett. 21, 637 (1968).

8. R. W. Hunstead, Ap. Lett. 12, 193 (1972).

9. A. Sandage and W. C. Miller, Ap. J. 144, 1238 (1966).

10. J. E. Gunn, Ap. J. 164, L113 (1971).

11. H. C. Arp, Ap. J. 162, 811 (1970).

12. L. B. Robinson and E. J. Wampler, Ap. J. 171, L83 (1972).

13. J. N. Bahcall, N. A. Bahcall, and G. R. Burbidge, Ap. J. 166, L77 (1971).

14. H. Arp, Science 174, 1189 (1971).

15. G. R. Burbidge, Nature Phys. Sci. 246, 17 (1973).

16. A. R. Whitney, I. I. Shapiro, A. E. E. Rogers, D. S. Robertson, C. A. Knight, T. A. Clark, R. M. Goldstein, G. E. Marandino, and N. R. Vanderberg, Science 173, 225 (1971).

17. M. H. Cohen, W. Cannon, G. H. Purcell, D. B. Shaffer, J. J. Broderick, K. I. Kellerman, and D. L. Jauncey, Ap. J. 170, 207 (1971).

18. M. H. Cohen, in Proceedings of the Seventh Texas Symposium on Relativistic Astrophysics, Dallas,

Dec., 1974 (to be published).

19. P. A. Strittmatter, in Proceedings of the Seventh Texas Symposium on Relativistic Astrophysics, Dallas, Dec. 1974 (to be published).

20. G. R. Burbidge, T. W. Jones, and S. L. O'Dell, Ap. J. 193, 43 (1974).

21. J. Terrell, Science 156, 265 (1967).

22. J. Terrell, Science 159, 291 (1968).

23. J. Terrell, Physics Today 22, No. 11, 11 (1969).

24. J. Terrell, Scientific American 225, No. 2, 6 (1971).

25. J. Terrell, Nature 236, 166 (1972).

26. S. K. Luke, 1971 (unpublished).

27. W. J. Luyten, Minn. Univ. Astron. Obs. Publ. 3, No. 13 (1963); W. J. Luyten and J. A. Smith, Ap. J. 145, 366 (1966).

28. W. H. Jefferys, III, Astron. J. 69, 255 (1964).

29. G. R. Burbidge and F. Hoyle, Ap. J. 138, 57 (1963).

30. T. A. Matthews, W. W. Morgan, and M. Schmidt, Ap. J. 140, 35 (1964).

31. G. Burbidge, Nature 216, 1287 (1967).

PARTICIPANTS
High Energy

Stephen L. Adler
Institute of Advanced Studies

Barry C. Barish
California Institute of Technology

Bruce Barnett
University of Maryland

Itzhak Bars
University of California at Berkeley

Sidney Bludman
University of Pennsylvania

Laurie Brown
Northwestern University

Peter A. Carruthers
Los Alamos Scientific Lab.
University of California

Demetrios Christodoulou
International Centre for Theoretical Physics
Trieste, Italy

W. John Cocke
Steward Observatory
University of Arizona

Fred Cooper
Belfer Graduate School
Yeshiva University

Joseph R. Cox
Florida Atlantic University

Richard Dalitz
Oxford University

P. A. M. Dirac
Florida State University

Paul Fishbane
University of Virginia

Daniel Freedman
State University of New York at Stony Brook

Howard M. Georgi III
Harvard University

Frederick Gilman
Stanford Linear Accelerator Center
Stanford University

Sheldon Glashow
Harvard University

Ahmad Ali Golestaneh
Mount Union College

O. W. Greenberg
University of Maryland

Gerald Guralnik
Brown University

Leopold Halpern
Florida State University

Roman Jackiw
Massachusetts Institute of Technology

Arthur M. Jaffee
Harvard University

Hans A. Kastrup
Institut für Theoretische Physik der Rheinisch-Westfälischen Technischen Hochschule
Aachen, Germany

Nicholas Kemmer
University of Edinburgh

Abraham Klein
University of Pennsylvania

Behram Kursunoglu
Center for Theoretical Studies
University of Miami

Christian LeMonnier de Gouville
Center for Theoretical Studies
University of Miami

Harvey Lynch
Stanford Linear Accelerator Center
Stanford University

K. T. Manhanthappa
University of Colorado

Sydney Meshkov
National Bureau of Standards
Washington, D. C.

Stephen Mintz
Florida International Univ.

R. Mohapatra
City College of the City University of New York

Robert J. Oakes
Northwestern University

Reinhard Oehme
University of Chicago

Heinz R. Pagels
Rockefeller University

Leonard Parker
University of Wisconsin at Milwaukee

Jogesh Pati
University of Maryland

Arnold Perlmutter
Center for Theoretical Stds.
University of Miami

Donald Pettengill
Center for Theoretical Stds.
University of Miami

Paul Roman
Boston University

Igor Saavedra
Universidad de Chile

Abdus Salam
International Centre for Theoretical Physics
Trieste, Italy

John H. Schwarz
California Institute of Technology

Charles Sommerfield
Yale University

Karl Strauch
Harvard University

E. C. G. Sudarshan
University of Texas, Austin

Leonard Susskind
Yeshiva University

Ivan Todorov
Institute for Advanced Studies

Hiroomi Umezawa
University of Wisconsin at Milwaukee

Kameshwar Wali
Syracuse University

Ming-Yang Wang
Center for Theoretical Stds.
University of Miami

Fredrik Zachariasen
California Institute
of Technology

Anthony Zee
Princeton University

PARTICIPANTS

Laser Fusion and Lasers

R. Andrews
U.S. Naval Research Lab.
Washington, D. C.

John Apel
University of Miami

Uri Bernstein
Center for Theoretical Studies
University of Miami

Kenneth Billman
NASA/Ames Research Center
Moffett Field, California

John S. Blakemore
Florida Atlantic University

Jean Louis Bobin
Commissariat A L'Energie Atomique, France

Stephen Bodner
U. S. Naval Research Lab.
Washington, D. C.

Ronald Bousek
University of Arizona

Keith Boyer
Los Alamos Scientific Lab.
University of California

Arthur Broyles
University of Florida

C. D. Cantrell
Los Alamos Scientific Lab.
University of California

George Chapline
Lawrence Livermore Lab.
University of California

Mikael Ciftan
Army Research Office
Durham, North Carolina

C. B. Collins
University of Texas, Dallas

Ralph Cooper
Los Alamos Scientific Lab.
University of California

K. Das Gupta
Texas Technical University

J. D. Daugherty
AVCO Everett Res. Lab.
Everett, Massachusetts

Raymond Elton
U. S. Naval Research Lab.
Washington, D. C.

J. Forsyth
University of Rochester

John Garrison
Lawrence Livermore Lab.
University of California

Damon Giovanielli
Los Alamos Scientific Lab.
University of California

Arthur Guenther
Air Force Weapons Lab.
Kirtland Air Force Base

Dale Henderson
Los Alamos Scientific Lab.
University of California

Robert Hofstadter
Stanford University

Heinrich Hora
Australian National Univ.
Canberra, Australia

Charles Hendricks
Lawrence Livermore Lab.
University of California

Joseph Hubbard
Center for Theoretical Studies
University of Miami

John L. Hughes
Australian National Univ.
Canberra, Australia

Reed Jensen
Los Alamos Scientific Lab.
University of California

O. Dean Judd
Los Alamos Scientific Lab.
University of California

Arthur Kantrowitz
AVCO-Everett Res. Lab.
Everett, Massachusetts

W. L. Kruer
Lawrence Livermore Lab.
University of California

Willis E. Lamb, Jr.
University of Arizona

Benjamin Lax
Massachusetts Institute of Technology

Melvin Lax
City College of the City University of New York

Leslie Levine
U. S. Naval Research Lab.
Washington, D. C.

John Lindl
Lawrence Livermore Lab.
University of California

William Louisell
University of Southern California

Moshe Lubin
University of Rochester

Philip Mallozzi
Battelle Memorial Institute

Robert Malone
Los Alamos Scientific Lab.
University of California

James Maniscalto
Lawrence Livermore Lab.
University of California

P. L. Mascheroni
University of Texas, Austin

Robert McCarthy
University of Arizona

R. McCorkle
I.B.M. Corporation
T. J. Watson Research Ctr.

William McCrory
Los Alamos Scientific Lab.
University of California

William McKnight
University of Alabama

William Mead
Lawrence Livermore Lab.
University of California

Laurence Mittag
Center for Theoretical Stds.
University of Miami

David Mosher
U. S. Naval Research Lab.
Washington, D. C.

John Nuckolls
Lawrence Livermore Lab.
University of California

Erol Oktay
Atomic Energy Commission
Washington, D. C.

Lars Onsager
Center for Theoretical Studies
University of Miami

Harry Robertson
University of Miami

Helmut Schwarz
Universidade de Brasilia

Marlan Scully
University of Arizona

John F. Seely
University of Southern California

Robert Shnidman
U.S.A. Ballistic Res. Lab.
Aberdeen Proving Grounds

George Soukup
Center for Theoretical Studies
University of Miami

Ian Spalding
UKAEA Research Group
England

Edward Teller
Lawrence Livermore Lab.
University of California

F. Winterberg
University of Nevada

E. A. Witalis
Research Institute of the Swedish National Defense
Stockholm, Sweden

Jack Wong
Lawrence Livermore Lab.
University of California

Lowell Wood
Lawrence Livermore Lab.
University of California

Gerold Yonas
Sandia Laboratory
Albuquerque, New Mexico

SUBJECT INDEX